FROZEN FUTURE

A Prophetic Report from Antarctica

FROZEN FUTURE

A Prophetic Report from Antarctica

*Edited by Richard S. Lewis
and Philip M. Smith*

*With an Introduction by Walter Sullivan
Science Editor of The New York Times*

QUADRANGLE BOOKS

A New York Times Company

CONTENTS

PART II
*Report
on International Scientific
and Operational Activities
in the Antarctic as Reported in the
"Antarctic Journal of the United States"*

Introduction

WALTER SULLIVAN

After several hundred thousand years of evolution, through a succession of ice ages, through the development of agriculture, the emergence of national states and the industrial revolution, mankind now faces the ultimate challenge. Our impact on the environment is becoming so catastrophic and so rapid that the world cannot long remain habitable unless our social and political institutions can find ways to live in harmony with our limited resources of air, land and water, sharing them with the other creatures of this earth.

As pointed out, in this book, by the Soviet scientist Yevgeny K. Fedorov, the precedents for international cooperation established in Antarctica—that frigid continent lying at the bottom of the world—will prove, it is hoped, to have begun creating conditions conducive to an ultimate solution.

Those precedents have arisen from the special circumstances of Antarctica and the provisions of the treaty that has made that continent an international laboratory are not directly applicable to other areas of international tension. But they arose from a recognition by governments with opposing ideologies and rival territorial claims that the laying aside of such considerations in favor of cooperation were

essential in attacking the scientific and environmental problems of that vast and hostile region.
Nationalism and militant ideologies have been sub-
ordinated to the common interest of all and the
effect is already manifest in international measures
outlawing military activity on other celestial bodies,
such as the moon, and on the sea bed.

So remote is Antarctica that many inhabitants of
the Northern Hemisphere are not even aware that it
is a continent. American perspective tends to be
centered on North America. Maps of the world published in Europe show that region as central. Such
maps, as a rule, omit entirely the great continent at
the South Pole.

Yet Antarctica, with its soaring mountains, its
vast, flowing fields of ice, its scattered "oases" of
bare land and its strangely tame natives—seals and
penguins—dominates the climate of one quarter of
the earth. Its effects are felt far beyond that part of
the globe. It provides a reservoir of mineral resources that will probably remain untouched for a
long time, but whose ultimate exploitation is bound
to come. It stands as a challenge to man's fortitude
and to his ingenuity, not only in finding ways to
cope with its severe climate, which is by far the
most inhospitable on earth, but also in devising
political institutions that will keep it what it has—
perhaps only temporarily—become: a highly successful experiment in international cooperation.

Because the continent is surrounded by a broad
zone of drifting pack ice and icebergs, it was largely
inaccessible to explorers until the advent of modern
icebreakers and long-range planes with a combination landing gear whose wheels enable them to take
off from ordinary airfields and whose skis allow
them to land on compacted snow.

No human foot is known to have been planted on
the continent until 1895 and it was the lure of such
exploratory feats as reaching the South Pole or

being first to cross the continent from Atlantic to Pacific that drew expeditions south during the early decades of this century. This "Heroic Age" of Antarctic exploration developed into the "Air Age" of Byrd, Ellsworth and Wilkins. It culminated in what might be called the present "Scientific Age," initiated by the extraordinarily ambitious undertakings of the International Geophysical Year of 1957-58.

This, for example, led to the establishment of an American scientific station at the South Pole and a Soviet station at the so-called Pole of Inaccessibility —the point farthest from any coastline. No one had ever come near the latter point and the only ones to have reached the South Pole (where all directions are north) were the Norwegian and British teams that raced there in the Antarctic summer of 1911-12. (Summer in the Southern Hemisphere coincides with winter in the North.) The losers in that race, led by Robert Falcon Scott of Britain, never made it back to their main base.

In 1955 only four nations had outposts in Antarctica and most of the outposts had been set up to underline rival territorial claims to sectors of the continent. The Argentines had 7 stations, the British 8 and the Chileans 4, almost all of them on islands alongside the long peninsula that reaches toward South America and was claimed by all three countries. There was also an Australian station on the opposite side of the continent, making a total of 20 stations, manned by 179 men.

To support their territorial ambitions each claimant of the peninsula—which is longer than the Italian "boot"—had bestowed its own name on the land. The British called it Graham Land, for a former First Lord of the Admiralty. The Argentines and Chileans had named it for national heroes— San Martin Land and O'Higgins Land, respectively. The United States, which officially had made no

claims to Antarctic territory, still asserted the region was discovered by an American sailor, Nathaniel Palmer, and called it Palmer Land.

Within two years all of this had changed. Narrow
national considerations were set aside and the establishment of coastal stations for the I.G.Y. of 1957-58
began during the Antarctic summer of 1955-56 when
the first American and Soviet bases were set up at
McMurdo Sound and Mirny, respectively. By the
time the I.G.Y. got under way 11 nations were operating 48 stations around the entire periphery of
the continent and at scientifically strategic points
within its interior. They were manned by 912
year-around personnel and the summer population
swelled to about 5,000. It was an extraordinary
change for a continent seen by no human eye until
the Nineteenth Century.

The participants included all nations that had
made claims to sectors that, like pie slices, con-
verged at the South Pole: Argentina, Australia,
Britain, Chile, France, New Zealand, and Norway.
Two—the Soviet Union and United States—had
"reserved their rights" to make territorial claims
and the other participants—Belgium and Japan—
had taken part in earlier exploration of the Antarctic.

Not long thereafter a number of the participants
informally agreed on a compromise name for one
of the longest peninsulas in the world. It is now
called the Antarctic Peninsula. The British and
Americans have agreed to call its northern sector
Graham Land and its southern sector Palmer Land.
It was an arrangement typical of recent developments in that region.

The establishment of the I.G.Y. stations was one
of the great logistic feats of all time. Construction
materials and bulldozers for the Pole Station were
brought in to McMurdo Sound by ships whose route
through the ice floes was broken by icebreaker. The

cargo was transferred to mammoth sleds, hauled to a makeshift airfield, prepared for parachuting and dropped by Air Force planes over the Pole. (One 'chute failed to open properly and a plummeting tractor dug a deep hole in the polar ice sheet.) The Soviet inland stations were primarily supplied by giant tractors hauling cargo sleds.

Now almost two decades have elapsed since the launching of that great enterprise and the pace has hardly slackened. All of the participants in I.G.Y. Antarctic work were still operating stations there in 1971, except Belgium and Norway, both of whom sent scientists to work with other expeditions in the summer of 1970-71. All told, 39 stations were functioning during that season, all but seven of which were also manned the following winter.

What has been gained from this great international effort? Can the continued investment of millions of dollars a year be justified at a time of pressing needs closer to home? The proposed American budget for Antarctica in the fiscal year 1972 was $19.3 million.

In other words: where do we go from here? To assess this question the *Bulletin of the Atomic Sciences* devoted one entire issue to a diverse series of articles, here reprinted in full with minor corrections and additional material. They reflect varied national points of view, but a common conviction that the international effort in Antarctica has played a role of major importance in setting precedents. The Antarctic Treaty of 1959 has set an entire continent aside as a laboratory open for research by all and open to inspection by signatories who seek assurance that its provisions against military activity or nuclear testing are being adhered to.

Devoting its December, 1970, issue to this subject was an appropriate undertaking for the *Bulletin*, which was founded in 1945 by scientists, then large-

ly centered at the University of Chicago, whose
consciences were deeply troubled by the consequences of the atomic bomb that some of them had
helped produce. It has evolved into a journal more
broadly concerned with the interactions of science
and public affairs.

As this book goes to press it is evident that some
curtailment of American activity in the Antarctic
is inevitable. After the summer of 1971-72 Byrd
Station, in the hinterland, will be closed as an all-
year outpost, although automated data-collecting
will probably continue. Such automation may ultimately reduce considerably the number of men who
have to endure the tedium of the long winter period
of confinement and unrelieved darkness.

National pride still plays a role and there is
reluctance to close the American outpost at the
South Pole for that reason. The fact that the Soviet
Union is maintaining six year-around stations, compared with four of the United States, has also not
been overlooked in Washington.

More important, as will be evident from the chapters of this book, the scientific assets to be gained
by continued Antarctic research are so great that
any close-down of all the stations there is almost
unthinkable. Not only does the continent generate
much of the world's weather, but combined observations with ground stations and earth satellites could
reveal trends in its accumulation of ice and its discharge of icebergs into the sea—changes that could
presage major climate changes and even the start
of a new ice age.

There is a small school of scientists who believe
large sections of the Anarctic ice sheet sometimes
slip off the continent, abruptly raising sea levels
everywhere. They find fragmentary evidence suggesting that such devastating rises have occurred
in the past. If so, the prediction of such "surges"
could save millions of lives in coastal areas. It is

also argued that Antarctica is an ideal place from which to monitor overall pollution of the world's air and water—remote from local effects. The plants and animals of Antarctic seas contains a multitude of biochemical substances unknown elsewhere and of possible medical use. Confirmation that Antarctica once served as the central piece in a jigsaw assembly of continents means that geologic structures there will eventually be used to discover new ore bodies not only in Antarctica but also in other land masses that once lay alongside those ore bodies.

It is even suggested in these chapters that, since the blue whale—largest creature on earth—has been grossly depleted by whaling ships, its chief food might now be exploited for human use. This food is a tiny, shrimp-like crustacean known as krill.

But the Antarctic resource typically overlooked by scientists and government analysts in their reports—though not in their personal experience—is the extraordinary beauty of that continent. Exploration of the moon has stolen public attention from Antarctica, but the moon is a drab and forbidding place compared with the southern continent, with its black, brown and grey mountains, draped in white, soaring against a sky bluer than any visible in more polluted latitudes, all girdled round with the blue-green sea. To watch the foolish antics of of Adelie penguins, or the ridiculous dignity of Emperor penguins is an experience being exploited more and more by those who run tourist trips to McMurdo Sound or the Antarctic Peninsula.

The Antarctic Treaty calls for periodic consultative meetings and at the one held in Tokyo in 1970 these tourist "invasions"—still on a small scale— were a subject of concern. The Antarctic nations are committed to preservation of its wildlife and they have not yet worked out legal machinery to deal with that problem nor to provide for what is to be done, for example, when a crime involving citizens of several nations is committed in that region.

When all is said and done, however, perhaps the most important reason to sustain the international enterprise in Antarctica is to keep before the world its demonstration that diverse nations can work closely together when they put their minds to it. Fedorov, the Soviet contributor to this series and an important figure in the Soviet scientific heirarchy, argues that within perhaps a century human activities will have to be coordinated on a global scale if man is to survive. As a loyal communist he hopes that the world by then will be "a single socialist society." But, he adds, even if diverse social systems persist, a "correct interaction of man with nature" may be achieved if, throughout the world, there is created "roughly the same type of interaction among countries as we have already attained and are realizing over a period of almost two decades in Antarctica."

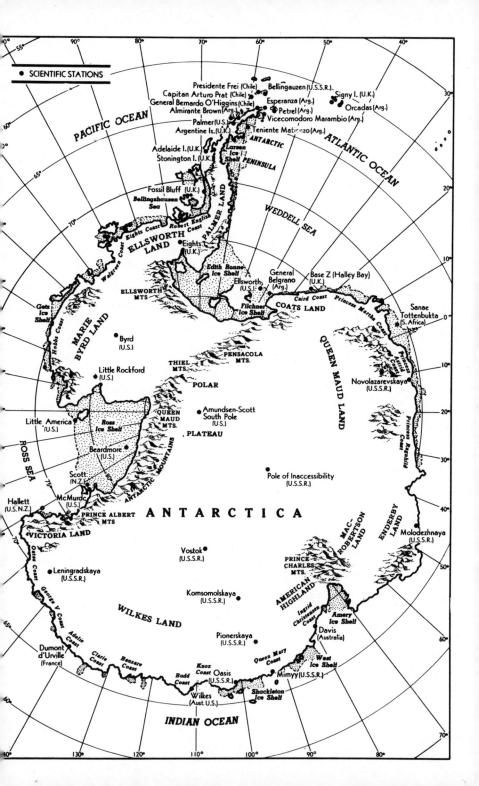

PART ONE

An Assessment of the American
Stake in Antarctica
at a Turning Point
in American Policy Making
as Published in the
"Bulletin of
the Atomic Scientists"

ANTARCTICA
SINCE THE IGY

Antarctic Research and the Relevance of Science

RICHARD S. LEWIS

The scientific investigation of Antarctica, which began on the present scale with the International Geophysical Year, has been the most successful program of international research in the history of science.

It has opened up the last, land frontier on this planet to human habitation the year around. It has shed new light on the great geophysical questions which have challenged science in this century. It has laid a foundation for the understanding of global atmospheric, oceanic and climatic processes, so that the world-wide effects of man's pollution of the environment can be assessed in a reasonable way.

From this investigation, also, there has evolved a mode of coexistence and cooperation among the

1

scientists of many nations on an unprecedented
scale. This has led to one of the great landmarks
in diplomacy, the Antarctic Treaty of 1959. In it,
12 nations with antarctic interests agreed to set
aside territorial claims for at least 30 years and to
dedicate the ice-clad region as a continent for
science.

In the United States, changes in social outlook
and mood during the years the Antarctic Research
Program has been operating as a low-key, low-
budget effort ($5 to $7 million a year) have challenged its relevance, along with that of other long-
term programs, to the immediate concerns of
mankind.

All science is relevant to man's concern for knowledge, but that is no longer sufficient justification
for support among Congressional pragmatists who
perceive science mainly as a kind of medication for
the ills of civilization. The scientific revolution of
the 1950s and early 1960s has given way to a
counter-revolution which deems pure science irrel-
evant if not inimical to the real concerns of society.
It provides a rationale for cutting long-term but
promising cancer research; for curtailing the exploration of the moon simply to save the cost of
operating rockets and spacecraft now standing in
storage bays and for drastically cutting federal support of graduate science education. The fundamental research programs of the Department of
Defense have been restricted to military applications only by the Mansfield amendment (Sec. 203)
to the 1970 Defense Appropriations Act. The im-
plied dictum: "If the troops can't use it, forget it"
may become the epitaph of the military establishment's effort in basic research.

In this context, the directions of science tend
to be dictated by assumptions, often capricious,
of socio-political priorities and by military requirements. The worth of research is judged by its ap-

ANTARCTICA

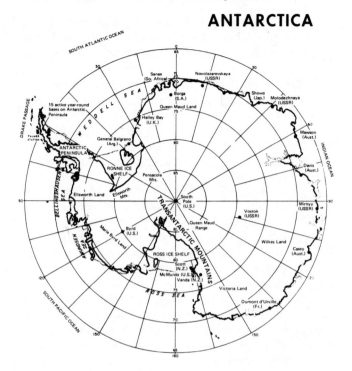

parent usefulness in fixing areas of breakdown in the social structure. But nature is intolerant of man's caprice. Rising population pressure and soaring pollution have forced industrial societies to assign a high priority to the relationship of man and the environment. For the first time, millions of people feel threatened by the unrestricted pollution of their habitat. For the first time, millions realize that Earth's resources are finite and exhaustible. In the face of possible catastrophe, man must turn to basic research as a means of assessing and modifying the threat to his survival.

Much of the concern for the environment has been stimulated by doomsday predictions of lethal changes in the atmosphere or in the environment as a result of man's pollution. Such predictions are often extrapolations based on limited investigation, or guesswork. They have yet to be supported by reliable data.

What is really happening to the atmosphere? Has the release of carbon dioxide from the burning of coal, oil and gas altered its chemical balance? Its thermal properties? Have pesticides and other poisons man has dumped into the biosphere affected the oxygen production of plants in the forests and the oceans? What effects do pollutants have on climate—particularly water vapor if discharged in large quantity in the stratosphere by future supersonic transports?

In a calm and thoughtful review of Critical Environmental Problems at Williams College last summer, a group of 100 scientists concluded that man simply did not know the answers to these questions, (*Bulletin*, Oct. 1970). The assembly urged that more research in ecology, meteorology, oceanology and climatology is essential if man is to predict the outcome of intended or accidental modifications of the environment.

Thus, it would appear that research which enables the scientist to predict the effect of technologically developed societies upon the environment would meet even the most narrow specifications for relevancy. In this respect, the Antarctic Research Program becomes a basic necessity. Not only does it focus on a region where environmental change has been dramatic, but it provides essential information for the understanding of planet-wide environmental processes. As William D. McElroy, director of the National Science Foundation, observes, man must continue to increase his knowledge of his planet in order to live productively on it.

RECORD OF THE REPTILES

When Ernest Shackleton found coal in the Transantarctic Mountains nearly 70 years ago, it became evident that Antarctica had not always been covered by seven and one half million cubic miles of ice, as it is in this century. Once, it had been fair and open to the sun. A carboniferous forest grew where, today, no single blade of grass has sought the sun for six or seven million years.

There were other clues to the dramatic environmental change which had drowned this land in ice. Fossils of the southern hemisphere fern, *Glossopteris*, which once covered most of the lands of the Southern Hemisphere, were found with the bodies of Robert Falcon Scott and his men who perished in the austral autumn of 1912, struggling back to their base at McMurdo Sound from the South Pole.

Could a coal forest thrive in a region where day and night are six months long? Perhaps, the continent had moved and its relationship to the sun had changed. This evidence supported the idea of continental drift, a theory which many Earth scientists rejected as heresy for decades.

Campbell Craddock describes how the painstaking and dangerous geological investigation in Antarctica during the 1960s, culminating in the discovery of fossilized bones of Southern Hemisphere Triassic Reptiles in the last two years, added confirmation to accumulating evidence for continental drift. The hypothesis of a Southern Hemisphere supercontinent called Gondwanaland became an acceptable probability. The records of the rocks indicated it had been split by sea-floor spreading which had ripped Antarctica from Australia some 40 million years ago and rotated it southward to the south geographic pole. The ice sheet formed, Craddock suggests, about seven million years ago.

Antarctica has been more than a laboratory for the study of the evolution of the continents. It provides a platform to observe the workings of what Joseph Fletcher calls the Global Climate

Machine.

The study of climatic processes requires a record of climate past. A substantial piece of the record, extending back in time more than a thousand centuries, is buried in the ice. It can be read in the ratios of oxygen and hydrogen isotopes found in summer and winter snowfall each year. These ratios (0^{16} to 0^{18} and H^1 to deuterium) represent a temperature history of the air masses as they moved over the planet from warmer to polar regions in the year the snow fell. Ratios in several summer and winter snow layers indicate average world climate at the time of the snow falls.

In this way, the summer and winter layers of snow in a vertical cross section or core of ice represent a natural file of climatic information. The U.S. Antarctic Research Program supported deep drilling all the way through 7,100 feet of ice in Marie Byrd Land by the U.S. Army's Cold Regions Research and Engineering Laboratory (CRREL). CRREL also perforated the Greenland ice cap, reaching bottom at a depth of 4,461 feet.

Isotope studies of air trapped in ancient ice from near bottom of both holes have shown that there were past periods of much colder climate than now preceded by climatic periods like today's.

THE OZONE SHIELD

One of the questions which deep drilling may settle is whether climatic changes occur simultaneously in both hemispheres or at different times in each. Synchronous change would suggest changes in solar radiation; non-synchronous change would point to localized events, such as the freezing or un-freezing of the Arctic ocean.

In their discussion of the CRREL drilling program, B. Lyle Hansen and Chester C. Langway, Jr. report that isotope studies indicate that climate changes in Antarctica during the late Pleistocene are essentially in phase with those in the Northern Hemisphere.

In recent years, observes Robert A. Helliwell, such practical problems as air pollution and ionizing radiation have been added to the list of those requiring more fundamental knowledge about atmospheric processes. We are uneasy about the effect, he points out, of pollution-stimulated changes in the composition of the lower atmosphere upon the amount of ozone in the upper atmosphere. Ozone is the shield that absorbs deadly ultraviolet light before it can damage living organisms on the Earth's surface.

Because of its remoteness from major pollution sources and its almost complete lack of vegetation which might affect seasonal carbon dioxide variations, Antarctica can serve as a "bench mark" in determining long-term trends in atmospheric pollution, Morton J. Rubin suggests. The ozone and carbon dioxide content of the atmosphere have been measured in the antarctic since the IGY. Now, the rise of carbon dioxide, DDT and radioactivity indicates that even this last frontier is becoming contaminated. Rubin urges that stations should be set up now to monitor contaminants and establish the base-line for assessing future conditions.

A CRIME-FREE LAND

Antarctica has been a conspicuously successful model as a laboratory for human and international relations. In more than 70 years of human occupation, usually under trying conditions, not a single, major crime of violence has ever been recorded there. In this cold, icy desert, man finds himself increasingly dependent on his fellows for physical safety and psychological comfort the longer he stays.

The intense national competition which characterized antarctic exploration in the early part of

this century faded away with the realization that
any bonanza in mineral riches was unreachable.
Even today, Neal Potter says, hopes for discovering
workable minerals appear quite dim. "On the ice-
covered continent," remarks Gordon deQ. Robin,
"exploitation is directed at providing new scientific-
knowledge of our planet."

It may be that Antarctica became a continent
for science because it was useful for nothing else.
The Treaty broke new diplomatic ground by prohibiting the testing of nuclear weapons and providing unlimited inspection of stations and installations. "Nowhere," Paul Daniels tells us, "has the
close relationship between the official actions of
government and the private actions of the international, scientific community been demonstrated
more clearly than in the consultative meetings
which led to the Treaty."

While the Treaty has served as precedent for the
Treaty on Outer Space and for discussions on the
use of the seabed, Finn Sollie points out that the
Antarctic Model is a complex structure particular
to the antarctic experience. Its blend of arms control, political agreement on a modus vivendi and
mixed scientific and governmental cooperation is
adapted to the special situation and conditions of
Antarctica.

Wholesale transfer of the Antarctic Model may
neither be desirable nor practical, Sollie feels. Yet,
the precedent of internationalization of new lands
is transferable to other environments—to space,
the moon and the planets.

Antarctica, the Continent for Peace, as Ye. K.
Fedorov calls it, has evolved in human conscious-
ness through three ages, each corresponding to ages
in techno-scientific development. Laurence Gould
refers to the Age of Mythology and Hypothesis
in classical times, when the existence of Antarctica
was merely imagined; the Heroic Age of geographic

exploration at the start of the century, when man pitted his courage and endurance against the unrelenting cold, and, finally, the Scientific Age.

"At last, Antarctica has become an international laboratory, a far cry from the days when plans and movements were discussed in code or cipher, lest someone else should forestall the next move," writes Sir Vivian Fuchs.

Thomas O. Jones suggests that scientific programs can blaze trails in new areas of foreign relations in ways diplomats cannot. On an intragovernmental level, the Antarctic Program represents a successful partnership between NSF and the Navy, which transports the scientists and their equipment to Antarctica and provides them with food, shelter, medical care and transportation on the ice.

The region is more than a geophysical laboratory. Biology research has revealed fascinating systems of adaptation to the cold by fish, seals and penguins. One of these is the glycoprotein antifreeze evolved by *Trematomus* fish. George Llano's description of biological discoveries in antarctic seas explains their fascination for scientists studying the short and long-range effects on life forms of environmental change.

Antarctic veterans see the necessity for change. Albert P. Crary, looking back over the last 12 years, wonders: "could we have done all that was really needed to be done at half the cost?" He would consider limiting the antarctic effort to one, three-year expedition each decade. No one scientist would be permitted to accompany a second expedition. This would give younger scientists a chance to do original work. The older ones, says Crary, don't seem to fade away fast enough.

What of the future? Philip M. Smith suggests that the antarctic investigation has generated scientific possibilities requiring greater resources than any single nation is likely to assign to them. Among these is an assessment of the erosion of environmental quality on a global scale.

In 70 years, Antarctica has evolved from the arena where Amundsen and Scott raced their yelping dog teams for the pole to an international cluster of scientific settlements, often working in concert. In this frigid land, where there is no cold war nor crime, man has been able to perceive his survival in terms of cooperation rather than conflict.

Perhaps the greatest experiment in this icy laboratory has been man himself, and his ability to adapt his outlook and his drives to an environment which requires cooperation. This experiment is still in an early stage. Another century may pass before its outcome is known.

RICHARD S. LEWIS

Emergence of Antarctica

The Mythical Land

LAURENCE M. GOULD

There have been three ages in the human conception of Antarctica. They parallel man's own intellectual development. In classical times, the ice-clad region existed as a myth. It evolved in later centuries, up to the 20th, as a hypothetical continent. The Heroic Age of antarctic exploration then occupied the first one-third of the 20th century. It was characterized by the exploits of Scott, Shackleton, Amundsen and Byrd. Then came the modern, Scientific Age, in which Antarctica has emerged as a vast, natural laboratory where man can observe the experiments which nature has performed over thousands of millenia. No one today is more qualified to describe this evolution than Laurence M. Gould, professor of geology at the University of Arizona and one of the great, explorer scientists who opened the modern era in antarctic research. Professor Gould was second in command of the Byrd Antarctic Expedition of 1928-30 and a veteran of arctic explorations as well. During the International Geophysical Year, he directed the United States Antarctic Program.

The idea of a southern continent is one of geography's most ancient assumptions. During the sixth century B.C. Pythagoras postulated a spherical earth. With the Greeks' love of symmetry this persuaded his followers to assume that there would be large masses of land in the southern hemisphere to balance those which formed the inhabited earth.

The most noted geographer of antiquity, the Roman Claudius Ptolemaeus or Ptolemy, who lived in Alexandria during the second century A.D., drew an immense southern landmass which he called "Terra Incognita" connecting Africa with the Malay Peninsula on the east, making the Indian Ocean a closed sea. This conception was not disproved until nearly the end of the fifteenth century.

The idea of a spherical earth was not compatible with early Christendom's dedication to a flat saucer-shaped planet. Ptolemy's ideas languished for a long time but the idea of a spherical earth and the likelihood of reaching India by sailing west from Spain was kept alive by monastic scholars. Then in the late fifteenth century stirrings of the Renaissance began. In addition to its greatness in art and science the Renaissance was man's first space age. Here was sparked the greatest era of geographical exploration in man's history — a period of exploration during which the size of the known world was doubled and which was not equaled until the International Geophysical Year. Ptolemy's geography was revived and during the late fifteenth century many maps appeared in Europe based on his concepts, with his "Terra Incognita" changed to "Terra Australis."

The first major reduction in the supposed southern landmass came with the rounding of the Cape of Good Hope by Vasco de Gama in 1497 which led many geographers to believe there was no continent at all south of Africa. In a way this was offset by Magellan's magnificent voyage around the world during which he discovered the Straits of Magellan in 1520. Geographers immediately assumed that Tierra del Fuego, the land south of the Straits, was a part of the great southern contnent.

Terra Australis first appeared on a world map by Orontius in 1531 and was copied by Mercator in 1538. This map was remarkable: based on pure guesswork, its outline was surprisingly like that of the real Antarctica as we know it except that it was about one-third larger with a huge bulge opposite Australia. This was the smallest "Antarctica" from the time of Ptolemy's projections until the continent was finally circumnavigated in the latter part of the eighteenth century by Captain Cook.

In 1578 Queen Elizabeth sent Sir Francis Drake to find the great southern land. His ship, the *Golden Hind*, was blown way south of Cape Horn, proving that the Atlantic and Pacific were one ocean there. Thus another great piece of Terra Australis was cartographically sunk.

Geographers were not deterred. The discovery of the Solomons and other Pacific Islands in the late sixteenth century and of New Zealand by the Dutch in 1642 were taken as further evidences of the South Polar continent. The myth further developed that such a continent was a veritable paradise with fertile lands and happy peoples. The economic motive to find the new land became stronger than ever.

THE FIRST EXPLORER

Early in the eighteenth century a young Frenchman, Bouvet d' Lozier, was probably the first explorer to discover the real nature of the antarctic regions. On New Year's Day 1739, a snowy land loomed out of the fog through which his ships were steering a dangerous course south of Africa.

This became Bouvet Island. Bouvet skirted ice fields for a thousand miles and found no land except for the island that bears his name, but he did see great tabular icebergs and guessed quite correctly that they could only be produced from some great landmass to the far south. Such a landmass, he reasoned correctly, must be harsh and disagreeable in contrast to the rich lands which, the geographers of France and Britain had expected explorers to find.

It was left to James Cook, greatest of all antarctic explorers and, in my opinion the greatest ship explorer of all time, to erase forever the idea of a fertile populated southern continent. During his first voyage, from 1768 to 1771, he circumnavigated both islands of New Zealand and thereby took another big slice away from the unknown southern landmass. On his second voyage, from 1772 to 1775, Cook circumnavigated the continent of Antarctica without actually sighting it. He deserved to discover Antarctica for he came close to it several times and was the first explorer ever to cross the Antarctic Circle. Upon Cook's return he observed with prophetic clarity that if there was a southern continent it would be so cold and inhospitable that it could not possibly be suitable for human habitation.

After Napoleon's disastrous retreat from Moscow, Russia emerged as a world power and the expansive mood of the Kremlin stimulated expeditions to both the north and south polar regions. In 1818, Czar Alexander I dispatched a well-equipped expedition under the command of Captain Thaddeus von Bellinghausen to make discoveries "as close as possible to the South Pole." Between 1819 and 1821 Bellinghausen, using Cook's charts, circumnavigated the continent penetrating farther south than Cook and adding important discoveries to those of Cook. Although Bellinghausen's course shows that he was near enough the continent to have seen it, he does not record such a landfall in his log. He was much surprised to find sealers in the sub-antarctic islands.

On his triumphant return in 1775 Cook had reported an abundance of fur seals in South Georgia which stimulated a great increase in their exploitation by British and American sealers. At the height of this slaughter more than 100 vessels were operating in a single season. It would have been strange if some of them had not inadvertently discovered the continent.

Most American students of the problem believe that a youthful New England sealing captain, Nathaniel Palmer, was the first to sight the continent in November 1820. The British are equally sure that it was first sighted by an Englishman, Captain Edward Bransfield, on January 30, 1820. After an examination of the records of his voyage the All-Soviet Geographical Congress concluded in 1949 that von Bellinghausen had discovered the antarctic continent in the Palmer Land sector (northward extension of what is now called the Antarctic Peninsula).

All of these contenders have one thing in common: the assumed achievement of the discovery of Antarctica on the part of all three rests on the interpretation of imperfect records by modern investigators. It is unlikely that the matter will ever be settled to the satisfaction of all concerned. Hopefully it will forever be an item of academic interest only.

A CONTINENT FOUND

The development of steam-powered ships and the gradual replacement of modern ships with iron or iron-clad vesels put greater reliance upon the magnetic compass. The Earth's magnetism became a field of great scientific importance. Sir James

Clark Ross had discovered the north magnetic pole in 1831. Sparked by the work of a great German mathematician, Karl Friedrich Gauss, who predicted that there was a south magnetic pole opposite the north one and that it would be found in latitude 66° south, longitude 146° east, three expeditions were dispatched to search for it during the years 1838 to 1843.

In January 1840, a French expedition under Dumont d' Urville sighted continental land between latitudes 120° and 160° east in the region of the magnetic pole, although d' Urville did not describe his discovery as part of a continent.

An American expedition under the command of Lieutenant Charles Wilkes was dispatched by the U.S. government in 1838 to further knowledge of the prospects for southern whale fishery as well as to carry out scientific exploration. Like d' Urville he was thwarted in his quest for the south magnetic pole since it is well inland, but he did cruise along 1,500 miles of the coastline charting many landfalls along the coast which now bears his name. On January 30, 1840, he wrote: "I make this bay in longitude 140° thirty minutes east, latitude 66° forty-five minutes south and now that all were convinced of its existence I gave the land the name of the Antarctic continent." This is the first confident statement of the reality of a continent. Since Wilkes did not land, his strong statement was something of a guess but modern mapping has shown his discoveries and assumptions to be valid.

SCIENTIFIC PENETRATION

On August 16, 1840, Sir James Clark Ross, with the best equipped ships yet designed for navigation in sea ice, sailed southward from Australia and was able to penetrate through the belt of pack ice that surrounds the continent; this had

Antarctica . . . "the greatest piece of geographical exploration still to be undertaken" (1895 International Geographical Congress).

never been done before. Although he did not reach
the south magnetic pole, Ross did sail to the head
of navigation of the huge embayment that bears
his name, making some of the greatest geographic
discoveries in the history of antarctic exploration.

Following this first scientific penetration, Antarctica was neglected for half a century. Then in
1893 reports of the Challenger expedition, which
had circumnavigated the globe from 1872 to 1875,
were released and greatly influenced the thinking
of the International Geographical Congress held in
London in 1895. The Congress declared that investigation of Antarctica was "the greatest piece of
geographical exploration still to be undertaken."

In 1898 Dr. John Murray, biologist on the Challenger expedition, described the great collection of
rock fragments dredged up from the sea bottom
around Antarctica, which were varied kinds of continental rocks as gneisses, granites, diorities, sand-
stones, limestones and shales. Murray observed
that "there can be no doubt of their having been
transported from land situated near the South
Pole."

While Wilkes was sure he had sighted a continent in 1840, the idea continued to persist that
Antarctica might be a gigantic archipelago smoth-
ered beneath the great inland ice sheet. Most
geographers agreed with Murray's belief that Antarctica was indeed a major continental landmass.
Yet as late as the beginning of the International
Geophysical Year (1957-1958) some Russian scientists supported the belief in a great archipelago.

Actually we know now that both assumptions are
valid for different parts of the continent. Seismic
soundings which reveal the thickness of the inland
ice show that if it were all to melt, East Antarctica
would be revealed as a true continental shield.
On the other hand West Antarctica would become
a great archipelago. But the continent is made one

by its great cover of glacial ice, for ice is just as truly a rock as gneiss or schist or granite.

THE HEROIC AGE

The response to the plea from the International Geographical Congress of 1895 has come to be known as the "heroic age" in antarctic exploration, which lasted from the nineteenth century well into the second decade of the twentieth. This was the most extensive geographic exploration of the continent which had yet been attempted and whose results will stand for all time among the great ones in the history of geographic exploration.

While scientists had played important roles on many of the early expeditions — especially those of Cook, Wilkes and Ross as well as some of the sealing and whaling expeditions — it was not until the turn of the century that teams of scientists were an important integral part of the voyages. All of the expeditions of this era, except that of Amundsen, included teams of scientists who carried out extensive programs in their own fields of research, but it was in the realm of geography that the major discoveries were made. It was during this time that the real nature of Antarctica and its environment were first understood and revealed. Extensive mapping of the coastal areas, the first sighting of the inland ice, significant geological and glaciological discoveries which furnished the basis for subsequent work and conquest of both the geographic and magnetic poles are but a small part of the achievements of this age.

This was an heroic age, both in terms of its achievements and in the caliber of its explorers. A Belgian, Adrien de Gerlache; Erich von Drygalski, a German; Robert Falcon Scott, an Englishman; Sir Ernest Schackleton, a second equally great Englishman; Otto Nordenskjold, a Swede; Jean Charcot, a Frenchman; Roald Amundsen, a Nor-

wegian and Sir Douglas Mawson, an Australian,
are but a few of the leaders who justified the name
of this age.

POSTWAR INTEREST

In the twilight of the Heroic Age, after its inter-
ruption by World War I, interest in Antarctica
was revived and a new, still continuing phase in
its exploration began, made possible by new advances in transportation and communication. For
almost four decades a series of British, Australian,
Norwegian, American, Argentine, Chilean, French
and Russian expeditions added greatly to our knowledge of Antarctica. Among them was the first
continuing program of scientific research in Antarctica; it was primarily oceanographic and marine
biological research, which was carried out by Scott's
old ship *The Discovery* which made 13 voyages
from 1923-39.

The most important development in the whole
field of logistics during these interim years was
the introduction of aircraft.

Before the advent of the airplane no part of the
interior of Antarctica except that adjacent to the
sledge routes of Amundsen, Shackleton and Scott
to the south pole had been uncovered. Exploration in depth beyond the coastal margin of the
continent had to await aircraft.

Three men may be said to have brought the
air age to Antarctica. The first flight was made
by Sir Hubert Wilkins on December 20, 1928,
across what is now the Antarctic Peninsula. Lin-
coln Ellsworth, after two failures, made a successful transantarctic flight in 1935-36 with one com-
panion in a single engine plane — one of the most
remarkable flights in the history of aviation.

Both Wilkins and Ellsworth were concerned
solely with demonstrating the practicality of the

airplane for antarctic exploration. But to Commander (later Rear Admiral) Richard E. Byrd belongs credit for opening up Antarctica to the air age. Indeed, he was the dominant figure in antarctic exploration for nearly three decades. He led two expeditions of his own and played leading roles in three others.

The first Byrd Antarctic Expedition of 1928-30 was the first American expedition since that of Wilkes 90 years before and the first ever to winter over in Antarctica. On January 5, 1929, Byrd made his first flight. Twelve days later a flight farther east produced his first major discovery, the Rockefeller Mountains.

On November 29, 1929, Commander Byrd and two companions flew over the pole. This much publicized flight enabled the expedition to get the financial backing, which made possible important scientific programs, including extended flights over what was later to be called Marie Byrd Land and the first geological survey of the Queen Maud Mountains.

Most of the techniques of travel and communication which make the greatly extended scientific study of Antarctica possible today were pioneered on the first Byrd Antarctic Expedition. Today aircraft are immeasurably more flexible and efficient; oversnow vehicles are immensely more effective, and radios perform better.

In 1946 and again in 1947 the United States dispatched the largest expeditions that had ever explored Antarctica and which made extended use of ships and ship-based aircraft.

The usual follow-up of territorial claims on the basis of discoveries characterized most of the expeditions of these years. Scientific cooperation did not exist except for the Norwegian-British-Swedish Expedition of 1949-1951 which carried out a suc-

cessful exploration in Queen Maud Land. This was
the first truly international exploration in Antarctica. In a way it was the forerunner of the International Geophysical Year.

THE IGY

There had been an International Polar Year in
1882-83 and a second in 1932-33 but it seemed
unwise to wait another 50 years for the third.

In 1950 a formal proposal was placed before
the International Council of Scientific Unions "that
the Third International Polar Year be nominated
for 1957-58 and that in view of the length of time
necessary for adequate organization, an International Polar Year Commission be appointed in
1951 to supervise the planning." The resolution
was approved and at the suggestion of the World
Meteorological Organization the concept of a Polar
Year was extended to include the entire earth.
Thus was born the International Geophysical Year,
which Hugh Odishaw, Executive Director of the
United States National Committee, has aptly called,
"the greatest peacetime activity in man's history."

The ICSU Special Committee, which met in
Rome in 1954 to consider national programs, singled
out two areas for special attention — outer space
and Antarctica — observing that Antarctica was
"a region of almost unparalleled interest in the
fields of geophysics and geography alike." Very
little geophysical work had ever been done in Antarctica and on the eve of the IGY almost half the
continent had not yet been seen by man.

Such significant results were achieved in both
areas that it is a matter of record that the scientific uncovering and exploration of Antarctica was
second only to the space satellite program among
the achievements of the IGY.

The first Antarctic Conference was held in Paris

"The planet Earth . . . is the laboratory; nature performs the experiments and man makes the observations."

from July 6 to 10, 1935. Gen. G. R. Laclavere was elected president and in his opening remarks set the tone for this conference and for the whole program that was to follow. He emphasized the technical character of the conference, excluding problems of finance and politics. Tensions due to overlapping political claims in Antarctica which were evident at the beginning of the sessions were laid to rest, and the following motion by General Laclavere was unanimously adopted: "The Antarctic Conference entirely endorses M. Laclavere's statement of purposes of the opening session and specifically his affirmation that the overall aims of the Conference are entirely scientific." This was a significant decision of great historic importance. Matters of strategic and political concern were set aside as the Antarctic IGY program was dedicated to the sole purpose of scientific exploration. Previously, the climate caused by competitive territorial claims had discouraged the exchange of scientific information.

COOPERATION

This was the beginning of Antarctica's emergence as a great natural and political science laboratory.

From the beginning differences melted away and the willingness to adjust national programs for common goals prevailed. There was flexibility and simplicity and freedom from political considerations without precedent in international scientific cooperation. When all the problems of this initial meeting had been ironed out, the antarctic program emerged as the combined effort of 12 nations — Argentina, France, Australia, Belgium, Chile, Japan, New Zealand, Norway, South Africa, the United Kingdom, the United States and the Soviet Union — with a total of 48 new stations on the margins and in the interior of Antarctica in addition to seven stations already established by Argentina, Chile and the United Kingdom in the Antarctic Peninsula.

The planet earth in its entirety is the geophysicist's laboratory; nature performs the experiments and man makes the observations. The IGY consisted of those programs which were inherently global in character. For Antarctica there were 11 programs: Aurora, cosmic rays, geomagnetism, glaciology, gravity, ionospheric physics, meteorology, international weather central, oceanography, seismology and biology and medicine.

Impressive records were made in all these fields and in the further geographic exploration which resulted in the discovery of the last unknown major physical features on the continent.

Early in the IGY a program for the exchange of scientists was begun whereby research workers of one country joined in the programs of others. This made possible the free and prolonged exchange of scientific information which has continued with increasing scope during the years since the IGY.

The International Antarctic Weather Central at Little America was a further instance of effective international cooperation. Although it was established by U. S. scientists, the weather central was truly international in character with scientists from Argentina, Australia, France, New Zealand, South Africa and the USSR participating fully in its work.

Even before the IGY began it was clear that its program of 18 months would enable scientists to uncover but a small part of Antarctica's secrets. Upon the recommendations of the last Antarctic Conference before the IGY began, ICSU approved the creation of a permanent committee to continue the scientific cooperation of IGY. The new committee held its organizing meeting at The Hague in February 1958. It was designated the Special Committee on Antarctic Research (SCAR). Later the word "Scientific" was substituted for "Special." The new committee consisted of delegates from each nation actively engaged in antarctic research and representatives of various scientific committees which would have overlapping interests in antarctic scientific activity.

There was an important increase in scientific programs beyond geophysics with the advent of SCAR for not only do the various disciplines of geophysics need information for their fulfillment which can come only from Antarctica, but Antarctica presents environmental conditions not duplicated elsewhere on earth. It therefore presents enormous opportunities for biological research. To to IGY programs SCAR added biology, cartography, geology and geodesy. Antarctica had now fully emerged as the greatest natural laboratory on earth. In establishing continuing permanent programs SCAR had now confirmed Antarctica as "A Continent For Science."

POLITICAL LABORATORY

Important as the scientific results of the IGY antarctic and global programs were, in the long run it may be the human and social results which will prove to have been most important. This vast global effort was carried out in a period of almost unprecedented worldwide turmoil and unrest. However, in the midst of all the political tensions, scientists of the IGY demonstrated that reasonable and rational conduct at the scientific level was possible. And it was the IGY cooperative efforts in Antarctica, coldest of all the continents, that witnessed the first thawing of the cold war.

To be sure, international scientific cooperation is not new. It has existed for many centuries, but the IGY did add a new and significant dimension. It demonstrated, as never before, that the international community of science is the most hopeful of all examples of world cooperation and organization.

Scientific cooperation in Antarctica led to the creation of the first treaty ever designed to protect a scientific program; the Antarctic Treaty is a political document without precedent.

HISTORIC BREAKTHROUGH

In my capacity as chairman of the Committee on Polar Research of the National Academy of Sciences, I made the following statement before the Senate Committee on Foreign Relations concerning the proposed treaty:

We know that civilization has evolved largely on the basis of precedents and that a peaceful world depends on the chance of international cooperation. I think it was our hope during the IGY that the intergovernmental cooperation which characterized this vast program would find its way into some kind of permanent cooperation. I believe the Antarctic Treaty is a breakthrough of historic importance. I believe the IGY and es-

pecially the Antarctic program has laid new
foundations for unifying our planet. It ushered
in a new world of cooperation. I believe if the
spirit which obtained during the IGY and
which finds expression in the Antarctic Treaty
is nourished and spreads as it should, history may take a new and more hopeful direction in our time.

The Antarctic Treaty is indispensable to
the world of science which knows no national
or other political boundaries; but it is a document unique in history which may take its
place alongside the Magna Carta and other
great symbols of man's quest for enlightenment
and order.

That my optimism had some foundation is illu-
minated by the following excerpt from a "New
York Times" editorial on December 9, 1969, the
eve of the tenth anniversary of the signing of
the Treaty.

There can be little doubt that this precedent helped to create the foundations of mutual confidence on which the great diplomatic
landmarks of the past decade have been based,
notably the test ban treaty of 1963, the space
compact of 1967, and the nuclear nonprolif-
eration pact of 1968. In effect, Antarctica
has become a political science laboratory, and
the Antarctic Treaty a historic, successful experiment pointing the way for future progress
toward international cooperation.

Now the task is to apply the lessons learned
from that experiment to all of the great contemporary problems where needless suspicion
and rivalry waste huge resources and endan-
ger earth itself.

POLITICAL
LABORATORY

The Antarctic Treaty

PAUL C. DANIELS

One of the milestones in international diplomacy is the Antarctic Treaty of 1959. Not only was it the model for international agreements on the exploration of the moon and other bodies in space, but it was the first to put aside, temporarily at least, national claims in a new region. Nowhere has the close relationship between official actions of government and the private activities of scientists been more clearly demonstrated than in the development of this historic document. Mr. Daniels, now retired from the U.S. State Department, was one of the architects of the Treaty.

There is a close relationship between science and international cooperation. Science, by its very nature, does not recognize national boundaries. Scientific knowledge may advance more rapidly in some countries than in others, at least for a time, but in the long run it becomes the common heritage of man. Among dedicated scientists all over the world there is a desire to share the results of fruitful research in the hope that all will benefit

Paul C. Daniels signing the Antarctic Treaty. Standing: Herman Phleger, Chairman of the U.S. delegation. Seated, extreme left: Christian A. Herter, former Secretary of State.

by a broadening of the base for further investigation. Obviously the complete sharing of technological advances in some fields of applied science, as in the development of military weaponry, is unrealistic in today's disordered world. However, this does not contradict the main point: that science is earth-wide in scope. It would be absurd to think of American chemistry, French physics, English biology or Russian meteorology. Similarly, international cooperation, a political ideal, is aimed at reducing the barriers to peace and progress frequently created by national boundaries and the resultant rivalries and frictions. Thus, science and international cooperation can and should go hand in hand. That this is possible is borne out by the work of the United Nations in such fields as health and meteorology. Even more far-reaching in many ways is the unique and unprecedented agreement embodied in the Antarctic Treaty of 1959.

SEVEN CLAIMS

Before considering some of the major provisions of the Antarctic Treaty, it will be conducive to a better understanding of the matter if we glance back briefly at the origin and antecedents of the Treaty. As a result of many expeditions of exploration and discovery, and a growing interest in this newly discovered continent, a number of countries asserted claims to certain sectors of Antarctica between 1908 and 1940. By mid-century seven nations claimed territorial sovereignty over defined sectors extending from the coast line southward to the pole, each tapering to a point like a slice of pie. These seven sectors covered all of Antarctica except for the part, mostly ice, lying between 90° and 150° west longitude. In alphabetical order, the seven claimant nations are Argentina, Australia, Chile, France, New Zealand, Norway and the United Kingdom.

From the standpoint of the claimant countries, this arrangement seemed simple and orderly. There were, however, three major difficulties: the claims were not generally recognized by the other countries; three of the claims overlapped; and the United States, which had been more active by far than any other country in Antarctica, neither made any territorial claims of its own nor recognized any of those made by others.

SHOTS FIRED

The three claims that overlap are those of Argentina, Chile and the United Kingdom, all on the great Antarctic Peninsula and terrain adjacent thereto. This is obviously a situation fraught with dangerous possibilities; in fact, in 1952, shots were fired by the Argentine navy on some British who were attempting to establish a meteorological station at Hope Bay.

The position of the United States was stated by Secretary of State Charles Evans Hughes in 1924:

> It is the opinion of this department that the discovery of lands unknown to civilization, even when coupled with the formal taking of possession, does not support a valid claim of sovereignty unless the discovery is followed by actual settlement of the discovered country.

In recent years there have been established a number of year-round stations in Antarctica, the largest being the American base at McMurdo Sound. But the policy of the United States remains as stated above.

Accordingly, in the mid-1950s, there was no undisputed title to land (or ice) in Antarctica, there was no agreed legal system, but there was an international political problem of serious implications. This was the situation when, for reasons far removed from the arguments of the foreign offices, far-seeing and imaginative scientists from many lands were making plans for the greatest international cooperative effort in history to gain wider and deeper understanding of the natural geophysical phenomena of the planet Earth. The International Geophysical Year (IGY), which actually was extended to a year and a half — from July 1957 through December 1958 — had the objective of undertaking a worldwide, coordinated, research program in many disciplines so that the results obtained in any one locality would contribute to the value of those from other localities, and therefore have more scientific value than the data obtained from any one isolated program.

The importance of Antarctica in this international program can be judged by the fact that 12 nations participated in the scientific investigations carried out in Antarctica and sub-antarctic areas. In addition to the seven claimant nations mentioned above, active work was carried on by Belgium, Japan, the Union of South Africa, the Soviet Union and the United States. Expeditions were launched, new stations were erected and the antarctic phase of the IGY was successfully inaugurated in July 1957.

GENTLEMAN'S AGREEMENT

Hardly had the IGY embarked on its great work of coordinated scientific investigation, however, than concern began to be manifested in various quarters as to what would happen in Antarctica after the IGY. The various governments concerned had reached a sort of gentleman's agreement not to engage in legal or political argumentation during that period, in order that the scientific program might proceed without impediment. With the impending end of the IGY there was danger that the moratorium on political activity might also end. If this were to happen, the various political differences referred to above might come to the fore again, perhaps in exacerbated form because of the continuing use of some of the stations established for the IGY.

The dangers inherent in this situation were perceived by several governments. In the United States it led to a comprehensive review by the Department of State, in the fall of 1957, of our entire antarctic policy. After many months of consultation with other interested government agencies, and some healthy arguments, it was decided to sound out the other 11 governments directly concerned to see if agreement could be reached on a program which would contribute both to the maintenance of peace in that area and to scientific research. Confidential consultations with the other governments gave assurance that this might be possible. Accordingly on May 2, 1958, the United States addressed identical notes to those countries, setting forth this program and proposing that a conference be convened to conclude a treaty to give it legal and lasting effect. The broad objectives of the United States' note were set forth in the third paragraph as follows:

> The International Geophysical Year comes to a close at the end of 1958. The need for coordinated scientific research in Antarctica, however, will continue for many years into the future. Accordingly, it would appear desirable for those countries participating in the Antarctic program of the International Geophysical Year to reach agreement among themselves on a program to assure the continuation of the fruitful scientific cooperation referred to above. Such an arrangement could have the additional advantage of preventing unnecessary and undesirable political rivalries in that continent, the uneconomic expenditure of funds to defend individual national interests, and the recurrent possibility of international misunderstanding. It would appear that if harmonious agreement can be reached among the countries directly concerned in regard to friendly cooperation in Antarctica, there would be advantages not only to those countries but to all other countries as well.

After reaffirming the basic rights of the United States in Antarctica, the note proposed that the

12 countries having a direct interest in that area conclude a treaty which would have the following peaceful purposes:

A. Freedom of scientific investigation throughout Antarctica by citizens, organizations and governments of all countries; and a continuation of the international scientific cooperation which is being carried out so successfully during the current International Geophysical Year.

B. International agreement to ensure that Antarctica be used for peaceful purposes only.

C. Any other peaceful purposes not inconsistent with the Charter of the United Nations.

In addition, the note put forward five suggestions for consideration by the other governments: (1) That no nation be required to renounce any rights or claims; (2) that such rights and claims would remain unaffected during the life of the Treaty; (3) that no new claims would be made by any country during the life of the Treaty; (4) that provision be made for such joint administrative arrangements as might contribute to the accomplishment of the agreed objectives; and (5) that the cooperation of the specialized technical agencies of the United Nations would be sought.

It is of interest to note that all the objectives and suggestions listed above were subsequently embodied in the Antarctic Treaty.

ALL IN FAVOR

Because of the prior consultations which had been held with the other governments, the replies to the United States' note of May 2, 1958, were received within a short space of time. All were favorable. The question then arose as to how to proceed at this point. It was generally agreed that to convene an international conference dealing with such novel and controversial questions would be unwise, and possibly dangerous, unless adequate preparations were made. Accordingly, and always in consultation with all the governments concerned,

Paul C. Daniels

it was decided to hold preparatory talks in Washington with a view to analyzing in detail the various points which had been proposed and others which might arise, in the hope of reaching a broad area of agreement which would ensure the success of the conference to be convened at a later date.

These preparatory talks began in June 1958, and were continued for well over a year. In the course of the talks agreement was reached on the major provisions of the proposed treaty, subject, of course, to the decisions to be reached at the conference.

INSURING FAIRNESS

Two features of these preparatory talks should be mentioned. First, they were held in the strictest of secrecy, to avoid the disadvantages which would ensue if the controversial subjects under discussion were to be debated publicly by the news media and the politicians in the various countries. This secrecy was conscientiously observed by all the representatives of the 12 governments, so much so that not even the place of the meetings was known to the public. (As a matter of fact, most of the meetings were held in the well-appointed board room of the National Academy of Sciences.) Second, in order to further a sense of joint participation in this effort, the chairmanship of the meetings was rotated, in alphabetical order, at each meeting. As a result the working papers produced by these preparatory talks, which were drafted in the form of articles suitable for a treaty, represented a joint effort and not the proposal of any one country.

Upon the conclusion of these preparatory talks, it was announced around mid-1959, again with the prior approval of all 12 governments, that the proposed conference would be convened in Washington on October 15, 1959.

As agreed, the Conference on Antarctica convened on that date with the presence of distinguished representatives from all 12 countries. The delegates to the Conference had before them the working papers already drafted in the course of the preparatory talks. This was a novel situation, because frequently specific treaty proposals are advanced by a given country, and sponsored by it, rather than by representatives of all participating countries acting jointly.

The delegates to the Conference entered into their negotiations with diligence and in the relatively short time of six weeks reached agreement on the final draft. The Treaty was signed on December 1, 1959 and the Conference was closed on that date.

For the Treaty to become fully effective, ratifications were necessary. Each country, in accordance with its constitutional procedures, set about this task. All 12 ratified the Treaty, the last ratifications being deposited on June 23, 1961. On that date the Antarctic Treaty entered into force.

It is unnecessary in this brief article to analyze each of the various articles of the Antarctic Treaty. However, the significance of some of the major provisions merit comment. For example, Article I provides that Antarctica shall be used for peaceful purposes only; and Article II provides for freedom of scientific investigation in Antarctica and for cooperation toward that end. In other words, the first two articles of the Treaty reflect the thought expressed in the opening paragraph, i.e., that science and international cooperation go hand in hand. This same thought is further reinforced by Article III, which provides that information regarding plans for scientific programs shall be exchanged to permit maximum economy and efficiency; that scientific personnel shall be exchanged between the various expeditions and stations; and that the scientific observations and results obtained shall be exchanged and made freely available. None of these requirements could be successfully accomplished in an atmosphere of international hostility; on the other hand they all contribute to the political ideal of international cooperation.

AVOIDING PROBLEMS

Another article of the Treaty having great significance is the one providing for periodic consultative meetings of representatives of the participating governments to consider and recommend to their governments measures in furtherance of the principles and objectives of the Treaty. This requirement is significant for three reasons:

1. The opportunity afforded to exchange information and to discuss current problems of mutual

interest gives some assurance that misunderstandings will not arise and that friendly cooperation will continue. If each of the participating governments were to go it alone in Antarctica, without such continuing consultation, there might result a loss of efficiency and economy.

2. The measures recommended by these consultative meetings, when approved by all the participating governments, become effective and are applicable throughout Antarctica the same as the Treaty under which they are formulated. This permits the gradual development of a body of administrative arrangements and regulations throughout Antarctica, something which has not previously existed.

3. From the very outset the consultative meetings have relied heavily on the experience and technical advice of the Scientific Committee on Antarctic Research (SCAR). This circumstance is of significance in demonstrating once more the close relationship between the official actions of governments and the private activities of the international scientific community. The mutual support which they lend each other is advantageous to both.

NUCLEAR BAN

The consultative meetings are likewise significant because of the continuity which they give to the Antarctic Treaty. Some treaties are negotiated after long and arduous negotiations and, if ratified, may be put away in the file cabinet to gather dust. This cannot happen to the Antarctic Treaty. Its continuity is assured so long as the Treaty is in effect. Already five consultative meetings have been held: Canberra, 1961; Buenos Aires, 1962; Brussels, 1964; Santiago, 1966; Paris, 1968; Tokyo, 1970. In addition, there have been meetings on specialized subjects such as telecommunications and logistics. Through these meetings the Antarctic Treaty acquires vitality, and a practical aspect going beyond the more abstract and political concepts contained in the Treaty. Whether this increasing activity in a number of fields will require some sort of a permanent secretariat, or special funds to be expended on joint administrative measures, it is too early to tell.

For *Bulletin* readers Article V is of special interest, in that it prohibits nuclear explosions in Antarctica. Although this article does not prohibit the use of an atomic plant for light, heat and power, there is a complete ban on nuclear explosions throughout the vast expanse of Antarctica. Neither the United States, France, Russia nor any other country can test nuclear bombs. This article has given rise to no controversy but it is worth mentioning as one small step in the right direction.

Another article of the Treaty merits special mention. This is Article VII, which provides for unlimited inspection by any of the participating countries of any station or installation in Antarctica. The United States and several other countries have already carried out inspections under this article of the Treaty. There is no reason to suspect that any country is deliberately violating any provision of the Treaty, but it has been felt that the exercise of this right in a routine manner will promote mutual confidence among all countries active in Antarctica, and give added assurance that the provisions of the Treaty are in fact being observed.

Notwithstanding the many major problems which have been dealt with in the Antarctic Treaty, it would be a mistake to view the Treaty as an international agreement which has served its purpose and can now be neglected. To be sure, it has operated successfully so far and as of today there are no major controversies among the participat-

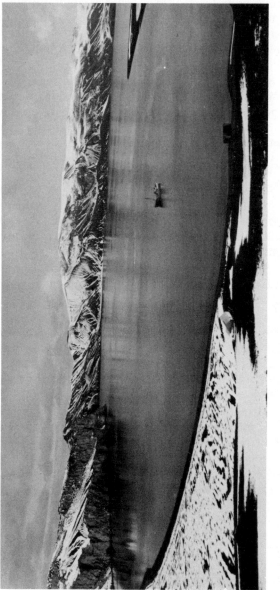

"In view of the fact that Antarctica is a relatively unspoiled and uncontaminated part of the world, perhaps now is the time to engage in joint discussions regarding the rational control of pollution and contamination."

ing governments. However there is much unfinished business. There are a number of problems which either have arisen or may arise requiring international agreements and joint decisions. Among these problems are the following:

1. Because of the basically confused legal situation in Antarctica there is no general agreement on the exercise of jurisdiction in civil and criminal cases. So far this lack of an agreed jurisdictional system has not led to any serious controversies, but it would obviously be useful if some broad basis of agreement could be reached.

2. The development and exploitation of living resources, particularly in the waters adjacent to Antarctica, is a matter which could be further discussed with a view to reaching agreement on regulations fair to all concerned.

3. Similarly, if any mineral resources of commercial value should be discovered, questions would arise as to the rights of ownership and development.

4. In view of the fact that Antarctica is a relatively unspoiled and uncontaminated part of the world, perhaps now is the time to engage in joint discussions regarding the rational control of pollution and contamination.

5. Already a number of recommendations have been approved through the consultative process regarding telecommunications, tourism and the conservation of living resources, but much more remains to be done.

Already more than 10 years have elapsed since the Treaty was signed on December 1, 1959. The Treaty is to remain in effect for 30 years from the date of its entry into force on June 23, 1961. Four years can be added to that period because of the procedures provided for withdrawal and possible termination. Accordingly, the Treaty is safe until 1995. But the future of the Treaty should be considered in broader terms than merely referring to its stated duration. What is more important is that the broad principles embodied in the Treaty, if not the Treaty itself, continue on indefinitely. This will not happen automatically. It is essential that the governments give continuing attention to problems such as those indicated above in the hope of reaching rational agreement long before they reach the point of controversy. This can best be done quietly through informal consultation among officials of the various governments, prior to public discussions at the consultative meetings. There is good reason to hope that agreement may be reached on existing problems in this way, and by utilizing the procedures set forth by the Treaty for formalizing them. What is essential is that there be continuing consultation among the participating nations. The Antarctic Treaty can and should be preserved, and points of possible difference settled in a rational manner. If this can be accomplished, then from that most remote and inhospitable part of the earth there will radiate a warm glow of human understanding which should have a beneficial influence in more troubled areas. If this same spirit of Antarctica can be applied successfully to the problems of outer space and the deep seas, then mankind has an opportunity to come ever closer to the fulfillment of three of our noblest aspirations: the pursuit of knowledge, friendly cooperation among the peoples of the world and the maintenance of peace.

The Political Experiment in Antarctica

FINN SOLLIE

The antarctic model of politico-scientific co-operation is a complex structure. Its blend of arms control, political agreement on a modus vivendi and mixed scientific and governmental cooperation is adapted to the special conditions of Antarctica. Such a blend may not function so well on other international science frontiers, such as the bottom of the sea and outer space. In fact, wholesale transfer for the antarctic model may neither be desirable nor practicable. Finn Sollie is director of the Fridtjof Nansen Foundation at Polhogda, Norway, and a specialist in international law.

The experience of the last decade is generally accepted as ample proof that the three main objectives of the Antarctic Treaty have been successfully attained and the success of the antarctic sys-

tem naturally attracts attention to it as a possible
model for application in other and more or less similar environments. The arctic, the seabed under the
high seas and space are such new environments,
where the nature and magnitude of the task of exploration call for international cooperation

The main objectives of the Treaty were to prevent any but the peaceful uses of Antarctica, insure free access and avert discord by waiving for a
time claims to territory and to secure the continuation and further development of scientific exploration. The realization of these aims had been facilitated by the fact that at the time of treaty negotiations, an international apparatus for scientific cooperation on a permanent basis had emerged from
the International Geophysical Year. This was the
Special Committee on Antarctic Research (SCAR),
which the International Council of Scientific Unions
had set up before treaty negotiations started to
plan for post-IGY scientific exploration of Antarctica. The Committee convened in February 1958
and has since become a permanent organization,
with its own secretariat. In 1961, its name was
changed to the Scientific Committee on Antarctic
Research.

SCAR, like its parent organization ICSU (International Council of Scientific Unions), was a nongovernmental institution representing the scientific
interests of its member countries. It did not have
political responsibilities and was not subject to control or supervision by the interested governments.
Consequently, there was a need for defining the
role and functions of this scientific organization and
its activities in relation to problems of a political
nature which required governmental action. This
could be done either by including such provisions
in necessary detail in the treaty itself, or by having
the relationship between science and politics worked

out gradually in the continued process of cooperation. In the latter case, there would be a need for
organized liaison between the governments after
the treaty entered into force. As it turned out, this
was the solution agreed upon, and this combination
of nongovernmental and governmental elements of
organization and the interaction between them is
one of the most interesting features of the antarctic
system. While this relationship, which was in large
measure a result of the chronology of events, is
determined by the special conditions and the situation in Antarctica, it is also an experiment in the
combination of governmental and nongovernmental
elements of cooperation in a new environment that
may be of value for similar experiments in other
regions.

In the case of the Arctic, there is a growing interest in scientific quarters for cooperation along the
pattern applied in Antarctica, a fact that is clearly
reflected, for example, in the 1970 report on polar
research prepared by the U.S. Committee on Polar
Research, and which has caused SCAR to focus attention on scientific cooperation also in the Arctic.

MODEL LIMITATIONS

In this connection, however, it is necessary to
emphasize that the antarctic model is a complex
structure composed of all the elements indicated
above and that its blend of arms control, political
agreement on a modus vivendi and mixed scientific
and governmental cooperation is adapted to the
special situation and conditions of Antarctica.
While some of the elements of this model may be
applicable to other regions, wholesale transfer of the
antarctic model to other environments may be neither desirable nor practicable. Thus, in the case of
the Arctic the question is not about a region far removed from the centers of communication, economic
development and military power, but about an area

where the political, economic and strategic interests of several nations are directly and immediately involved. In the case of the seabed, economic interests already are involved and, in addition to the difficult problem of establishing an agreed line of demarcation between areas reserved for the exclusive control of coastal states, there is worldwide interest calling for a solution within the framework of the United Nations which obviates the more exclusive system of cooperation between a small number of states. In the case of space, the situation is again different, because only the superpowers possess the capability for active participation.

On the other hand, while the complete structure of antarctic cooperation may not lend itself to transfer to other regions, elements of it may be suited for adaptation to new environments. It is a system of scientific cooperation through an international nongovernmental committee combined with an agreement, tacit or explicit, that operations under such an arrangement shall not constitute a basis for national claims nor, indeed, for internationalization at the political level. Such a system may prove to be a working formula also for other environments. Potentially, as in the case of Antarctica, it may also prepare the ground for improved political relationships and international cooperation at the governmental level.

OUTER SPACE TREATY

The fact that operations in Antarctica are so predominantly concentrated on scientific exploration does not signify that cooperation there is primarily a technical matter, nor does it mean that antarctic cooperation is not important in the wider and more political perspective of international relations. It is obvious that Antarctica rates far below a great many, probably most, other regions in political importance. Those who are familiar with antarctic affairs, however, know that political considerations are important. This was particularly true, of course, during the renegotiation of the Treaty. As one of the participants at the Washington Conference in 1959 has remarked: "The Conference was all politics and very little science." Significantly, he also added that when it became evident that the Conference would succeed, "we all felt elated and knew that something important was about to happen." The Treaty itself, therefore, as well as the subsequent experience of its functioning in practice may offer lessons in international cooperation that can be of use in a wider international perspective than that encompassed by the 60° southern parallel. In fact, according to H. G. Darwin (The Outer Space Treaty, in "British Yearbook on International Law 1967"), the Antarctic Treaty began "one of the most rapidly growing branches of international law which concerns the peaceful and orderly regulation of new environments opened up with new techniques. . . ." More recent shoots on this branch are the Outer Space Treaty (1968) and the current active debates on regulation of the seabed. Also the Nuclear Test Ban Treaty (1963) and the Non-Proliferation Treaty (1968) may be considered as belonging to this new branch, although the environment they are concerned with is of a rather special nature.

While Antarctica was the first of these new environments where peaceful regulation was provided, the regime established there remains as the most comprehensive both in terms of the range of problems it covers and in terms of the scope of its regulations. The reason for this can safely be assumed to be that Antarctica has offered more favorable conditions than other environments for regulation and for active and continuous international cooperation. As a contrast, it may be mentioned that scientific cooperation was also sought for the Arctic in connection with the IGY, but with no success; and attempts at limited arms control in the Arctic, for example, the U.S. proposal in 1958 that the U.N. Security Council should consider a proposal to establish a "northern zone of interna-

"The conditions of Antarctica, in contrast to other new environments, restricts the likelihood of copying the Antarctic regime elsewhere. . . ."

tional inspection against surprise attack," have been abortive.

The conditions of Antarctica, in contrast to other new environments, restricts the likelihood of copying the antarctic regime elsewhere, but they also offer opportunity for continued and more active experimentation. Although new approaches and techniques may be more easily developed and tested in Antarctica than in other environments, they can prove to be valuable for progress in those other environments. Primarily, however, Antarctica may be used as a proving ground for its own future development. The antarctic system is neither complete nor fail-safe, and unless contingencies are provided before new needs for orderly regulation become immediate and pressing, the present system of cooperation may suffer severe strains. Antarctica's potential role as a political laboratory, however, calls for a closer look at the present system and its operation in practice.

From a disarmament point of view, the Antarctic Treaty provided a near maximum solution by prohibiting "inter alia, any measures of a military nature, such as the establishment of military bases and fortifications, the carrying out of military maneuvers, as well as the testing of any type of weapons." The prohibition was rendered less than total by the provision that the treaty "shall not prevent the use of military personnel or equipment for scientific research or for any other peaceful purpose," an exception that was made necessary by the fact that the navies of some of the parties had long been engaged in antarctic exploration and that military equipment and personnel were—and still are—widely used for logistics and support activities. The danger of breaches against the 'military prohibitions was foreclosed by the treaty's provisions for inspections and by the obligation imposed upon

the parties to give advance notice of intended operations.

FREE INSPECTION

No restrictions were set for the right to carry out
inspections: observers "shall have complete freedom
of access to any and all areas" and "all stations,
installations and equipment within these areas, and
all ships and aircraft at points of discharging or embarking cargoes or personnel in Antarctica, shall be
open at all times for inspection. . . ." Aerial inspection, the method first proposed by President Eisenhower in the general "open skies plan" at the
Geneva summit meeting in July 1955, and later proposed for a limited zone in the Arctic (but both
times rejected) also may be carried out in Antarctica. An important feature of the inspection system
is that inspections are to be carried out unilaterally,
by observers appointed by each party. This has
the advantage, of course, that inspections may be
as effective as each of the parties is determined to
make them, since they are neither dependent upon
advance agreement or approval in each instance
nor subject to the tactics of obstruction that may
be used when inspections are carried out by multi-
national teams or international commissions. On
the other hand, and this shows one of the difficulties
of creating a perfect inspections system, the fact
that inspections are to be carried out unilaterally,
and not by a joint agency set up for that purpose,
leaves the smaller nations in a less than satisfactory
situation since only a large power will have the
resources and capability effectively to inspect activities in a region with such vast distances and
harsh conditions as Antarctica.

For the smaller nations, the main security will
lie in the deterrent effect of an arms ban combined
with the obligation of the parties to give advance

notice of "all expeditions to and within Antarctica
—all stations—and any military personnel or equipment intended to be introduced. . . ." While this
may not prevent the large powers from disregarding
the arms ban in an emergency or crisis situation—
and then they might not be stopped by any inspection—the deterrent effect may be sufficient to prevent minor incursions that can erode the arms ban
gradually over a long period and to exclude lesser
attempts to "cheat the rules" that military estab-
lishments may sometimes feel tempted to make.

The right of inspections has not been widely used.
Only five countries—New Zealand in 1963, Australia and Great Britain, jointly in 1963, Argentina
in 1965 and the United States in 1964 and again
in 1967—have carried out inspections. Of these,
only the U.S. inspections have included a large
number of installations in wide areas, while the
others have been limited to a few stations in a
small area. In no instance were indications found
of malpractice or nonobservance of the Treaty or
agreed rules and regulations. The limited number
of inspections apparently reflects a general feeling
that there is little need for the parties to check on
each other, as well as the fact that inspections are
costly and must have low priority. With the exception of the United States, the parties do not seem
to have taken great interest in making inspections
a normal and regular part of their activities.

JOINT INSPECTION TOURS

While this reticence with regard to inspections
is easily explained and understood, those who look
at inspections in Antractica in the perspective of
the general international disarmament effort may
nevertheless find it deplorable. To them it will seem
that while there may indeed be scant reason for any
of the parties to feel that inspections are necessary

in Antarctica, at least for the time being, and that even if the cost of inspections is considerable in terms of the funds available for activities in Antarctica, a more active inspections policy might be in order. In this connection it may be observed that in addition to the value of more regular inspections as a means to strengthen the inspections concept generally, a more active policy also may promote experimentation and the development of new techniques that can be important in the general disarmament effort. As mentioned above, the smaller nations will have great difficulty in carrying out inspections effectively under a system where each country has a right to inspect the activities of the others. They can, however, as was done by Australia and Great Britain in 1963, organize joint tours. If they did this on a regular basis, they might develop experience and techniques for organizing systems of control that could strengthen the position of smaller nations in the general disarmament talks. So far, the antarctic example has made no significant impact upon the disarmament effort in other parts of the world, even though it is true that the Antarctic Treaty's provisions for arms prohibition, free access and inspections have been fairly closely copied in the Outer Space Treaty. With a more active policy in this regard, the parties might possibly be able to make a larger contribution.

NUCLEAR TEST BAN

Today, the value of the nuclear test ban in the Antarctic Treaty is mostly historical. It deserves mention, however, because it was the first general international test ban and one which was adopted only on the very eve of the Washington Conference after long and difficult negotiations. Agreement to prohibit "the testing of any type of weapons" was reached at an early stage of the conference; but this left open the possibility of nonmilitary nuclear

explosions for peaceful purposes including such experiments as, for instance, that of excavating artificial harbors with nuclear energy. Upon the insist-
ence of some of the parties, especially some of the
southern hemisphere countries which may have
been more concerned with the dangers of radioactive
fallout than with the difficulty of distinguishing
between peaceful explosions and military tests, it
was finally agreed that "any nuclear explosion in
Antarctica and the disposal there of radioactive
waste material shall be prohibited." Thus, the Antarctic Treaty was to be a forerunner of the Nuclear
Test-Ban Treaty, as well as of an early agreement
to prevent environmental pollution from radioactive
waste.

As might be expected in the case of an issue where
opinions were sharply divided and where clear
national interests were involved, the Antarctic
Treaty's measures to prevent discord through an
agreement on the sovereignty issue barely moved
beyond the absolute minimum required for temporary political pacification.

While the first claim to antarctic territory had
been made as early as in 1908, by Great Britain, a
rush to secure a slice of the frozen land developed
only shortly before World War II. The first demòn-
stration of dramatic competition came in 1939,
when Norway hurried to annex Queen Maud Land
and forestalled German occupation of the same
area. Then Chile, in 1940, and Argentina, in 1942,
claimed sectors that partially overlapped, and both
of them conflicted with the previous British claim.
Antarctica, therefore, was ripe with latent conflict
and a potential danger zone. In an episode in 1952
shots were fired.

The disagreement was not only about who should
have a share of Antarctica and about the criteria
for determining the legitimacy of claims, but also
a more basic difference of opinion on the principle

of annexation itself. As a matter of principle, reinforced by the fact that they had let their opportunity slip by so that only the least desirable parts
of Antarctica remained open for new claims, several
nations maintained that national claims to antarctic territory could not be recognized, that the
whole region must still be regarded as a "no-land's
land" and that the only solution was to arrange for
internationalization of the whole territory. The
arguments here were fairly similar to those involved
in the seabed issue, although the theory of con-
tiguity—of territorial rights through an area's near-
ness to the national territory—applies only to some
of the claims to Antarctica.

After a series of preliminary discussions in which
a trusteeship for Antarctica under the United Nations was also considered, a definitive proposal for
internationalization was made in 1948. In a note
to the seven countries with previous claims, the
United States proposed that they, together with
the United States, set up a condominium or co-
government for Antarctica. The plan, however, did
not win general approval from the seven and it soon
became apparent that an exclusive condominium
might cause Antarctica to become an additional
issue in the cold war which had reached a critical
stage with the Berlin blockade in June 1948. The
Soviet Union obviously could not be expected to
accept the antarctic solution proposed by the United States unless she was herself included as one of
the condominium states. Diplomatic representa-
tions were made and books and articles published
in the Soviet Union served to emphasize the historical bases for Soviet interests in Antarctica, as
well as the Soviet Union's general right to participate in any antarctic settlement.

A NON-SOLUTION

The Antarctic Treaty's solution to these prob-

lems was in the form of nonsolution, a type of con-
structive evasion based on a proposal for a modus
vivendi with regard to claims that Chile had made
in reply to the U.S. condominium proposal. As
stated in Article IV of the Treaty, it was agreed
that nothing contained in the Treaty should (1)
imply a renunciation of existing claims or asserted
rights, nor (2) involve any diminution of any basis
for claims nor (3) should it prejudice the position
of any of the parties with regard to recognition or
nonrecognition of claims. Furthermore, and this
was the crux of the compromise, it was agreed that
while the treaty was in force no acts or activities
should constitute a basis for asserting, supporting
or denying claims, and that no new claims should
be made as long as the treaty was in force. Through
this moratorium on claims with its preservation of
the status quo, all of the parties reserved their
rights for the duration of the treaty. The guarantee
that their claims would not be weakened or endan-
gered while the treaty was in force gave the states
with previous claims the assurances they needed to
agree to free and unlimited access and operation of
expeditions and stations from other countries within
their territories for a prolonged period. The non-
claimants and internationalists on their part had
their minimum requirement met when they got free
access to and freedom of scientific exploration in all
parts of Antarctica without conceding the rights
of any of the claimants or prejudicing their own
right either to make their own claims or to press
for internationalization if and when the treaty
should be terminated. A further advantage of this
arrangement was that by removing politics from
operations in Antarctica, it was possible to leave
science to the scientists themselves and to let them
continue to develop their own system of cooperation
within the nongovernmental organization that had
been developed in connection with the IGY.

For more than a decade, Antarctica has been an international haven for scientists. They have demonstrated their ability to develop their side of the antarctic system of cooperation for the benefit of science and without apparent side effects of a political nature. This does not mean that political considerations have been completely ruled out by the Antarctic Treaty; they are reflected in a num-

ber of ways in a number of cases large and small—
even down to the size of commemorative postal
stamps, whose design can cause problems—and bear
witness to the tentative nature of the political
settlement. (In 1965, for example, a separate recom-
mendation was adopted in connection with a commemorative stamp issue for the Antarctic Treaty
1961-1971, to the effect that stamps issued by the
parties should have as their most prominent feature
the "map of Antarctica which appears on the official documents of Consultative Meetings," i.e., without territorial claims drawn in, and that "any additional matter should be consonant with the provisions and spirit of the Antarctic Treaty.")

As a scientific body, SCAR has no political functions and care is always taken to maintain scrupu-
lously its purely scientific status, even to the extent
of reluctance at consultative meetings to adopt ver-
batim recommendations SCAR has prepared on request. On the other hand, the fact that, up to this
point, the major function of cooperation at the
government level has been to facilitate continued
scientific cooperation has given SCAR and the antarctic scientist a vital role in the total process of
antarctic cooperation. In addition to its own activities at the scientific level, SCAR is frequently called
upon for advice on matters brought up to consultative meetings, for example, in connection with measures for preservation and conservation of living resources. Furthermore, although practice may vary
from country to country, national scientific committees on Antarctica, which form the organization basis of SCAR, often are called upon to advise their
governments on antarctic matters. For these reasons, as well as because of the limited number of persons involved nationally as well as internationally in
antarctic affairs and because of the relative stability
of this personnel both in science and government,
antarctic scientists and their organization hold a

position of considerable influence. To what extent this influence, and its obviously beneficial effects upon cooperation also at the government level, may be maintained if and when other than scientific interests become actively involved is of course impossible to say.

ECONOMIC EXPLOITATION

Much of the success of antarctic cooperation during the last decade is certainly due to the fact that activities have been concentrated on science, and that scientific cooperation has not required a fully developed international organization at the government level nor substantial and substantive regulations involving controversial issues of jurisdiction and national prerogatives. There is, however, no reason to expect that such issues can be permanently avoided. It is when these issues are met head on that the antarctic system must prove how much of a success it really is.

One of the contingencies that may force such a test is the advent of economic exploitation. At present, the outlook for any significant economic development in Antarctica is bleak, and tourism still appears to be the only industry capable of any real growth there. However, exploration often is a forerunner of exploitation even in the most inaccessible environments, and tourism itself may raise jurisdictional problems that require a more positive agreement on the sovereignty issue than that reached in the current moratorium. The question, for instance, of who shall have jurisdiction if a French tourist who arrives at the U.S. McMurdo station on board a Norwegian ship on a tour arranged by a British agency and who becomes subject to a serious crime committed by a person of unknown nationality during his stay in the New Zealand sector may not be any easier to solve than the

question about the proper authority for regulation
of mineral prospecting and mining. The risks of
such unfortunate episodes, as well as the possibility
that other kinds of activities than the purely scientific will require positive regulation, appear bound
to increase with the passage of time. Here, provisions with regard to the duration of the Treaty
may give a false sense of security, but also an opportunity for experiments toward a gradual settlement
of controversial issues.

During the negotiations in 1959, proposals with
regard to the time period of the Treaty ranged from
a fixed 10-year period to indefinite duration. The
final compromise was that no fixed termination date
was set, but after 30 years any of the active parties
might request that a conference be called "to review
the operation of the Treaty." (There may be a
natural temptation in this to take a wait-and-see
attitude and to postpone consideration and consultation on difficult problems in the hope that they
will not develop to a crisis point before 1991. The
assumption that serious incidents and crises can be
avoided before that time, and that outstanding
problems can be effectively solved with one stroke
at such a conference, both will contain an element
of risk.

If no modification or amendment to the Treaty
is agreed to at such a conference, the Treaty will
remain in force as before and without a legitimate
cause for withdrawal from it.

If changes are agreed to and then ratified by all
of the active parties, the Treaty will remain in force
in its altered form and, unless a withdrawal clause
has been added, without legitimate cause for withdrawal.

If, on the other hand, modifications or amend-
ments to the Treaty are adopted by a majority at
the conference, but not ratified by all of the parties
and thereby do not become effective, any of the

parties can withdraw from the Treaty.

This rather unique procedure leaves a large amount of uncertainty as to the future of the Treaty. On the other hand, the moratorium provisions in Article IV insure that nothing that happens while the Treaty is in force shall imply or constitute a permanent modification of the status of previous claims or with regard to the rights of non-claimants. Thus the parties do in effect have an opportunity to make temporary arrangements without prejudicing their position. In the consultative meetings they have a mechanism for making such arrangements without amending the Treaty, even in matters that will be controversial if they are coupled to the sovereignty issue in such a way that they will permanently affect the status of or position on claims.

It would seem that under these circumstances the parties to the Antarctic Treaty can expand their active cooperation gradually in a step-by-step process and arrange for orderly regulation at an early stage also in matters where even now incidents may precipitate minor crises and in matters where latent issues may turn acute if and when antarctic operations move definitively beyond the stage of pure scientific exploration. They could, in effect, make Antarctica—which has for more than 10 years been an international laboratory for science—into an international political laboratory for further experiments in cooperation.

Antarctica

Experimental Proving Ground for Peaceful Coexistence and International Collaboration

Ye. K. FEDOROV

The antarctic from my point of view is useful as a testing ground for developing through experience forms of peaceful co-existence and close collaboration of various countries in mastering a difficult but very interesting region of our planet. Academician Ye. K. Fedorov is Chief, Hydrometeorological Service of the USSR.

In January 1820, Russian sailors under the command of Faddey von Bellingshausen and Mikhail

Lazarev for the first time caught sight of and discovered the continent of Antarctica while sailing around the world on a research mission in the small ships, *Vostok* and *Mirny*. In January 1956, the first Soviet Antarctic Expedition, led by Mikhail Somov, approached the antarctic coast near Haswell Island to establish a base for scientific investigation and build an observatory. In that interval, the uninhabited ice continent had not recorded many events. At the turn of the century, its glaciers were an arena for competing expeditions, each racing to be first to reach the South Pole. In summer, ships approached shore, simple shelters were set up on the rocks or just on the glaciers. Here expedition members lived through the winter in order to start for the Pole in the spring. In early spring, expeditions led by the Englishman, Robert F. Scott, and the Norwegian, Roald Amundsen, set out on different routes to reach the South Pole. Amundsen arrived there a month ahead of Scott. On the way back, Scott and five of his companions perished of exhaustion and cold. Amundsen, however, returned safely to his base. Incidentally, Russians were among the crews of both expeditions. They were A. Kuchin, D. Girev and A. Omel'chenko.

Once the South Pole had been reached, the problems of research and, possibly, development became uppermost. In the 1920s and 1930s several great expeditions equipped by various countries were active in Antarctica. Soviet polar explorers know well and respect the names of such explorers as the Australian, Douglas Mawson, and the Englishman, Ernest Shackleton. The American, Richard E. Byrd, who became an admiral after his successful flight over the North Pole, organized a large expedition to reconnoiter Antarctica from the air. He flew over the South Pole in an airplane.

Explorers discovered mountain ranges and the great mountain systems of Antarctica, in their rough features, began to appear on the maps. But the structure of this continent, the phenomena in the atmosphere above it and in the oceans around it remained unexplored, giving rise to many hypotheses—often contradictory ones.

Only in 1956 was broad research begun on the antarctic as part of the vast program of the International Geophysical Year. Twelve nations apportioned their scientists, resources and apparatus to study the ice-clad region. Actual international collaboration was established. It was the first and most effective instance of an understanding concerning the peaceful utilization of a vast region of the Earth for joint scientific work.

Soviet scholars performed a significant share of this joint effort. Among them were experts who had received experience and training on drifting stations in the Arctic Ocean: A. F. Treshnikov, E. I. Tolstikov, E. S. Korotkevich, P. K. Sen'kow, V. A. Bugayev, A. P. Kapitsa, A. G. Avsyuk, P. A. Shumsky, M. G. Ravich and many others.

Fifteen years have passed. The 16th Soviet Antarctic Expedition left Leningrad in October 1970 to replace the 15th expedition on the ice continent. More than 200 Soviet citizens, working in Antarctica in rotation, continue the scientific investigation. Opposite the western coast of Australia, in the region where the first Soviet Expedition arrived in Antarctica, Mirny Station was built, named for one of the ships of von Bellingshausen and Lazarev.

In 1956-57, this settlement consisted of some 20, well-appointed huts, supplied with light and heat by a central power plant. A powerful radio station guaranteed communications with other stations in the antarctic and with Moscow.

However, during the construction of Mirny, our

explorers were unable to consider all the peculiarities of the chosen spot. Strong and continuous winds, together with the character of the terrain on the minute section of rocky shore jutting out from the glacier, caused all the huts to be covered by a thick layer of snow after several years. One has to descend two or three flights of steep stairs before entering a hut. Not a sound reaches down there from the surface, nor does any light filter through. In summer, when it thaws, streams flow from the ceilings of the rooms. They are diverted by various, clever devices under the floor—where a lake forms beneath each hut.

A NEW STATION

For this reason, the principal base of our Expedition is being moved to Molodiozhnaya, a new station now being completed. It is about 2,000 kilometers to the west, roughly on the meridian that passes through Madagascar. Facilities have been provided there for carrying out the most diverse investigations, including the launching of meteorological rockets to an altitude of 100 to 200 km. A radio center and good living quarters have been built. About 1,400 km to the west and 100 km from the coast is the small Novolazarevskaya Station. In the central part of Antarctica, 1,400 km south of Mirny, is Vostok Station, named for the second of the Russians ships in the von Bellingshausen-Lazarev Expedition of 150 years ago.

Vostok probably is the most difficult place to live in the world. It is located at an altitude of 3.5 km which makes life difficult enough. The winter temperature often falls below −80°C and −60° or −70°C are common occurrences. A "hot" day in summer there is about −30°C. Nonetheless, scholars live and work there.

At the beginning of 1968, Soviet polar explorers built their fifth antarctic station called "Bellings-

The first hut at the USSR station Leningradskaya.

hausen" on Waterloo, a small island near the Drake
Strait which separates Antarctica from South
America. It is 3,000 km from the nearest Soviet
station, Novolazarevskaya, but next door (100
meters) from the Chilean Station, President Frei,
built later. We are preparing to open our sixth
station at the end of this year on the still uninhabited Pacific littoral of Antarctica in the area
called Oates Land. It will be named Leningradskaya in honor of the city where most of the participants in Soviet Antarctic expeditions live and
work.

BENEATH THE ICE

During these years our scientists have carried
out many traverses on tractor trains. We use high
capacity tractor vehicles containing living quarters
and laboratories. They are equipped with navigational instruments and geophysical apparatus and
radios. They haul a string of steel sledges, loaded
with tens of tons of fuel, equipment and provisions.

These transport annually about 150 tons of supplies for Vostok as well as traverse all Antarctica on scientific missions. Their tracks stretch across the least explored regions of the continent. Several mountain ranges and individual peaks have received Soviet names, and deposits of useful minerals have been found. Of prime importance is the fact that the ice surface and the structure of the land beneath the ice have been determined.

Until recent years, this work was done by the very laborious method of seismic soundings. In order to determine the thickness of the ice cover, one had to set off here and there a small number of explosive charges and carefully observe the propagation of seismic vibrations. Now in our country, and others, radar has been developed and tested for this purpose. It is a very much more effective and simpler method. Beams from special radar sets in tractors or aircraft pierce the entire, three-kilometer deep ice mass. The beams are reflected from the sub-ice surface of the continent revealing not only the thickness of the ice but the contour of the ground beneath it.

Meteorological observations are systematically carried out at the station. We now know about peculiarities in the antarctic climate and we follow the movements of glaciers and the accumulation of snow upon them.

Magnetologists carefully investigate fluctuations of the south magnetic pole, study the polar lights (auroras) and other phenomena.

A great task has fallen in the antarctic to polar aircraft pilots. They deliver urgent supplies to stations, re-supply the tractor trains out on the ice and have assisted expeditions in trouble. On the whole, enormous work requiring great selflessness, persistence, enthusiasm and scientific initiative has been carried out in the antarctic by Soviet expeditions.

ATLAS COMPLETED

The results have been tens of volumes of scientific work, diagrams and descriptions. It is likely that about one-quarter of all the information which world-wide science has obtained about the antarctic has been collected, evaluated and synthesized by Soviet scientists. In 1969, the fundamental two volume "Atlas of the Antarctic" was completed and published in the Soviet Union. It contains the basic conclusions from the work of Soviet and foreign scientists, and it already commands great respect throughout the world.

Broad investigations of Antarctica began in the period of preparation for and execution of the International Geophysical Year (IGY). However, they were not completed at the end of this international scientific program. Although a few countries shut down their stations in Antarctica after the IGY was over, the greater portion of the expeditions organized during the IGY continue their work to the present. More than that, the volume of investigations of the antarctic has grown continually, and their range has expanded. The work of the Soviet Antarctic Expedition as well as of the antarctic stations of the United States, England and other countries is broadening.

What has caused this? What attracts scientists of many countries to this remote continent? One may suppose that in the period of the International Geophysical Year, consideration of prestige played a role. Often the interests of the armed forces are the basis of large scientific enterprises. Do not these play a certain role in antarctic research?

The international treaty on collaboration in the antarctic forbids the use of the continent for military purposes, and forbids testing of any type of weapon or carrying out other kinds of military preparation. All of the participants in the exploration of this continent abide by this agreement. No one carries out weapons tests, atomic explosions or any similar operations.

True, the presence of a very great number of Seabees at the antarctic stations of the United States evokes some surprise among Soviet scientists. The treaty does not forbid using military personnel to help with scientific investigations. However, for each American scientist in the antarctic there are no fewer than 10 enlisted men and officers of the armed forces of the United States. Evidently the personnel in the armed forces are training for work in polar conditions. Probably they are carrying out experiments on transportation methods and equipment. Nonetheless, I think that for the United States as well as for the other countries the interests of the armed forces are not first and foremost in the organization of antarctic research.

Of course, cognitive interests play a serious role in the earth sciences—the possibility of solving some important problems relating to this science. However, I doubt whether purely cognitive interests are the basic stimulus for antarctic exploration.

I claim that the basic stimulus is the sharply increasing practical necessity at the present time for information—pertaining to the entire earth—about the state of natural environments. It is just this that evokes the interest in Antarctica, compelling many countries to spend significant means and forces to carry out exploration.

The earth sciences have always dealt with phenomena and processes taking place over our whole planet or in major regions of it. However, corresponding to practical needs and the process of its development, each of these sciences at particular times has concentrated its attention on problems which might have had a global, a regional or a local character.

Cognitive interests require solving global problems. By analyzing phenomena occurring over the whole terrestrial globe, in the entire atmosphere, in the oceans or in the hard shell of the Earth, it may be easier to understand the nature of this or that process. Until recent decades practical interests pushed mainly the study of regional and local problems—in weather prognosis, analyzing climate, studying geological structures or evaluating seismic dangers—primarily for national purposes.

In recent times not only cognitive but also practical interests more and more often direct their basic attention to research in the area of earth sciences, to phenomena embracing the entire terrestrial globe. Doubtless, this is connected with the growth of "global elements" in practical activities. Lines of aerial communication become longer and longer, and the areas of development of the oceans' riches move further and further away from one's native coasts. Finally, cosmic flights and all the activity in the zone of the inner cosmos naturally have a global character.

In this connection information about the state of natural environments on the entire terrestrial globe and understanding the processes unfolding on the surface of the entire planet acquires great practical significance.

In connection with these circumstances there is developing the so-called Worldwide Weather Service, a new level of collaboration among the meteorological services of all countries. Its basic idea is to provide uniform, reliable and rapid weather data for the entire terrestrial globe. These data are available to the meteorological services of any country. Analogous ideas were set forth in the Global Atmospheric Research (GARP) Program, which is now a fundamental and extremely serious program for the scientific collaboration of meteorologists from all countries. The necessity for global information about the state of natural environments is bound to grow further still. This relates to the entire terrestrial globe and, in particular, to its antarctic region.

In Antarctica, however, some additional phenomena appear related to both cognitive and practical interests. Let us dwell on some of them:

The regularities of the general circulation of the atmosphere now constitute the basic problem whose solution attracts eminent meteorologists of all countries. Development of a quantitative theory of general circulation allows creation of reliable numerical methods for long-term prognosis of weather. The air heated in the tropics, rising, moves to the polar regions of the planet where, being cooled, it sinks down and returns then to the tropical zone in the lower layers of the atmosphere. This simple diagram is complicated over and over by the influence of the earth's rotation, the position of the continents, oceans, mountain ranges, etc.; but the heating at the equator and the cooling in the polar regions is the basic factor which sets the entire terrestrial atmosphere into motion.

The planetary "refrigerators" in the arctic and in the antarctic, however, are not symmetrical. Antarctica is a very cold continent, surrounded by the relatively warm waters of the southern portions of the World Ocean. The central portion of the arctic presents the opposite picture: a comparatively warm ocean, surrounded on all sides by cold continents. In this asymmetry there are factors determining essential features of the general circulation of the atmosphere of our planet.

The basic elements in the climate of any region on the Earth are the radiation and heat balances and the circulation of moisture. In summer the energy coming from the sun balances the loss caused by reflection and radiation of heat from the surface of the antarctic continent covered with snow. But during the polar night, radiation of heat into space exceeds incoming energy from the sun and, on the whole, the radiation balance of the antarctic is negative for the year. The constancy of the average yearly temperatures on the continent is due to the transfer of heat to Antarctica from the relatively warm ocean to the north by means of moving masses of air.

To calculate atmosphere circulation it is extremely important to evaluate the quantity of heat which Antarctica absorbs from the terrestrial atmosphere. It probably changes somewhat. This determination permits us to calculate more precisely the energetics of atmospheric circulation.

The circulation of moisture in Antarctica is also particularly interesting. We know that there was a time when Antarctica did not have an ice cover. The ice was formed, probably, over a period of millions of years. And what is happening to it now? Is it decreasing or increasing? Everyone knows that the melting of antarctic ice would cause a change in the level of the Pacific Ocean of several tens of meters, which would bring about the inundation of many thickly-populated territories.

Up to the present time, however, we do not know whether the ice cover is in essential equilibrium, is gradually increasing or gradually decreasing. An enormous supply of fresh water is concentrated in it: about 15 per cent of all the fresh water contained on the surface of the Earth or in the atmosphere. Naturally, the behavior of this depository is of substantial interest for evaluating the water balance of the entire terrestrial globe.

AN IMPORTANT GLACIAL PROBLEM

It seems to me that a precise determination of

nected with the ice continent. This is a difficult problem. But in recent times several additional possibilities of its solution have appeared.

The systematic photography by Soviet and American meteorological satellites flying above Antarctica permits us to make an evaluation of the loss of ice in the form of icebergs from the antarctic continent. Observations of changes in ice cover, snow accumulation and the movement of ice, particularly in the littoral zone of Antarctica, should help us evaluate all the elements of equilibrium in the ice cap. Drilling through the ice and analyzing the cores recovered at different depths permits analysis of the genesis of the ice formation.

Such tasks, it seems to me, should be set up as one of the most important problems in the international collaboration of research in Antarctica.

There is great interest in investigating electromagnetic phenomena occurring in the upper layers of the atmosphere and in the nearer zones of space. It is known that in the polar regions the magnetic poles of the Earth create a specific structure in the near regions of cosmic space. They affect the position of the radiation belts and phenomena occurring in the ionosphere.

Our station Vostok is located at the south magnetic pole. This station was built just for studying magnetic and ionospheric phenomena and, because of this, Soviet scientists and their frequent guests— foreign colleagues—work there continuously under difficult conditions.

Substantial interest is also shown in the study of the biological resources of the southern waters of the Pacific Ocean surrounding Antarctica. Whaling is now declining. As a result of the two-century-long exploitation of whales, a balanced whale population can be maintained only by killing such a small number that the industry will become uneconomic in a short time.

Of great interest, however, is the krill population. Since these tiny shrimp-like animals are the main food of whales, their quantity, as a result of the disappearance of their principal consumers, should show a significant increase. Krill represents a valuable biological raw material which perhaps could easily be transformed into food for domestic animals or perhaps even for man.

The southern waters of the World Ocean are rich. However, according to specialists, available food could support a much greater quantity of commercial fish than are found there now. Many varieties of valuable commercial fish in the northern hemisphere are absent from the southern hemisphere. They, themselves, cannot cross the warm tropical waters, but if they were transported to the Southern Ocean and set free amidst its rich food resources, perhaps they could flourish there.

MINERAL RICHES

Finally, the geological structure is very interesting. Its study allows the possibility of judging the genesis of the entire continent. Some data suggest, for example, that Antarctica is composed of two parts: one which earlier belonged to the South American continent, and the other to Asia. Further geological and paleomagnetic research will probably give an answer to this question. Many geologists are convinced that the mineral riches undoubtedly to be found on the continent may already, or in the near future, be the object of exploitation. One can hardly agree with this, but there is little doubt that at some time in the future the deposits of useful minerals in the antarctic will find their place in the balance of mineral raw materials.

One could also name other problems specific to the antarctic which attract the attention of scientists to this region of the terrestrial globe. For

USSR settlement Mirny under the snow. The entrances to the huts are visible.

example, the methodology of assessing the characteristics of the natural environment is of particular significance. In view of the great difficulties in setting up common methods of measurement at the international array of stations in the antarctic, it is expedient to employ standard automatic devices, movable platforms such as satellites or airplanes and other long-range apparatus.

It has already been noted that the current chart of the ice cover of Antarctica is being sketched on the basis of radar sounding of the continental ice.

A CONTINENT OF PEACE

Now I would like to dwell on the social-political aspect of antarctic exploration. The most important specific feature in this plan is the broad and very successful international collaboration. All work in Antarctica is carried out only for peaceful purposes. Within these limits any country is free to carry out any investigations, a situation conditioned by the free exchange of all scientific information received. This is, in fact, accomplished. It is not without reason that Antarctica is called the continent of peace. Besides the exchange of information and joint consideration of work plans the exchange of scientists is also widely practiced. Thus, scientists from the United States, England, France, the German Democratic Republic, Czechoslovakia, Hungary and Bulgaria have worked at the stations of the Soviet Union. It has become a tradition for Soviet scientists to send a representative each year to one of the stations of the United States and to accept American colleagues at its own stations.

Often explorers in Antarctica fall into difficult and dangerous situations. It is then that mutual assistance—not fixed by treaty but unfailingly carried out—comes into operation.

All of us approve of the principle of the Antarctic Treaty. And is it not an excellent precedent for many other situations in which agreement about activities is required among various countries? Is it not time to think of disseminating to the entire terrestrial globe the principles set forth in this treaty—namely, the close collaboration of countries with different social structures for the exploration of nature and the mastery of a broad region of our Earth for peaceful purposes?

This is far from a rhetorical question, and I would like to dwell on it in some further detail.

Of course, all progressive, or simply sober-minded, people—composing the vast majority of the population of the Earth—understand well that the peaceful coexistence of nations is the only form of international relations worthy of mankind, the only alternative to devastating wars. The majority of readers of the *Bulletin,* I suppose, not only understand this, but more or less actively work to support peace.

I suppose also (although I understand that many readers may not agree with this) that objectively functioning laws of social development will lead finally to the unity of mankind.

MAN AND NATURE

But now I would like to turn to one of the factors working in this direction. This is the interaction of mankind with the natural environment surrounding him.

The growth of global elements in the practical activities noted above is one of the peculiarities of the current stage of interaction between man and nature: the dissemination of our actions over the entire surface of the terrestrial globe, the exploitation of the ocean depths and the penetration of the cosmos.

Other characteristics of the current stage in this interaction relate to the use of natural resources

and to the influence on natural processes. These
are problems which now perturb everyone. Will
natural resources suffice to satisfy all of the increasing needs of mankind? Will not our ever intensify-
ing interference in natural processes finally lead
to fundamental changes in the state of the natural
environment?

The question of the sufficiency of natural resources, as is known, has been converted into a social
problem since the time of Malthus. Noting the
unconditional limits on the totality of all natural
resources on our planet, contemporary followers of
Malthus claim that this places limits also on
the development of society in general. It is in the
accelerating growth of the population of many developing countries, particularly in comparison with
still-low rates of economic development, that they
seek an explanation of the difficult economic positions of these countries, and see as the only way
out of them the curtailing of population growth.
Everyone is aware of the idea of the danger of the
continuing "demographic explosion."

What is the situation from our point of view?
Not being able to delve into this interesting question deeply, I wish nevertheless to turn our attention to the fact that through the entire history of
man the growth of the potential for satisfying man's
basic necessities in energy, food, materials, space,
etc., has always outstripped the growth of those
necessities.

Thus, for example, if we evaluate the quantity
of energy which might be produced per capita,
utilizing all the means already mastered and all the
known resources, then at present it appears perhaps 20 times greater than a century ago.

Already located supplies of useful minerals, including the most deficient, calculated per capita,
have also increased during the last decades, and

continue to grow. The continuing decrease in the proportion of the population employed in agriculture is witness to the rapid growth in the efficiency of it, as well as in other sources of productivity.

We talk of course about potentials, assuming a high level of technical progress. The practical possibility of supplying the needs of the population in this or that country (in particular the developing countries) may be completely different, but here we are already dealing with social factors—basically the result of former or continuing colonial exploitation, the lack of specialists, technical means, etc.

The discussions of contemporary partisans of Malthusian doctrines are based on extrapolating contemporary rates of population growth (which even in itself is arguable) and on the preservation, in principle, of current effectiveness (in the broad sense of this term) in using natural resources.

V. I. Lenin at the beginning of this century, while polemicizing with Malthusians of that time, showed that their views were inapplicable to those cases when technology progressed and the means of production were transformed.

BLIND ALLEY

It is essentially in this connection that the potentials of mankind, viewed as a whole, in relationship to all nature, grows more quickly than the necessities.

If the means of production and consequently the effectiveness of utilization of natural resources as a whole do not change, then the development of mankind would long ago have stopped in a Malthusian blind alley. Not only the current but even a much smaller population on the Earth, for example, could not be nourished by hunting.

In considering any growth in the effectiveness

of utilizing natural resources there is some definite limit imposed by the very mass and dimensions of the Earth. But it is exactly here that the above mentioned possibilities of man outstripping his needs looms large.

It is, of course, too early to conjecture on the forum of utilization of extraterrestrial resources by mankind, but is clear that the possibility of their use is approaching significantly faster than the time when no reserves will be left to us on Earth.

Does all this indicate that the problem of natural resources doesn't exist. Hardly. At the present stage of interaction with nature, we are approaching utilization of a noticeable share of the entire supply of irreplacable riches (e.g., minerals, living space) and an accountable portion of the balance of renewable resources (e.g., soil, forests, fresh water, oxygen, hydraulic energy, etc.).

From my point of view, the renewable resources take on particular significance. We are now using between a few per cent and several tens of one per cent of the accountable part of the balance. When we approach 100 per cent, then the most extreme measures to regulate the use and to restore the balance will become unavoidable on a world-wide basis. Mankind will have to use all of its resources to cultivate nature on a planetary scale.

With the same inevitability, the problem of man's influence on the natural environment grows before our eyes. We are already introducing new elements into it as a result of air and water pollution, the release of heat from industrial activities, the destruction of forests and various land reclamation projects. All of this already is beginning noticeably to influence natural processes. We still do not know precisely on what scale interference in nature will inevitably change the environment. However, we should keep in mind that, in addition to direct influence, small, indirect manipulations may produce enormous effects.

We take advantage of channels of control arising from time to time in the atmosphere for the active reforming of meteorological processes, such as cloud seeding to cause additional precipitation or hail suppression. However, such manipulations in other cases may bring about a circumstance in which a comparatively small influence may cause a large-scale, perhaps unexpected and unwanted change in the ordinary sequence of natural events.

Technical progress has developed rapidly the capability of controlling large scale processes in every area of human endeavor. Colossal quantities of energy are regulated in the centers of unified energy systems. Contemporary mass production may in a short time turn out huge quantities of any sort of products. Insignificant acts, even mistakes by particular persons, may lead even to the unleashing of a nuclear war. Naturally, an increase in the possibility of control should be accompanied by an increase in reliability and guaranty of effectiveness, since the scale of loss and misfortune for mankind increases at the same rate as control capability. An increase in reliability of control is actually occurring within the limits of particular enterprises, industrial unions and in planned, socialist economies —thus within the limits of entire nations. Obviously, however, this is not occurring within the framework of all mankind. There has developed an obvious gap between needs which have already appeared, and which are rapidly increasing, and the ability to implement global actions to deal with them. It is because of the absence of a corresponding social mechanism, not only for regulating such actions, but also for evaluating their effectiveness from the point of view of all mankind.

This gap is developing in various aspects of hu-

man activities. We are observing it now in the area
of interaction with nature. At some future time we
will not be able to allow ourselves independent uncoordinated actions with respect to nature. When
will this time arrive? As was already noted, we may
consider that it will arrive somewhat earlier than
the moment when the utilized share of renewable
natural resources approaches the full quantity of
the accountable portion of their balance. This will
probably be after several decades, but hardly later
than a century from now.

Should we then await some sort of catastrophe,
resulting from the sharp violation of the balanced
state of natural processes and the balances of renewable natural resources, caused by uncoordinated
acts of different parts of human society?

UNIFICATION OF MANKIND

Certainly not. History has proved to us that
the development of human society in interaction
with surrounding nature may be likened to a chain
reaction, each stage of which creates everything
necessary for significant growth and expansion of
the following stage. I believe that social progress
of mankind will progress so far that it will become
a single socialist society on the entire terrestrial
globe.

Perhaps some readers will not agree with this.
We shall not argue. Even before the unification of
mankind in a single social system— in the presence
of countries with different social systems—a correct interaction of man with nature may be constructed under conditions of peaceful coexistence
and broad international cooperation among all
nations. It will be possible if, over the entire
globe, there is installed, for example, roughly the
same type of interaction among countries as we
have already attained and are realizing over a period of almost two decades in Antarctica.

We may note that in this same period, the natural resources of Antarctica evidently have acquired significant importance for utilization in practical activities. Thus Antarctica, from my point of view, would be useful to observe as a testing ground for working and checking out by experience and perfecting methods and forms of peaceful coexistence and close collaboration of various countries in the general work of studying and mastering a difficult but very interesting region of our planet.

We wish success and prosperity to our colleagues —being united in a friendly international collective which is now carrying out its difficult scientific watch in Antarctica.

International Cooperation in Antarctica.

The Next Decade

PHILIP M. SMITH

"Nations working in Antarctica have the opportunity to create a leading role in international programs in conservation and in the solution of environmental problems affecting all mankind. . . . The decade of the 1970s must see a renewed effort in scientific cooperation if we are to achieve the full opportunity which has been afforded us under the terms of the Antarctic Treaty." Philip Smith is deputy head of the Office of Polar Programs, National Science Foundation.

The antarctic programs of the 12 nations that have worked there continuously since the mid-1950s have achieved a worldwide reputation as international cooperative efforts. In comparison to international cooperation in many other areas of science, antarctic cooperation has been notable.

However, the success itself has tended to obscure some of the problems inherent in planning for expanded cooperation. At the time of the International Geophysical Year (IGY) and the discussions concerning the establishment of a regime under the provisions of an international accord, the period of 30 or so years in which the Antarctic Treaty would foster a spirit of cooperation in science seemed like a rather long time. The 1960s have slipped away quickly; most countries are now planning their programs for the first half of the 1970s. We can project certain glaciological and meteorological investigations into the 1980s. Thus, the future has become a part of the present and even more quickly a part of the past.

It is my belief that the decade of the 1970s must see a renewed effort in scientific cooperation if we are to achieve the full opportunity which has been afforded us under the terms of the Antarctic Treaty. The problem now is to utilize the general framework of cooperation which has been established to enhance very specifically the scientific programs of all nations, and to provide an additional understanding among the countries, an understanding that slowly but surely may lead to resolution of the difficult, unresolved political and managerial problems in Antarctica.

Scientifically we have certainly arrived at an excellent multi-national understanding, with each country more or less fitting its overall scientific program into the framework of the broad scientific program agreed upon by the Scientific Committee on Antarctic Research (SCAR). Some investigations are now jointly planned by two or more countries where their scientific or geographical interests overlap. But antarctic scientific cooperation remains bi-national to a large degree. We are to some extent on a plateau of understanding that was arrived at as early as the IGY itself. Today few research projects are jointly conceived, planned and executed by several nations working together, and there is no single antarctic investigation presently in progress that requires concerted managerial effort by scientists and administrators of all 12 nations. Exchanges of men and data are sometimes almost personal affairs. They are research activities that have little real influence on the polar planning offices of the antarctic nations, let alone the larger governmental processes in the various nations. International planning in the context of multi-national cooperation presently practiced through SCAR is a very comfortable arrangement, but it is far short of what could exist were we to realize fully the opportunities of the Antarctic Treaty.

At the political level the unresolved problems include the question of "rights" on high seas, the impact of tourism and other economic development on the science programs and the continent itself and the effective method of handling jurisdictional problems, both administratively and legally. To these must be added the question of the claims themselves, perhaps a less immediate worry, but ultimately a question of great importance. We did not think in the mid-1950s that we would be facing the questions of antarctic tourism with such regularity as we are some 15 years later. The tourists come by ship each year and proposals for regular flights between New Zealand and the U.S. McMurdo Station have been seriously advanced. Interest in the oceanic and the terrestrial resources is growing. Pelagic sealing has been attempted and awaits only a technological development to achieve the total destructive success of the modern whaling industry. Geophysical surveys will undoubtedly be conducted although prospects of immediate economic return are small. Antarctica has become a continent for science, but it is not the scientists' continent. Painful as they are to consider, the unresolved management problems, the political problems and economic development must be addressed in the next decade.

CHALLENGING DEVELOPMENTS

Can our science and our international planning of scientific projects make additional contributions? I would tend to share the somewhat pessimistic view of my colleague, A. P. Crary, were it not for two compelling and challenging developments: First, the scientific problems in Antarctica which now need study are of an order of magnitude larger than the resources of any single nation. They are problems that demand additional cooperation if they are to be resolved. The second reason for hope is that the passage of time has pointed out the unique significance of Antarctica as a laboratory for assessing the subtle but continuing erosion of environmental quality which is taking place on a global basis. Environmental monitoring and protection relate not only to the protection of Antarctica. Nations working in Antarctica have the opportunity to create a leading role in international programs in conservation and in the solution of environmental problems affecting all mankind.

The scientific reconnaissance in Antarctica which has given a broad understanding of the natural processes themselves has been completed in large measure. The geography and general geology, the atmospheric circulation and the basic parameters of life processes within the fragile terrestrial ecosystem and richer marine environment have been sketched out.

The scientific challenge is not now a question of what is to be found in Antarctica or how it functions but one of specifically developing experiments which are designed to answer new questions posed in the course of the 15-year reconnaissance which has been underway. A number of specific projects are under discussion and can be cited as examples. They are significant not only because of the questions that will be addressed but also because they are large experiments that will require a new level of international collaboration in managing the studies. For example, within the field of geology we have the opportunity for study of continental drift after the breakup of Gondwanaland. It is a study requiring cooperation because other fragments of Gondwanaland—Australia, New Zealand, South Africa and India—are national territories where quite a different set of rules applies. If undertaken, a detailed study of continental fit will require international coordination of scientific and logistic effort on a larger scale than has heretofore been attempted.

FUTURE PLANS

Projects now under discussion or in the first planning phases that will lead to an increase of cooperation in science and the development of cooperatively managed programs include:

1. The International Antarctic Glaciological Project, in which scientists of Australia, France, the United States and the Soviet Union will examine the region of about a million square miles of the ice cap in East Antarctica. The studies will be conducted throughout the 1970s or possibly longer, and will involve cooperative planning in all phases from the methodology and design of the field experiments, through the actual conduct of surface and subsurface instrumentation and study of the ice cap, to the analysis and publication of the data. The planning committee is comprised of representatives from the scientific circles of the four nations, a representative from SCAR and representatives from the national offices responsible for the antarctic programs in each of the four countries. This arrangement falls between the official governmental

contacts provided for by the Antarctic Treaty in the consultative meetings and the more informal scientific contacts provided through SCAR.

2. A proposal for collaboration in studying geothermal and meteorological problems in the ice-free valleys near McMurdo, including the drilling of a number of bore holes into the bed rock, will result in further cooperation between Japan, New Zealand and the United States. Scientists from all three countries have worked in the ice-free valleys for many years. Their current plans to team up will require much greater collaboration between the national offices of the three countries as the project develops.

3. The prospect for developing unmanned automatic stations provides a kind of low-cost research facility which can be made available to scientists of several nations. Geophysicists in the Soviet Union have already installed several automatic recording stations for the measurement of magnetic phenomena in the area between Mirny and Vostok. In the United States, the prototype of a complex station which would transmit data from Antarctica to the other continents via a communication satellite is undergoing test. Discussions have been held by workers in the two nations on the feasibility of combining the sensor systems and the communication system. This planning may result in a network of geophysical stations that will operate at a cost far lower than the costs of the manned stations on the inland ice.

4. The Argentine, French, Japanese and Soviet expeditions have all experimented or are planning to experiment with meteorological rocketsondes. An antarctic meteorological rocket network could be in the offing, and will certainly eventuate if present planning continues.

5. Exploration of the areas beneath the floating ice shelves characteristic of Antarctica has been ad-

The National Science Foundation's research vessel *Hero.*

vanced at recent international meetings in geology and oceanography. Manned submersibles are still inadequate for such a task. Consideration is being given to the utilization of one or more drill holes through the Ross Ice Shelf to study the water column, the biology life, the underside of the shelf ice and the seafloor by remote instrumentation. The project will have particular relevance to the question of bottom water formation and, ultimately, the project can be expected to transfer from the Ross Ice Shelf to the area south of the Weddell Sea, thought to be the source of most of this water.

6. Astronomy, never before considered seriously as a subject for major antarctic research, is being examined as an adjunct to the development of a new U.S. station at the south geographical pole. The feasibility of the project may very well depend on an international evaluation of the research opportunities and the organization of the project so that scientists from many of the Antarctic Treaty nations may conduct research.

7. There are two formidable problems for which cooperation is sorely needed. The biological productivity of the Southern Ocean is cited as a great resource but it remains a largely unknown quantity requiring collaboration through multi-ship operations by several nations if the next steps toward an understanding of this marine resource are to be taken. Perhaps the most important question of all is that of air-sea interaction and the pack-ice. As so ably pointed out by Joseph O. Fletcher, the antarctic pack-ice is the largest single feature on the surface of earth that is in regular change. These investigations remain a mind-boggling prospect even in an era of "big science" and new technology. If they are to be undertaken, they must involve cooperation among many nations.

Management problems which will arise from the administration of the programs that may be undertaken in the 1970s will require a closer collaboration between the national offices which fund and plan the expeditions, and the scientists in the several countries. Such collaboration should move the Treaty countries perceptably closer to the ultimate goals of international cooperation in Antarctica and the surrounding ocean. There are, to be sure, many problems. One that is now coming to the forefront is the relationship between the antarctic community represented through SCAR and the more formal intergovernmental organizations: the World Meteorological Organization and the Intergovernmental Oceanographic Commission.

In the 1970s, the worldwide studies such as the Global Atmospheric Research Project will provide the new challenge in international planning for the close-knit small community of Antarctic Treaty nations that will be dealing in the larger arena of scientific and technical organizations. Can we utilize the services of United Nations groups to advantage without getting hopelessly bogged down in the sea of paperwork and discussion inherent in the very large scientific organization? The question will be answered in the next decade.

Environmental protection involves two problems, and opportunities—those which bear directly upon Antarctica and those which relate Antarctica to environmental protection and monitoring on a worldwide basis. We have found that many of the decisions which have been taken in the past in the area of antarctic conservation and environmental protection have benefited from a period of study by scientists themselves. This has often taken the form of discussion in SCAR, with recommendations made to the consultative meetings. SCAR and the governments are now addressing themselves to many conservation problems which have been apparent for some years.

Perhaps the most pressing problem facing the

nations working in Antarctica is the impact of science itself, especially on the ice-free land areas. A resource of minimal size, the ice-free land is subject to further problems because the research tends to concentrate itself in a few highly interesting regions. The scientifically interesting problems in areas such as the ice-free valleys near McMurdo motivate repeated visits by many scientists from different universities and institutions. We have learned that this annual traffic is causing a slow but irreparable decay to the environment, especially for some studies such as microbiology. Hence, there is now developing a concept of a scientifically managed area with greater coordination of research and minimal disturbance.

RESERVES FOR TOURISTS?

The problems, however, are not limited to the impact of science. Should special reserves be set aside for tourism? At first glance the idea seems preposterous but it may be a solution that would prevent a decline in the larger environment by the continuing visits of tourist groups. What does one do with the many forms of human waste? Should incineration be utilized instead of the dumping of wastes into the ocean, now the common practice? These kinds of questions are under discussion at all levels of our antarctic community—from the temporary field camp at a previously unvisited nunatak to the international assembly such as the Sixth Consultative Meeting held recently in Tokyo. I am optimistic that our antarctic community, which has demonstrated its concern and sensitivity for conservation, will develop an ever-increasing awareness of its special opportunity in the protection of the antarctic environment.

As understanding of atmospheric and oceanic circulation increases, it is becoming evident that the antarctic can serve as a kind of bench mark indi-

cator of general environmental changes on earth.
The challenges now are to develop methods of measurement which are designed for long-term monitoring and to implement the necessary networks of
stations and observing points on the continent and
in the Southern Ocean. In my estimation decisions
in this matter are among the highest priorities
facing us. If addressed effectively, our action will
further demonstrate our capability to work and
plan for the joint management of our projects and
of Antarctica itself.

Even within the framework of the international
cooperation established or hoped for by many of
us, there are problems which will require careful
consideration. Unanimity has been a key to the
success of antarctic affairs. Some of the matters
which need resolution cannot await unanimity if
the working out of an agreement takes a period of
four to six years, which has sometimes been the case
for items on the agenda at the consultative meetings. To what extent should a few nations provide
leadership through multi-national agreement and
to what extent should they wait for total agreement
of the 12? We must strike a balance between innovation on the part of some of the countries working together, and the interests of all.

AN ANTARCTIC AIR BUS

Where expenditure of funds are involved all governmental organizations tend to be conservative.
Our air logistic assistance which is occasionally
given to other countries could be utilized much more
effectively as a basis for a true intercontinental
and antarctic transportation system. Such a system might involve intercontinental flights on the
part of the United States, the Soviet Union, New
Zealand and Argentina (all of whom have the capability at present), and a kind of interline or feeder
service between antarctic stations jointly organized

and funded by several nations. A proposal to organize an antarctic "air bus" was advanced by Gordon Robin in 1968, but it has not been implemented. I believe that a large part of the reason may be the fear of "aid" criticism that could come in the annual trek to the financial authorities that each antarctic administrator must make on behalf of his program funds.

In the past we have depended upon the merit and momentum of science itself as a catalyst in solving difficult problems. The big science projects which must now be developed can possibly do just this in the 1970s, resolving questions such as those raised here. Sustained participation in an antarctic program is arduous for all concerned: the scientists, the pilots, personnel who maintain the stations, and even the administrators who, in the case of the antarctic, have an interesting mixture of field and office experience and incessant travel around the world on behalf of their programs. The value of the effort relates to the commonly held conviction that we have not run out of exciting problems and challenges that are worthy of the effort. Though the way is often not clear and the work sometimes arduous, satisfaction comes from the accomplishment of the difficult tasks. The next decade in Antarctica can and will be as exciting as the last.

SCIENCE
LABORATORY

Antarctic Geology and Gondwanaland

CAMPBELL CRADDOCK

One of the principal contributions of antarctic research to man's understanding of the history of the Earth is the geologic evidence uncovered there supporting the theory of drifting continents. The evidence accumulated in Antarctica strongly suggests that the continental landmass beneath the ice sheet is a fragment of an ancient, supercontinent called Gondwanaland. Spreading over part of the southern hemisphere, the supercontinent also included most of modern South America, Africa, India, Australia and adjacent islands. Campbell Craddock is professor of geology at the University of Wisconsin and for many years a principal investigator in the United States Antarctic Research Program.

Although ideas of drifting continents had been advanced earlier, it was not until late in the nineteenth century that geologists first suggested the existence of a large ancestral continent in the southern hemisphere in the geologic past. This hypothetical protocontinent — termed Gondwanaland — included present-day South America, Africa, Arabia, Madagascar, Ceylon, peninsular India, Antarctica and Australia (Fig. 1.) Because of its position in the reassembly, Antarctica must clearly play an important role in determining whether Gondwanaland actually ever existed. Despite its great importance to the concept, however, the geology of Antarctica was almost unknown when Gondwanaland was first postulated. Only in the past few years has our knowledge of Antarctica, the last fragment of the supposed protocontinent to be explored, advanced to a point where meaningful geologic tests of the Gondwanaland hypothesis are possible.

Antarctica was first sighted 150 years ago from ships sailing near the tip of the Antarctic Peninsula, confirming the suspected existence of a southern polar continent. Later expeditions collected continental rocks such as granite and sandstone from icebergs, but the first geologic specimens obtained on the continent were collected in the 1890s at Cape Adare, south of New Zealand. The ensuing 20 years was a period of vigorous exploration by expeditions from several nations, and the broad pattern of antarctic geology began to emerge. Other private and national expeditions before and after World War II added further geologic information, but large areas of the continent still remained unexplored and unknown up to 1955. Most of these early geologic observations were confined to the coastal fringe of Antarctica; except for the South Pole parties of Ernest Shackleton, Roald Amundsen and R. F. Scott — and the Laurence Gould party in support of Byrd's polar flight — the vast interior of the continent remained geologically unknown.

Eights Station at Palmer Peninsula, no longer in operation, was named for James Eights, first American scientist to visit Antarctica.

In 1937 the great South African geologist Alexander Du Toit published a book ("Our Wandering Continents") which must be rated among the most important ever written in the field of geology. In this brilliant synthesis he set forth in detail the geologic evidence then available for continental drift and for the existence of Gondwanaland. Regarding Antarctica, he stated:

> The role of the Antarctic is a vital one. As will be observed from Fig. 7 [present Fig. 1], the shield of East Antarctica constitutes the "key-piece" — shaped surprisingly like Australia, only larger — around which, with wonderful correspondences in outline, the remaining "puzzle-pieces" of Gondwanaland can with remarkable precision be fitted.

Because so little was then known about the geology of Antarctica, Du Toit's Gondwanaland reassembly in effect predicted the geologic patterns to be expected in the antarctic interior. It is a tribute to his genius and foresight that subsequent geologic studies in Antarctica have largely confirmed these predictions. When Du Toit's book was published, the Gondwanaland hypothesis had few advocates, at least among northern hemisphere scientists. Unfortunately, Du Toit did not live to see the wide respect and acceptance accorded his work today.

Ski-equipped aircraft and oversnow tracked vehicles have opened the entire continent to geologic study, since the start of the IGY, and only a few areas of significant rock exposure remain unvisited by geologists today. It is safe to say that our knowledge of the geology of this remote continent has more than doubled during the past 15 years.

EAST AND WEST

Early in this century, after geologic data became

available from the Antarctic Peninsula, the Ross
Sea region and other coastal localities, it was recognized that Antarctica could be divided into two
major geologic provinces. The first comprises the
larger part of the continent that faces mainly upon
the Atlantic and Indian Oceans; since most of this
province lies in the area of east longitudes, it is
commonly known as East Antarctica (see Fig. 2).
The second province consists of the smaller part of
the continent that faces mainly upon the Pacific
Ocean; it is commonly known as West Antarctica.
East Antarctica is a typical continental shield or
stable platform, consisting of a foundation of older
igneous and metamorphic rocks overlain by a sequence of younger, flat-lying stratified or sedimentary rocks. By contrast, West Antarctica is
composed of generally younger rocks that are widely deformed and metamorphosed. Intrusive and
extrusive igneous rocks are abundant, and some volcanic activity continues there today.

Rock exposures comprise less than five per cent
of the area of the continent, and those in East Antarctica occur in an oval belt that includes the coastal
region and the Transantarctic Mountains. The
nunataks (mountain tops protruding through the
ice) and mountain ranges within this belt reveal a
basement complex composed mainly of high-grade
metamorphic rocks and intrusive igneous rocks.
Gneisses of the granulite facies are the most abundant rocks, but lower grade metamorphic rocks of
the amphibolite and green schist facies occur in
some localities. A wide range of igneous rocks has
been reported, but felsic varieties such as granite
are most common. These crystalline basement rocks
record a complex geologic history involving several
cycles of deformation, metamorphism and emplace-
ment of igneous intrusives.

In contrast to the other continents, Antarctica
has so far revealed no rocks with apparent ages

greater than 2 billion years and, indeed, few greater
than 1.5 billion years. This fact may imply that (1)
the oldest rocks in the basement of East Antarctica
are truly younger than those of other continental
shields, (2) insufficient sampling has yet taken

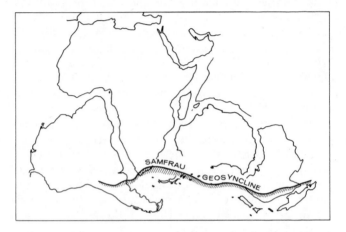

Fig. 1. Reassembly of Gondwanaland (after Du
Toit, 1937).

place to discover the oldest rocks present, or (3)
later metamorphic events, especially in the early
Paleozoic era have reset the mineral clocks, causing
apparent radiometric ages younger than the true
ages of the rocks (Fig. 3). The youngest known
rocks in the East Antarctic basement complex are
fossiliferous Upper Precambrian and Cambrian strata, generally folded and metamorphosed, that occur
in the Transantarctic Mountains and at a few
coastal localities.

Overlying the East Antarctic basement complex
is a succession of mainly flat-lying sedimentary and
volcanic rocks. These beds have been called the
Beacon Group (sedimentary) and the Ferrar Group
(igneous), and they represent the Gondwana sequence — as described from the other southern

continents — in Antarctica. The Beacon Group contains rocks as old as Devonian, and the Ferrar Group rocks as young as Jurassic. These groups are extensively exposed in the Transantarctic Mountains, but they have been found in place at only a few localities along the coast of East Antarctica.

The geologic history of West Antarctica is complex. All rocks whose ages are known appear to have formed during the last 600 million years, and no definitely Precambrian rocks have yet been discovered. In much of West Antarctica the oldest rocks are igneous intrusive and metamorphic varieties that form a basement complex believed to be Paleozoic in age. Sedimentary and volcanic sequences of probably Paleozoic and Mesozoic age are widely distributed, and most of these rocks are strongly folded and somewhat metamorphosed. Intrusive igneous rocks were emplaced across much of West Antarctica during the Mesozoic, and perhaps the early Cenozoic. Upper Cenozoic volcanic and sedimentary layers on the Antarctic Peninsula and to the west are flat-lying and undisturbed. Volcanism which began in the Miocene has continued into recent times in much of coastal West Antarctica.

The geologic composition and history of a continent can be effectively studied from a tectonic map, which shows the age and distribution of the major structural units that define the architecture of the continent. In particular, such maps portray shields (stable areas with a basement complex of ancient igneous and metamorphic rocks overlain by younger flat-lying strata) and orogens (belts of folded and metamorphosed strata, commonly intruded by large bodies of granite — the modern or ancient sites of mountain chains). A recent tectonic map of Antarctica consists of six tectonic units: the East Antarctic Shield, four orogens in the Transantarc-

tic Mountains and West Antarctica and a Cenozoic
volcanic province (Fig. 4, page 38). The delineation of these tectonic provinces allows a major test
of the Gondwanaland hypothesis, the geologic com-
patibility of the opposing coasts.

MAJOR EVIDENCE

In fitting Antarctica into his Gondwanaland reassembly, Du Toit had to depend largely on the
shape of the continent because so little was then
known about its geology. Since that time, progress
in antarctic geology has yielded a number of discoveries that bear on the Gondwanaland problem.
Eleven lines of evidence that seem especially significant are discussed below:

1. The basement rocks of coastal East Antarctica

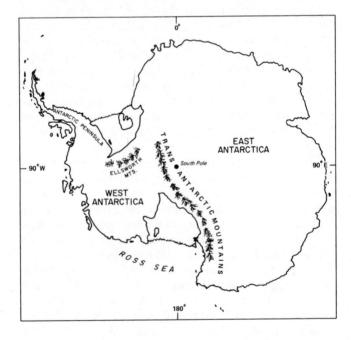

Fig. 2. Geologic provinces of Antarctica.

are similar, both in a general way and in some details, to those along the matching coasts of the other Gondwanaland fragments in Du Toit's reassembly. Work by geologists of several nations has shown that the structural grain in these ancient antarctic rocks is compatible with that in like rocks of the suggested matching coast. The basement rocks of all these areas are compositionally similar, consisting of high-grade metamorphic rocks such as granulite gneisses, along with igneous intrusives such as granite. In particular, an unusual hypersthene-bearing granitic rock, termed charnockite, is widespread in eastern Africa, Ceylon, eastern India and coastal East Antarctica.

2. The rocks of the Beacon Group in Antarctica are generally similar to the Paleozoic and Mesozoic Gondwana sedimentary sequences on the other southern continents and continental islands. The lower Beacon consists of detrital sedimentary rocks as old as Devonian in some localities. Beds of ancient tillite were first discovered in the Transantarctic Mountains in 1958, and many other tillite localities are now known in Antarctica. These tillites occur in the Beacon Group and are considered Carboniferous or Permian in age. Overlying these glacial beds are younger Permian strata which commonly include coal beds and bear the *Glossopteris* flora. This succession of distinctive rock types can be matched, at least in part, in Australia, India, Madagascar, Africa, the Falkland Islands and South America.

3. With the discovery of the tillites in Antarctica, evidence for late Paleozoic glaciation is now known from all the major Gondwanaland fragments. Similar deposits had been previously found in South America, Africa, India and Australia, and their existence in Antarctica had been predicted. The character and distribution of these ancient glacial beds imply the presence of Paleozoic ice sheets of conti-

nental dimensions. However, along some coasts directional indicators show the ice flowed onto the present-day continent from the adjacent ocean basin. If we accept modern geography as that of the Permian, both the anomalous flow directions and the wide latitudinal range of continental glaciation are awkward to explain. Recent studies have shown, however, that the Gondwanaland reconstruction presents an attractive alternative in understanding this early glacial period.

FOSSIL RECORDS

4. The Paleozoic and Mesozoic fossil record in Antarctica, only now emerging in detail, bears a strong resemblance to that found in the other southern continents. Marine faunas are as old as Cambrian and include archaeocyathids, trilobites, gastropods, bryozoans, fish, echinoderms, brachiopods and pelecypods. These animals flourished in shallow waters close to land under conditions similar to those on modern continental shelves. Although these fossil faunas are similar to those of Australia, South America and South Africa, it is unlikely that such animals migrated across deep ocean basins. Land animals are less abundant but also show close affinities to the faunas of the other southern continents. Recent discoveries of Triassic reptiles and amphibians in the Transantarctic Mountains are of great importance because these animals, such as *Lystrosaurus*, must have moved over land routes. Antarctic fossil floras, especially the Permian-Carboniferous *Glossopteris* flora, bear a strong similarity to other southern floras. The pronounced overlap between the *Glossopteris* floras of Antarctica and India, for instance, poses two questions if we suppose that Permian and modern geography are identical. Can a reasonable dispersal mechanism, such as wind or water currents, be found to connect these distant lands? And is it pos-

Era	Period	Epoch	Age in m.y.
Cenozoic	Quaternary		1-2
	Tertiary	Pliocene	11
		Miocene	25
		Oligocene	40
		Eocene	60
		Paleocene	70
Mesozoic	Cretaceous		135
	Jurassic		180
	Triassic		225
Paleozoic	Permian		270
	Carboniferous		350
	Devonian		400
	Silurian		440
	Ordovician		500
	Cambrian		600
Precambrian			

Fig. 3. Geologic time scale.

sible that these two widely separated lands, one polar and the other tropical, could support nearly identical floras when their climates would have been so different?

Thus, the fossil animal and plant record in Antarctica strongly suggests that the present geographic isolation of the continent did not exist during Paleozoic and at least early Mesozoic time.

5. The deformed and metamorphosed rocks underlying the Beacon strata in the Transantarctic Mountains can be compared to rocks in southeastern Australia. Strata in both areas were folded and intruded by granitic rocks during the Paleozoic era. Each continent reveals an early Paleozoic orogen paralleled by a middle Paleozoic orogen lying to the east, or away from the Precambrian shield. Structural trends in both areas are anomalous in being nearly perpendicular to the present shoreline, but they roughly parallel the coast in the Gondwanaland reassembly.

6. The Ellsworth Mountains fold belt formed in early Mesozoic time, and probably represents the continuation of the Cape fold belt of South Africa and a part of Du Toit's Samfrau geosyncline. Between the Transantarctic Mountains of East Antarctica and the coastal belt of West Antarctica lies a large region that has been explored only during the last 15 years. Bedrock exposures in this area are found in the Ellsworth Mountains and in nunatak groups and small ranges to the south and west. On the basis of lithologic similarity and structural continuity most of these outcrops have been assigned to a new tectonic province, the Ellsworth Mountains Orogen. The thick sedimentary sequence is mainly Paleozoic in age (some Precambrian strata may be present) and has undergone strong post-Permian folding. Some of these formations resemble the Beacon Group formations in the Transantarctic Mountains, but differ in being both

considerably thicker and distinctly folded. In part of the province these deformed Paleozoic strata are invaded by granitic bodies that were emplaced during late Triassic to early Jurassic time. In its present setting the Ellsworth Mountains fold belt is a puzzling tectonic fragment resting between East Antarctica and coastal West Antarctica. Both in stratigraphy and in structural style, however, it bears strong resemblance to the Cape fold belt of southern Africa and the fold mountains of eastern Argentina. In the Gondwanaland reassembly it represents the natural continuation of a fold belt that begins in Argentina and continues across southern Africa into Antarctica.

7. Jurassic igneous rocks, mainly basaltic in composition, are widespread in Antarctica. These rocks occur both as volcanic deposits and as shallow intrusive bodies such as sills and dikes. They are common throughout the length of the Transantarctic Mountains, where they have been termed the Ferrar Group. These Jurassic mafic igneous rocks may be compared to rocks of similar age and composition that occur over large areas of Brazil, southern Africa and Tasmania. In the Gondwanaland reassembly it is reasonable to interpret the rocks of all these areas as belonging to a single igneous province; one perhaps related to the initial fragmentation of the protocontinent. Jurassic volcanic rocks of more varied composition are abundant in the Antarctic Peninsula and common along the coast of West Antarctica. These latter rocks, along with counterparts in Argentina and Australia, may be the products of activity in a mobile belt along the margin of Gondwanaland.

8. Late Cretaceous to early Tertiary igneous bodies, mainly granitic in composition, are widespread in the Antarctica Peninsula and westward along the coastal sector of West Antarctica. Similar intrusive rocks are typical of the western margin of

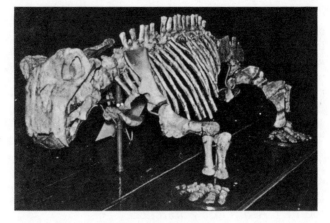

Lystrosaurus skeleton

the Americas from Alaska to Tierra del Fuego. The presence of such plutons, along with geologically young deformation and abundant Cenozoic volcanism, suggest that coastal West Antarctica may be properly considered a part of the circum-Pacific mobile belt of Mesozoic-Cenozoic time. Igneous and tectonic events in the southern hemisphere part of this mobile belt may be related to the break-up of Gondwanaland, since the belt lies along the leading edges of the drifting fragments. One anomaly is the presently aseismic character of Antarctica; elsewhere the circum-Pacific belt is typified by numerous modern earthquakes.

9. Magnetic anomaly belts parallel to and symmetrical about the mid-ocean ridges strongly suggest sea-floor spreading and continental drift have occurred. Within the last 15 years oceanographic surveys have revealed this unexpected pattern of alternating belts of high and low magnetic intensity, a pattern which initially defied explanation. Concurrent studies of paleomagnetism from both lava flow and marine sediment sequences, however, pro-

duced evidence that the earth's magnetic field appears to undergo periodic reversals of its polarity. If the alternating high- and low-intensity belts are ascribed to these polarity reversals, then the slowly spreading sea-floor can be though of as a magnetic tape which freezes in the effects of the existent magnetic field as new crust is formed at the mid-ocean ridges by the cooling of silicate melts from the earth's interior. If this interpretation proves correct, we may hope to learn both the rate of sea-floor spreading and the time when the various fragments of Gandwanaland began to separate. For example, present data — collected in the southern oceans by the National Science Foundation's *Eltanin* and several other research vessels — suggest that Antarctica and Australia were joined together until about 40 million years ago.

10. The Antarctic Ice Sheet appears to have formed at least 7 million years ago, suggesting Antarctica was a separate polar continent by that time.

Hypothetical reconstruction of a Glossopteris tree (about 10 m tall) with large leaves.

The late Cenozoic history of the continent is obscure because few deposits of this age are known in
areas of rock outcrop. A limited number of paleomagnetic measurements suggest that Antarctica
was in its present latitude even at the beginning
of the Cenozoic, 70 million years ago. Tertiary
floras from the Antarctic Peninsula area indicate
that moderate temperatures prevailed there during
part of the era, but fossil penguins have been recovered from beds considered Miocene in age. Early
Tertiary microfloras have been identified in glacial
erratics in the Ross Sea area, but these rocks have
not been found in place. Volcanic rocks at least 7
million years old overlie a glaciated surface in the
Jones Mountains of coastal West Antarctica, and
late Cenozoic volcanoes to the west in the same
province contain deposits that suggest eruption of
the lavas through the ice sheet. An interesting record of glacial and volcanic events of the last few
million years is preserved in some of the deglaciated
valleys of the Transantarctic Mountains. Thus although there yet remains much to be learned about
the Cenozoic history of Antarctica, it seems clear
that by 7 million years ago the continent was isolated from the other Gondwanaland fragments and
was in a geographic position favorable to the growth
of an ice sheet.

11. Better knowledge of the bathymetry of the
southern ocean allows more critical testing of the
morphological fit of the Gondwanaland fragments.
The earliest speculations about continental drift
were fostered by the similarity in shape of opposing
coasts, especially the Atlantic coasts of South
America and Africa. The coastline, however, may
undergo significant modification with only a small
change in sea level, and a more realistic comparison
may be obtained by using a submarine contour near
the edge of the continental shelf or part way down
the continental slope. Although subject to some

modification by erosional and depositional processes, such a contour is a natural border for the
continent and may be little changed in shape since
the time of separation from its adjoining landmass.
Recent oceanographic surveys have yielded greatly
improved bathymetric maps of the antarctic continental shelf and slope. Studies using these new
maps have shown that good morphological matches

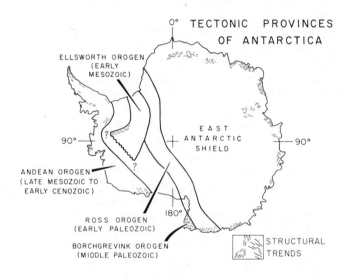

Fig. 4. Tectonic provinces of Antarctica.

can be obtained between Africa and Antarctica and
between Australia and Antarctica, as required by
the Gondwanaland hypothesis.

Du Toit's reassembly of Gondwanaland, if correct, requires that certain geologic features exist in
Antarctica. The basement rocks of coastal East
Antarctica must resemble in composition and structure those of the matching coasts of the other Gondwanaland fragments. The Beacon Group should be

present throughout the length of the Transantarctic Mountains and should resemble the Gondwana sequences of the other southern continents. Upper Paleozoic glacial beds should occur in Antarctica. The Paleozoic and Mesozoic fossil record should consist of forms resembling those elsewhere in Gondwanaland rather than unique forms developed in an isolated continent. The eastward extension of the Samfrau geosyncline and the Cape fold belt from Southern Africa should be found in Antarctica. The southward-trending Paleozoic orogens of southeastern Australia should continue in the northern Transantarctic Mountains. Jurassic mafic igneous rocks can be expected in the Transantarctic Mountains along with the strata of the Beacon Group.

The rapidly accumulating geologic data from Antarctic strongly suggest that each of these predictions will prove to be correct. The accuracy of Du Toit's predictions, the striking geologic similarities between Antarctica and the other southern lands and the new evidence from the oceans for seafloor spreading combine to provide a very strong case for the reality of Gondwanaland. (The current reassembly of Gondwanaland is presented in outline on the *Bulletin's* cover.)

Delineation of the tectonic provinces of Antarctica allows comparison with those of the other landmasses and permits a more accurate reconstruction. Tectonic ties between Antarctica and Australia are provided by the early Paleozoic Ross and Adelaide Orogens, and by the middle Paleozoic Borchgrevink and Tasman Orogens. The early Mesozoic Ellsworth Orogen in Antarctica is the continuation of the Cape fold belt in southern Africa. That the present map of Gondwanaland, based on the swift advances in Antarctic geology in recent years, differs so little from that drawn by Du Toit in 1937 is ample testimony to the skill and vision of that great geologist.

FUTURE RESEARCH

Although the Gondwanaland concept is winning wide acceptance, further testing of the hypothesis against the emerging facts of Antarctic geology is necessary. The geologic similarities established in a general way must be critically examined through local, detailed studies. While most of Antarctica has been geologically mapped on a reconnaissance scale, the remaining unknown areas must be investigated in the near future. At the same time, more detailed mapping of certain areas is necessary, both to clarify the structural framework of the continent and to test fully the correctness of Du Toit's predictions.

The basement rocks of East Antarctica require much more investigation. Those in the Transantarctic Mountains appear to be younger than those in coastal East Antarctica; if correct, this fact is important in understanding the tectonic evolution of the East Antarctic shield. Detailed comparative studies of the ancient rocks of coastal East Antarctica with their assumed counterparts on the matching coasts of Africa, India and Australia are needed. Radiometric age determinations on these igneous and metamorphic rocks will be a great help in testing the original continuity of basement rock terranes in Antarctica with those in the other southern lands.

Detailed studies of the Beacon Group are just beginning, and it deserves examination along the length of the Transantarctic Mountains to establish lateral changes in composition, age and origin of these strata. Thorough knowledge of the coastal localities is especially important to allow careful comparison with the Gondwana sequences in Africa, India and Australia. Additional fossil discoveries can be expected in the Beacon Group and in the stratified rocks of West Antarctica.

Two kinds of studies of the geologic structure in

Antarctica will enable further testing of the Gond-wanaland reassembly. On the one hand, additional knowledge of the areal geology will lead to better definition of the tectonic provinces of the continent, such as the Ellsworth Orogen, and to more accurate assessment of the continuity of these provincial boundaries between Antarctica and the other Gond-wanaland fragments. On the other hand, thorough study of the structural style within each antarctic province is necessary to evaluate the validity of its correlation with a tectonic province in another southern land.

ICE SHEET SURGES

Continued investigation of paleomagnetism in the rocks of Antarctica should provide valuable insights into its geologic history. Although this technique is commonly a complicated one in practice, under favorable circumstances it can be used to establish paleolatitudes. Thus, the paleomagnetism locked in antarctic rock specimens, together with the magnetic anomaly belts from the ocean floor, offers the hope of direct confirmation of not only the reality but also the chronology of continental drift.

Finally, studies of the Antarctic Ice Sheet during late Cenozoic time are sure to produce interesting and valuable data. We are only beginning to learn about the inception, growth and fluctuation of this enormous mass of ice. Because of its influence on both climate and world sea level, understanding the history and probable future of this ice sheet is of great practical importance to mankind. A recent analysis, for example, suggests that the Antarctic Ice Sheet periodically surges in rapid flow toward the sea, in the manner of a "galloping" valley glacier; such surges could cause rapid and significant rises in sea level. In this case, however, we may draw some tentative reassurance from the abundant evidence across the continent for ice surface levels

300 meters or more above that of the present; thus if surges do occur and are related to thickness, the present ice sheet appears to be well below the threshhold thickness. Studies of the ice sheet are truly multidisciplinary, and observations must be made from the surface of the ice sheet, on cores from within it, on deposits in land areas along its margin and on deposits on the antarctic sea floor.

Further geologic research in Antarctica should continue to yield important returns to both the scientist and society. Although great progress has been made, this remote continent remains the geologically least known of all the earth's major landmasses. The geologic history of the southern hemisphere will be fragmentary and unsatisfactory until we have learned much more about the role of Antarctica. Global tectonic theories, such as sea-floor spreading and continental drift, require testing in Antarctica and the adjoining seas. It is unlikely that Antarctica is a unique continent wholly devoid of mineral resources, but our present geologic knowledge is inadequate for establishing the nature, location and possible future value of such deposits.

Polar Ice
and the Global Climate
Machine

JOSEPH O. FLETCHER

While man has the engineering capability of influencing atmospheric circulation and, hence, climate, such an effort is not feasible now because our understanding of atmospheric and ocean dynamics and heat exchange is far too limited to enable us to predict the outcome. However, the inadvertent effects of man's activity may lead to catastrophic influences on global climate unless ways are developed to compensate for undesirable effects. Polar research is basic to any understanding of the Global Climate Machine. Joseph Fletcher is research professor in Atmospheric Sciences and Oceanography, University of Washington, Seattle.

Large variations in global climate have occurred in recent times and are occurring today. The climate of a particular region is determined by relatively static factors such as elevation, latitude, topography and type of surface and also by the properties of the air which passes over it. The dynamic factor is the circulation of the atmosphere.

Worldwide changes of climate are associated with variations in the general vigor of the global atmospheric circulation, with related latitudinal shifts of the main planetary wind belts and changes in the nature of their disturbances. Variations in the global circulation pattern are the common factor which makes possible a coherent interpretation of climatic data from all parts of the earth.

For example, from about 1890 to 1940 the general but irregular trend was toward growing strength of the global atmospheric circulation, northward displacement of the polar fronts in both the atmosphere and the ocean, northward displacement of ice boundaries in both the arctic and antarctic, weaker development of anticyclones over the continents and more northward cyclone paths. These dynamic changes were reflected by a dramatic warming of the arctic and of the North Atlantic, and aridity in the south central parts of North America and Eurasia. Conversely, recent decades have exhibited opposite trends: weakening planetary circulation, southward shifts of ice boundaries and cyclone paths and sharp cooling and different rainfall patterns over continents.

Our complex pattern of human activity is increasingly sensitive to these relatively small variations in climate — and they are small compared to even the recent past. Less than 20,000 years ago the Wisconsin ice sheet covered North America from the Atlantic to the Pacific and was up to two miles thick. Most of this vast ice mass melted during only a few thousand years, raising the level of the world ocean by several hundred feet. This warming culminated in a "climatic optimum" from about 4000-2000 B. C., during which world temperatures were four to five degrees warmer than they are now and rainfall patterns were very different.

The cooling from the warm optimum was abrupt from about 100 B.C. to about 400 B.C., ushering in a period of climatic stress on human activity. Increasing aridity afflicted the Mediterranean regions, and a period of stormy climate in the Baltic region about 120 B.C. set the Teutonic peoples on the move. By this time renewed warming had set in which continued until the secondary "climatic optimum" around 1000 A.D., a period characterized by a relatively dry, warm and storm-free North Atlantic which permitted the great Viking colonization of Greenland and Newfoundland. The decline, from about 1300 A.D., with one partial recovery from about 1400 to 1550, continued until about 1750, culminating in the "little ice age" of 1650-1840. During this cooling period, North Atlantic ice boundaries advanced and the Viking colonies were extinguished. The warming since the cooling climax of the 1700s continued irregularly up to the 1940s, when renewed cooling seems to have set in.

The basic causes of climate variations are not yet understood, but they are associated with variations in global patterns of heating and cooling which cause the motion of the atmosphere.

The global ocean/atmosphere system is a giant thermodynamic engine which transports heat from the warm tropics to the colder polar regions. The atmospheric motion is forced by pressure gradients arising from the pattern of atmospheric heating and cooling. The oceanic currents are moved by friction with the atmosphere, and they also transport an important fraction of the total heat toward the poles.

Most of the heat which generates atmospheric motion comes by way of the ocean surface, where solar energy is absorbed and stored. Thus, thermal energy from the ocean largely drives the atmosphere, and mechanical energy from the atmosphere largely drives the ocean. It follows that the fundamental problem in the study of climatic change is the development of a quantitative understanding of the general circulation of the atmosphere and ocean, including a quantitative understanding of oceanic heat transport and patterns. of ocean/atmosphere heat exchange.

NO ANALYTIC SOLUTION

Such an understanding should begin with the planetary distribution of solar energy and, by using the fundamental physical laws (largely embodied in the classical equations of motion and thermodynamics), should enable us to predict the global distribution of temperature, pressure, motion, water vapor, clouds and precipitation. In principle, such an analytic approach is straightforward, but in practice the equations are much too difficult for simultaneous solution by analytic methods. However, with the development of modern computer technology rapid progress is being made, for the equations can be replaced by their finite difference analogues and can be solved by high-speed computers. Already it is becoming possible to simulate mathematically some large-scale ocean/atmosphere processes in more detail than we observe them in nature.

This progress toward simulating the dynamics of climate calls for better understanding of ocean/atmosphere heat exchange in the real climate machine. Variations in equatorial heating and in polar cooling are poorly observed and only partially understood. It is known that substantial year-to-year variations do occur and do influence atmospheric dynamics. To further clarification of the tropical heat exchange processes, the forthcoming Global Atmospheric Research Program (GARP) envisions a series of tropical "experiments" aimed at better understanding of the primary heat source region.

In addition to understanding variations in the tropical "heat source" region, it is also necessary to understand variations in the two polar "heat sink" regions. A comprehensive program for monitoring ocean/atmosphere interaction over the arctic heat sink was put forward in early 1970 by the USSR for inclusion as a GARP sub-program. As yet, no corresponding proposal has been advanced for observing the antarctic heat sink.

The largest variations in the intensity of the polar heat sinks are associated with variations of ice extent on the ocean.

Ice cover on the ocean is a thermal "lever" which very effectively reduces heat exchange between the atmosphere and the ocean, both in winter and in summer. For example, in the central arctic in January the heat reaching the surface from below is very small even though the air is very cold, and only a few feet below the ocean waters are above freezing. If the ice were absent over a small area, the upward heat flow would be as much as 100 times greater; and if the ice were absent from the whole arctic, the total upward heat flow would be five or six times greater than at present. This would supply most of the planetary heat loss to space and thus reduce the transport of heat from lower latitudes.

Conversely, in summer the high reflectivity of ice reduces the solar heat input to the ocean by a factor of about four, so that, on the whole, both upward and downward heat exchange are drastically reduced by an ice cover.

Thus the extent of ice on the ocean regulates heat exchange between ocean and atmosphere and influences the pattern of net atmospheric cooling, thereby influencing the thermal forcing of the dynamic system. To put the matter in global perspective we might ask, "How much of the Earth's surface is subject to this thermal regulation, and how much does the ice-covered area vary during the year and from year to year?"

ARCTIC WARMING

In the northern hemisphere, the annual maximum extent of sea ice is about 5 per cent of the hemispheric area and the annual variation is about one-fourth of this. In the southern hemisphere the maximum sea-ice area is much larger, about 8 per cent of the hemispheric area, and the annual variation is about three-fourths of this. Thus, the annual variation in area covered by sea ice is roughly six times greater in the antarctic than in the arctic. We might expect that year-to-year variations are also larger in the southern hemisphere, but we do not have observational records from the antarctic to give a direct verification of this.

Records for the arctic are much better. During the warming of the early 1900s, variations in the mean area of arctic sea ice were roughly 10 to 15 per cent — about half of the variation from winter to summer. Variation in mean thickness may have been as much as one-third. These are substantial variations from a regional viewpoint, but since arctic ice extent is only about 5 per cent of the hemisphere, the long-term variation in area was less than one per cent of the area of the hemisphere.

A shrinking ice cover permits greater thermal participation by the ocean and thus reduces poleward temperature gradients and forcing of atmospheric motion, but the observed trends in the arctic were opposite to this. Warming of the arctic coincides with a period of increasing vigor of global atmospheric circulation, while the cooling of recent decades has been accompanied by weakening global circulation. We must therefore conclude that the warming and cooling of the arctic, with associated variations of ice extent, cannot have been a contributing cause of the observed variations in global circulation. On the contrary, the influence on thermal forcing of the observed variations in arctic ice extent would have dampened the observed variations of global circulation, the causes of which must lie elsewhere.

Examination of the surface radiation budget (Fig. 1) shows why the arctic pack ice is sensitive to

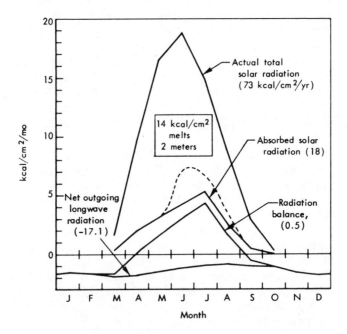

Fig. 1. Radiation components at surface in central arctic, long-term mean values. Only 18 of 73 kilocalories per square centimeter per year of solar energy at surface is absorbed. An earlier melting date might increase absorptivity as illustrated by the dashed line, thus capturing more heat. Rectangular area shows amount of heat to melt about half of the pack ice thickness.

small changes in atmospheric heat advection during early summer (early winter in the southern hemisphere). Maximum absorption is in July rather than in June, when solar energy is maximum, because a sudden increase in absorptivity occurs in mid-summer when melting produces puddles of water on the ice. A warmer than usual summer advances the melting date and heat budget variations during this brief summer season are as great as 10 per cent of the total annual heat advection by the atmosphere from lower latitudes.

During the northern summer the kinetic energy of the southern hemisphere circulation is about four times greater than that of the northern hemisphere, the meteorological equator is far north of the geographic equator and momentum is being transported across the equator from south to north. It is thus to be expected that southern hemisphere trends would be dominant in influencing the global system, partly because of the greater energy of the southern hemisphere circulation, but also because the winds over the equator, which cause important year-to-year ocean variations, are a feature of the southern hemisphere circulation.

Variations in the extent of ice on the Antarctic Ocean does seem to be an important factor influencing global climatic trend.

The high average intensity of the southern hemisphere circulation is partly due to the high, cold, white continent of Antarctica, which is a heat sink for the global system even in mid-summer. However, because it is always cold and white, its properties do not vary much from year to year. On the other hand, the sea ice surrounding the continent is in winter about 8 per cent of the hemisphere (more than one and a half times the area of the continent), and in summer shrinks to about one-fifth of its winter maximum. Variations in sea-ice extent around Antarctica thus offer a high

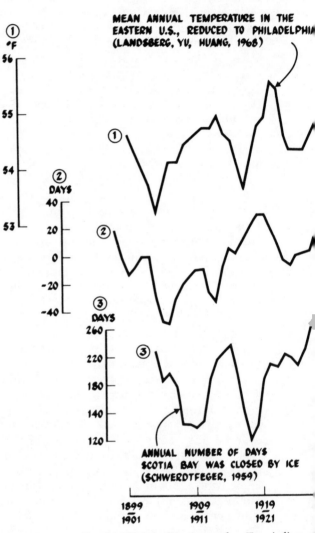

Fig. 2. Global climatic trends. Two indices c
circulation compared with iciness of th

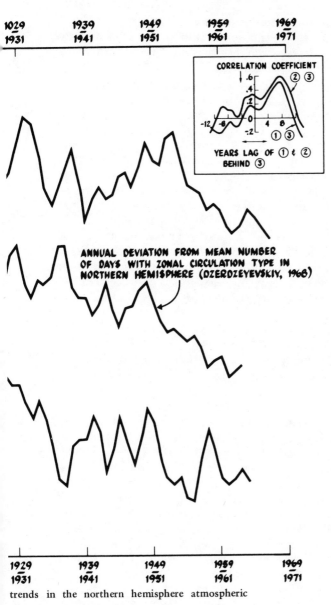

1029
1931
1939
1941
1949
1951
1959
1961
1969
1971

CORRELATION COEFFICIENT

.6
.4
.2
0
-.2

② ③

-12   -8   4   8

① ③

YEARS LAG OF ① & ②
BEHIND ③

ANNUAL DEVIATION FROM MEAN NUMBER
OF DAYS WITH ZONAL CIRCULATION TYPE IN
NORTHERN HEMISPHERE (DZERDZEYEVSKIY, 1968)

1929
1931
1939
1941
1949
1951
1959
1961
1969
1971

trends in the northern hemisphere atmospheric
Southern Ocean (three year moving averages).

potential for influencing the global system, and should do so in the sense that greater ice extent corresponds to stronger thermal forcing and more vigorous global circulation.

The data available to test this conclusion are very meager. There is no long-time series of direct observations of antarctic sea-ice extent. The only long-time series of meteorological data for the region of variable sea ice is from the South Orkneys, where data on freezing and opening of Scotia Bay have been recorded since 1903. Figure 2 compares the trends reflected by these data with climate trends for the northern hemisphere. These trends demonstrate the unity of the global system and also show the expected opposite phase between the antarctic ice region and the northern hemisphere. Global atmospheric circulation was strongest when iciness was greatest and vice versa. Northern hemisphere temperature trends follow global circulation intensity.

The climate history of the northern hemisphere has been documented for the last millennium, and it would be especially interesting to extend the comparison with variations of the southern heat sink back much farther than 1903. The first big question, of course, is to find out if the opposite phase relationship between antarctic sea ice and northern hemisphere temperature held true during and before the "little ice age" of the 1700s. We can get at this question indirectly by noting that iciness at Scotia Bay is closely paralleled by snow accumulation at the south pole, both being greater during periods of more vigorous atmospheric circulation (Fig. 3). The record of snow accumulation goes back much farther and can serve as a substitute index. Figure 4 shows the record for the last four centuries. The overall picture suggests that the "Little Ice Age" of the northern hemisphere corresponded to weaker global atmospheric circulation and in the antarctic by less snowfall at the pole and presumably minimal iciness of the Southern Ocean.

Going even further back, we would like to compare the warm epoch which reached its climax in the north about 100 A.D. and the subsequent cooling interrupted by a brief reversal about 1500 A.D. We do not yet have snow accumulation records from Pole station for these periods, but one time series has been constructed by pollen analysis from a peat bed at Kerguelen Island, slightly north of the present sea-ice zone at the longitude of India. The evidence is consistent with the foregoing relationships. In 100 A.D. it was cold at Kerguelen, after which warming occurred except for a short reversal about 1500 A.D.

The basic causes of these variations in the global climate machine are as yet unknown. Many suggestions have been offered, but we must learn much more about how the machine works before basic causes can be reliably evaluated.

Thus the reconstruction of past extremes of global climate is an urgent task which has been dramatically advanced by paleotemperature analysis of deep ice cores from Greenland and Antarctica. In general, the colder temperatures at such inland stations are associated with the intensity of the temperature inversion in the lower atmosphere and, thus, inversely with the general vigor of atmospheric circulation and frequency of cyclones. Similarly, analysis of ocean sediments can reveal the history of ocean temperatures and the displacement of such crucial dynamic features of the global climate machine as the antarctic convergence zone.

Whatever the basic physical causes of these planet-wide variations, sea-ice extent acts as an amplifying lever. For example, a reduction of solar intensity would cause cooling and expansion of sea-ice area. The greater sea-ice area amplifies the

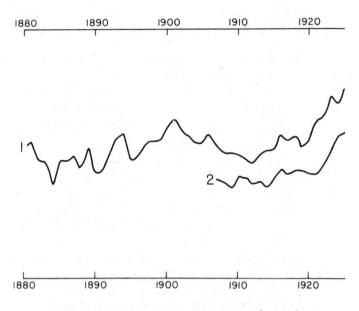

Fig. 3. (1) Ten-year moving average of annual snow accumulation at the south pole (Giovinetto and Schwerdtfeger, 1966); (2) Iciness of the

cooling by reflecting a greater fraction of solar energy away from the surface. An increase of solar intensity would reduce sea-ice extent and thus amplify the warming effect. An important task of climate investigations is to evaluate quantitatively these amplifying effects. An initial attempt has been reported by M. I. Budyko, who, on the basis of empirical data on solar variations and climate variations, suggests that a 1 per cent decrease in solar intensity would advance ice boundaries by 10 degrees latitude to cause a total planetary cooling of 5° C.

A 1.5 per cent decrease would advance ice boundaries 18 degrees and cause 9° C cooling, while more than 1.6 per cent solar decrease would advance ice boundaries to cover all the oceans, thus reducing

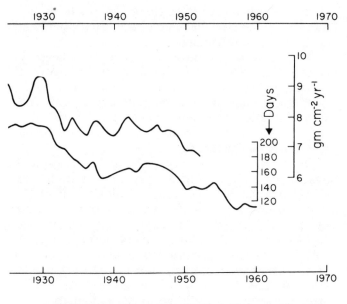

Weddell Sea, Antarctica. Number of days with
ice on the bay at Orcadas, 10-year moving average
(Schwerdtfeger, 1959).

the global climate to a very cold and stable condition. If this is true, the quaternary ice advances
were uncomfortably near to this critical instability
of the planetary climate machine.

MAN'S INFLUENCE

Man's inadvertent influences on global climate
up to now are small compared to natural variations, but in only a few more decades they may
become dominant.

The influencing pollutants most frequently suggested are carbon dioxide, heat and stratospheric
dust and moisture. Although the complexities of
the global system are still too poorly understood
to assess confidently the dynamic response of the
system to changes in these constituents, rough

estimates can be made of the effects of these pollutants on the heat balance of the atmosphere and on global mean temperature.

Carbon dioxide pollution is generally believed to be most important. It is one of the three important radiation absorbing gases in the atmosphere (along with water vapor and ozone), and more CO_2 substantially affects the amount of energy radiated to space (because the radiation comes from a higher and hence cooler level).

During the last century, CO_2 in the atmosphere has increased by about 11 per cent, and this increase is enough to account for about half of the $0.6°C$ mean hemispheric warming that occurred before 1940. With the accelerated burning of fossil fuel that is expected during the next three decades, the CO_2 level will be increased by about 50 per cent (to 450 parts per million) and global warming attributable to this cause will be about $1°C$. Such a strong warming would be further reinforced by substantial changes in sea-ice extent and might trigger other important internal variables in the climate machine. Thus it appears the CO_2 influence on climate may soon become critical. On the other hand, other influences may counter these trends. For example, the cooling of the 1950s and 1960s shows that some other factor is more than countering the warming effect of CO_2. Stratospheric dust from increasing volcanic activity reflects more sunlight away from the earth and thus causes cooling. This may account for recent trends, but records of dust load in the atmosphere are inadequate for a reliable evaluation. Man's contribution to the atmospheric dust load is increasing at an exponential rate with a doubling time in the 10 to 20 year range. A 10-year doubling time would more than compensate the warming due to CO_2, a 20 year doubling time would compensate only partially. Thus it appears that the influence of each of these factors, dust and CO_2, will become large compared to natural variations, but the net effect is difficult to estimate without better data.

Other forms of pollution may also be of comparable importance. Creation of high, thin cloudiness by aircraft is very influential in modifying the heat budget of the system. For example, a 10 per cent change in CO_2 is compensated by only 1 per cent change in mean cloudiness (or 3 per cent change in water vapor). Depending upon whether the region is in a sunlit or dark part of the earth, the effect of stratospheric clouds could be toward net cooling or net warming. It is thus a factor of potential use in managing climate influences, for cruising altitudes could be specified as in the stratosphere or below the stratosphere if it were important to do so.

In short, we may conclude that man's activities are already influencing global climate and that these influences will increase at exponential rates, becoming dominant over natural causes in a few decades. Before these inadvertent influences become critical, we must learn to exercise some purposeful control of climatic processes.

It is within man's engineering capability to influence global climate, but purposeful use of this capability will not be feasible until we understand how the global climate machine works and can simulate its behavior to predict the consequences of a given change in the system.

Many schemes have been put forward for influencing climate, but they will not be listed here. To appreciate the urgency of the problem, it is sufficient merely to recognize that avenues for purposeful influence exist, if we knew how to use them. For example, it has already been noted that the creation or dissipation of high cloudiness has an enormous influence on the heat budget of the atmosphere and of the surface. Moreover, under certain conditions, only one kilogram of reagent can seed an area of several square kilometers. It is estimated that 60, C-5 aircraft could deliver one kilogram per square kilometer per day over the entire arctic basin (10^7 km^2).

Thus it is a large but not impossible task to consider seeding such enormous areas. Assuming that such seeding were effective in creating or dissipating clouds, it is of interest to estimate the effect of such cloudiness on the heat budget of the surface/atmosphere system. The presence of average cloudiness over the arctic in July decreases the radiative loss to space by about 10 per cent from what it would be without clouds. For comparison, 100 per cent cloud tops at only 500 meters would decrease radiative loss by only 2 per cent while 100 per cent cloud tops at 5,000 meters would decrease radiative loss by about 30 per cent. These numbers

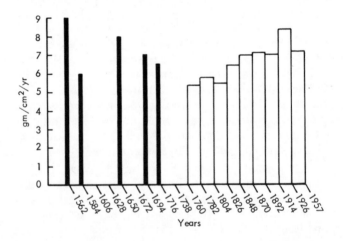

Fig. 4. Snow accumulation at south pole during "Little Ice Age"—after 1760, 22-yr means; before 1760, short-period samples (adapted from Giovinetto and Schwerdtfeger).

demonstrate not only the enormous thermal leverage that might be exercised by influencing mean cloudiness, but also the range of influence that might be possible, depending on cloud type, height and its influence on the regional heat budget during periods of sunlight and darkness.

Similarly, it may be noted that, under certain conditions, influencing the surface albedo of arctic pack ice is not beyond the capability of present technology. Since the presence of sea ice effectively severs the intense heat flux from ocean water to cold atmosphere, regulating the extent of sea ice is still another possible way of exercising thermal leverage on patterns of thermal forcing of atmospheric motion.

Influencing the temperature of the ocean surface over extended areas by changing the courses of certain ocean currents in various ways has also been proposed. These schemes involve large but not impossible engineering efforts. The principal difficulty, however, is that present understanding of ocean dynamics is too rudimentary to predict reliably the effects of such projects and, even if this were possible, the dynamic response of the atmosphere to the new pattern of heating must also be predicted.

CONCLUSIONS

These various examples are enough to demonstrate the following essential conclusions:

1. It does appear to be within man's engineering capacity to influence the heat loss and gain of the atmosphere on a scale that can influence patterns of thermal forcing of atmospheric circulation.

2. Purposeful use of this capability is not feasible because present understanding of atmospheric and oceanic dynamics and heat exchange is far too imperfect to predict the outcome of such efforts.

3. Although it would be theoretically more effi-

cient to act directly on the moving atmosphere, engineering techniques for doing so are not presently available.

4. The inadvertent influences of man's activity may lead eventually to catastrophic influences on global climate unless ways are developed to compensate for undesired effects. Whether the time remaining for bringing this problem under control is a few decades or a century is still an open question.

5. The diversity of thermal processes that can be influenced in the atmosphere, and between the atmosphere and ocean, offers promise that, if global climate is adequately understood, it can be influenced either to maximize climatic resources or avoid unwanted changes.

In the limited time available before inadvertent effects become critical, we must learn how to manage climatic resources.

It is convenient to think of needed progress in four stages: observation, understanding, prediction and control. We must observe how nature behaves before we can understand why. We must understand before we can predict. And, we must be able to predict the outcome before we undertake measures for control. Much progress is needed in all four areas to achieve the degree of control over climatic processes that is becoming necessary.

1. Observation of global heating patterns and ocean/atmosphere dynamics must be expanded. Until recently no more than about 20 per cent of the global atmosphere was observed at one time, and that very incompletely. With the advent of satellite observing systems some quantities can be observed over the entire planet every day. This observational breakthrough makes possible the synoptic surveillance of the entire global system, and the sophistication of satellite observations is rapidly increasing.

Synoptic observations of the global system have further emphasized the necessity of observing certain regions in great detail for a limited period in order to understand the heat exchange processes taking place and their influence on the atmosphere and the ocean. This is especially important in regions which play an important role in the thermal forcing of atmospheric and oceanic circulation, and where large year-to-year variations can occur. In the equatorial heat source region, variations in the intensity of the tropical convergence zone seem to be associated with changing global climate. In the two polar heat-sink regions, variations in extent of ice cover on the ocean also seem to be associated with changing global climate. Both the causes and the effects of these variations are obscure and will be revealed only by systematic observations of natural behavior in careful coordination with development of global climate models.

The tropical regions are receiving increased attention in recent years and several large observational programs have been conducted there: "The Indian Ocean Experiments," 1964; the "Line Island Experiment," 1966; the "Barbados Experiment," 1968, and the "BOMEX Experiment," 1969. Similar planning is needed for regions of large heating anomalies at high latitudes. Such a program for observing air-sea interaction for the arctic and for the ice-free ocean down to 50°N was announced in early 1970 by the USSR and is now under discussion by international planning groups.

Careful consideration should also be given to needs for data from the southern "heat sink." Since the southern hemisphere circulation seems to dominate the global system, it is especially important to piece together the climatic history and the past behavior of the more variable features of the dynamic system, for example antarctic sea-ice extent and the position of the antarctic convergence, which marks a sharp thermal discontinuity in the ocean.

2. An understanding of contemporary and future climatic changes can hardly be achieved without understanding the large climatic changes of the past. Defining the patterns of these changes is a way of observing nature's own "climate control experiments." Yet the collection and systematization of paleoclimatic evidence has been both meager and uncoordinated. The records from deep ice cores taken in both Greenland and Antarctica have demonstrated their enormous potential for describing past climates. Records from ocean sediments can be expected to reveal past variations of the important oceanic discontinuities. A more systematic effort is needed to bring together all the diverse sources of evidence to produce a more coherent overall picture of global climate variations.

At the same time it should be noted that the polar regions offer unique opportunities for monitoring such important global pollutants as CO_2, dust, ozone, etc., far from local sources of contamination. Such "background" measurements are necessary to reveal worldwide trends, and data taken in the antarctic have demonstrated the unique potential of "polar environmental observatories." Systematic measurements over long periods of time are essential. Understanding and prediction can be advanced by evaluation of the circulation changes resulting from specific variations of boundary conditions — "climate experiments" in the laboratory.

3. An adequate theoretical basis has not as yet been developed for explaining the interactions of the global heat engine and for accounting for observed changes in climate. Casual relationships are obscured by the multitude of factors operating, and problems for investigations are often ill-defined. Research methods have been painfully slow and frustrating and thus appear less attractive than

the more direct methods of experimental sciences: observation of physical behavior, formation of a hypothesis, deduction of consequences from the hypothesis, and the testing of deductions by physical experiment. These limitations are also changing rapidly, for the rapid increase in computer power, coupled with the parallel development of mathematical models of atmospheric and oceanic circulation make it possible to conduct laboratory experiments to find out how the ocean/atmosphere dynamical system responds to a specific change in heating pattern. A model which realistically simulates the dynamics of the global system can be used to evaluate theories of climatic change. With these tools, a resurgence of interest in explaining climatic changes can be expected — with rapid progress toward understanding how our climate machine works.

HEAT BUDGET CALCULATIONS

For example, a number of theories for explaining climate variations invoke the supposition that an ice-free ocean characterizes an alternative stable state of the global climate machine. This argument has been advanced by C. E. P. Brooks, W. M. Ewing and W. L. Donn and M. I. Budyko; the key idea being that the heat budget of an ice-free arctic would be such that it would remain ice free for a long period of time. Simple heat budget calculations are inconclusive, for it appears that the annual heat budget of an ice-free arctic ocean would be almost neutral; whether it was positive or negative would probably be determined by the response of the global atmospheric circulation to such a change in heating pattern.

Thus, to answer this question it is necessary to simulate global circulation with an ice-free arctic and compare the dynamical behavior with that for a normal ice-covered arctic. Such experiments, involving the largest plausible heating anomalies, are now under way. Evaluations of the influence of smaller anomalies will follow as simulation models are improved.

4. Control can be advanced by evaluating ways of influencing large-scale heat exchange processes. Examples have already been given of various ways to influence the heat budget of the surface or the radiative properties of the atmosphere. Such techniques should be systematically evaluated, and new ones discovered. In general, such tests must be conducted under natural conditions and be designed to trigger cumulative effects on natural heat exchanges. Nature sets a limit on the rate of such experimentation, as the annual cycle occurs only once a year. We should expect that when rapid experimental progress becomes urgent this limitation will be severely felt. Meanwhile, it would be wise to initiate a small but systematic program of field evaluation of such potential techniques for large-scale weather modification.

INTERNATIONAL COOPERATION

Finally it must be emphasized that management of climatic resources is a problem shared by all nations. The global ocean/atmosphere is a single interacting physical system, in which an action anywhere may influence behavior everywhere. We are rapidly approaching the time when progress toward learning how to manage global climate will be proportional to the purposeful investment of scientific efforts. Coordination of these efforts is in everyone's interest. More effective arrangements are needed for coordinating the efforts of different countries. And all countries should be encouraged to conduct complementary and mutually supporting field observation programs with pooling and full dissemination of data. During 1970 both the Soviet Union and the United States have announced plans for ambitious observational programs in the arctic. The USSR Ocean/Atmosphere Interaction Experiment and the U.S./Canadian Arctic Ice Dynamics Joint Experiment, developed quite independently of each other, are in no way duplicative but are complementary. The inherent potential for international cooperation is a challenge to government and scientific leadership in all countries.

Antarctic Meteorology

MORTON J. RUBIN

"The question of world-wide pollution is a pressing one at the moment and promises to become even more serious. The rise of CO_2, DDT and lead in Antarctica indicates that it is becoming contaminated by man-made pollutants. It is now time to establish stations to measure all aspects of this contamination in order to provide a base-line against which to compare future conditions." Morton Rubin is chief of Office of Special Studies, National Oceanic and Atmospheric Administration. The views expressed are those of the author and do not necessarily reflect those of NOAA.

The development of meteorological knowledge about Antarctica was slow and incomplete until relatively recently. More than 100 years after men had first wintered-over, only imprecise estimates were available of the extreme temperatures likely to be experienced when the United States and

Soviet expeditions were planning to establish stations in the interior of the continent for the International Geophysical Year (IGY), 1957-58.

The unique international effort during the IGY
and the continuing cooperation afterward resulted
in a marked increase in knowledge about antarctic
metorology and climatology. An important element
in the cooperative program was the exchange of
scientific personnel and the pooling of scientific
efforts such as the operation of the IGY Antarctic
Weather Central at Little America. As program
leader for that activity, I can attest to its success
both as an operational and a research project.
Meteorologists representing six countries worked in
a common cause to provide the weather maps and
other charts for the antarctic continent and surrounding ocean. These charts, used for operational
purposes, also provided the basis for research on
the synoptic processes of the high latitudes of the
southern hemisphere. There were other cooperative
programs in which Soviet and American meteorologists, of which I was one, spent as much as a year
or more as participants on the meteorological team
of the other. These exchange programs, not limited
to meteorology, provided participants with a rare
opportunity to become conversant with the techniques and procedures of the others. I have no
doubt that much of the success of the antarctic
meteorological program is due to that kind of continuing cooperation.

From their sense of symmetry, the ancient Greek
philosophers deduced that there was a large polar
landmass to balance the land areas in the north.
It was not until Captain James Cook's second expedition that Western man was able to show that
there was such a cold region. In January 1774, at
latitude 71°10'S, longitude 106°54'W, Cook judged
from the sea ice and his observations of 97 icebergs
that "the ice extended quite to the Pole, or perhaps

joined to some land to which it had been fixed from earlier times."

In all of the voyages of exploration and discovery in the nineteenth century, meteorology was an integral part of the scientific program. Expeditions in the twentieth century contributed still more to the developing store of meteorological data and increasing understanding of climatic conditions. Climatic records in Antarctica, of course, cannot compare in length to records elsewhere on earth, but some of the specialized or routine meteorological observations being made in Antarctica today were attempted years ago: the first data on sunshine were recorded in 1898-1900; atmospheric ozone observations—crude and unsuccessful—in 1901-04; atmospheric electricity data in 1910-13; upper-air soundings (kites and airplanes) in 1928-30; and radiosondes in 1939-40.

Without question, the IGY brought about a rapid and unparalleled increase of knowledge of the climatic and meteorological characteristics of a previously unknown region. These characteristics of Antarctica, which is a principal heat sink of the earth-atmosphere system, are best understood in the context of the heat and water-mass balance of the region and the physical processes which are factors in that balance.

The principal determining factor in the radiation balance and climate of Antarctica is, of course, its south polar location. This determines the length of day and night, winter and summer, and the maximum possible incoming solar radiation. Because the earth is at perihelion around the time of the southern hemisphere summer solstice, the south pole receives seven per cent more solar extra-terrestrial radiation than the north pole at summer solstice. The solar radiation is modified by the mean elevation (2,400 meters), the perpetual snow cover which strongly reflects solar radiation and strongly radiates the earth's long-wave energy, the clarity and dryness of the atmosphere, and by other atmospheric constituents.

At the south pole, the theoretical value of the incoming solar radiation at the top of the atmosphere is 133 x 10^3 langleys (calories per square centimeter, hereafter ly) per year (Fig. 1), rising rapidly from practically zero in September to 36 x 10^3 ly in December, and falling just as rapidly to zero in March. About 73 per cent of the annual total is during the three-month period centered on the summer solstice. At the polar circle somewhat less (33 x 10^3 ly) is received in December, but the greater total number of hours of sunlight per year provides over 160 x 10^3 ly of solar radiation, about 57 per cent of which is in the summer. Interior stations tend to have less of the solar radiation depleted within the atmosphere, resulting in higher values at the surface than stations at the lower elevations and latitudes. For example, the south pole December mean surface value is 28.5 x 10^3 ly, down 7.5 x 10^3 ly from the extraterrestrial value, while a station at the polar circle will have a mean surface value of 22 x 10^3 ly, down 11 x 10^3 ly.

Solar radiation is not very effective in heating the atmosphere directly; it does so mainly through absorption of short-wave radiation at the surface and by re-radiation in the long-wave lengths for which the atmosphere is relatively opaque. The bright, clean snow and ice surfaces of Antarctica reflect as much as 80 per cent or more of the solar radiation received at the surface, leaving little available to heat it and the lowest layers of the atmosphere.

Although the snow surface shows a net gain of heat (Fig. 1) through radiative exchanges for a short period in summer at most stations, it has a negative annual radiation balance. The heat to offset this negative balance does not come from the topmost layers of snow. At the south pole, for example, the flux from these layers is about 12 per cent of the long-wave radiative flux in winter. Measurements of the subsurface snow temperature at several depths show an annual cycle decreasing in amplitude to nearly zero at around 10 meters. Since the annual mean temperature of the snow surface shows little year-to-year variation, the radiative heat loss must be made up by other processes. These are mainly turbulent exchanges of sensible heat and latent heat between the atmosphere and the snow surface. The total turbulent exchange at the south pole, for instance, is about 8,400 ly for the dark six-month period and 4,400 ly for the light six-month period.

Calculations show that on the polar plateau the heat flux owing to water vapor can be of the same magnitude as the sensible heat flux in summer (about 10-20 ly per day), but in winter the latent heat flux is as low as two per cent of the sensible heat flux. Most commonly the latent heat flux results in the deposition of snow on the surface; this is said to amount to as much as 0.7 centimeters per month at the stations on the high plateau. Annual values at coastal stations and on the plateau in summer are higher because of the higher water vapor content during that season. Some months show a net evaporation from the surface; both at plateau stations and on the coast. The coastal stations which are under the influence of prevailing downslope winds may experience strong net evaporation, even resulting in a net loss of snow cover.

HEAT TRANSPORTED

The overall negative heat balance has to be made up since Antarctica does not appear to be cooling. This is accomplished through the transport of sensible and latent heat by the atmosphere from other regions with positive heat balances. This has im-

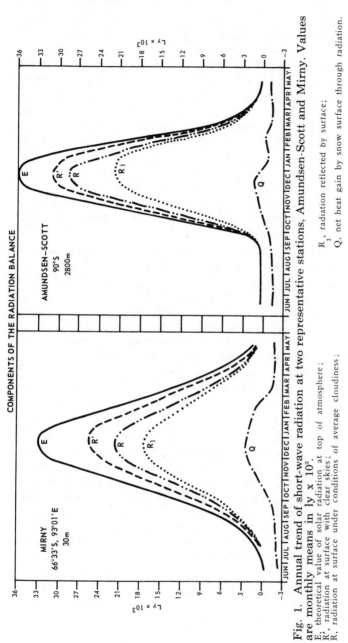

Fig. 1. Annual trend of short-wave radiation at two representative stations, Amundsen-Scott and Mirny. Values are monthly means in ly x 10³.

E, theoretical value of solar radiation at top of atmosphere;
R', radiation at surface with clear skies;
R, radiation at surface under conditions of average cloudiness;

R₁, radiation reflected by surface;
Q, net heat gain by snow surface through radiation.

portant implications in terms of circulation systems, precipitation, storm tracks, cloudiness, etc.

From IGY data, calculations of the amount of heat transported across 70°S latitude in the form of sensible heat gave a value of 13.2 x 10^{21} calories per year, with another 1.8 x 10^{21} in the form of latent heat. This total, 15 x 10^{21} calories per year, offsets the amount presumed lost by radiation from the top of the atmosphere to space. Recent calculations from satellite observations give a value of the heat loss of about 8.7 x 10^{21} calories per year. The value of the transport required to balance this heat loss is less than calculated previously, but it does not change the basic requirement that there be such transport.

Other factors that have to be considered in the overall heat balance are the total extent of the sea ice in different seasons and its variability within seasons, the extent of rock and bare soil and changes in cloudiness and albedo. For instance, it is known that albedo changes of the order of 20 per cent occur, depending upon the character of the snow and ice surface. The vertical flux of heat from the ocean can change perhaps by two orders of magnitude, depending on whether the sea is open or ice-covered. Rock and soil change the heat balance radically.

Consider, for example, the sea-ice cover, for which estimates have been made on the basis of satellite data and from surface observations. It has its minimum extent of 2.6 x 10^6 square kilometers in March, and maximum of 18.8 x 10^6 square kilometers in September. This is a sevenfold increase and has a strong influence on heat and moisture exchange, temperature gradient, cyclonic activity, etc. Variations in this cover, even of the order of 10 per cent, can result in large variations in the heat balance for certain regions and for given periods of time. The increase of sea ice, also, constitutes an increase in continental and ice surface from 17.2 x 10^6 to 33.4 x 10^6 square kilometers, essentially a doubling, which strongly influences the radiation and climatic regimes.

It has been determined that there has to be net advection of heat across the boundary of Antarctica if radiative heat losses are to be balanced. As a result of the data collection and analysis program beginning with the IGY, the details of the large-scale circulation and advection have become known, and calculations have been made of the magnitude and character of the advective transport. But the smaller scale details require a denser network of data than now exists. The large-scale processes over the oceans are not yet completely understood, although some of the recent studies, particularly those based on satellite and long-term statistical data, are revealing much about the zonal and meridional exchanges, storm tracks and synoptic developments.

The radiative imbalances which establish themselves early in the winter between Antarctica and the lower latitudes bring about a state in which

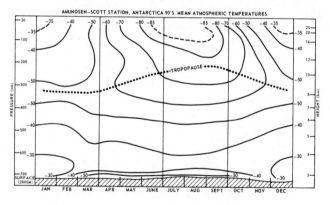

Fig. 2. Time-height section of monthly mean air temperature (°C) at the south pole.

cyclonic systems in the troposphere (the levels in the atmosphere below about 10 kilometers) move warm and moist air over the continent. These incursions of warm air are confirmed by daily map analysis, climatological statistics and other analyses. This is true for all stations. At the south pole station (Fig. 2) for example, the monthly mean temperature in the mid-troposphere varies by 10° C or less from mid-summer to mid-winter. The monthly mean surface temperature, because of strong radiative effects, varies by more than 20° C. The stratospheric temperatures vary by more than 50° C on the average because of the strong, stable circulation established early in winter which inhibits meridional exchange in the stratosphere.

HOME OF THE BLIZZARD

Generally, the lower elevations of West Antarctica are less of a barrier to the incursions of air from the oceans. This results in greater storminess and precipitation. In that region, the large-scale circulation seems to result in strong warm air advection and upward motion, with positive correlations between precipitation amounts and synoptic patterns. In East Antarctica, there is less warm air advection, much less precipitation, and generally subsiding air. This is in agreement with greater cloudiness over West Antarctica than over East Antarctica. For the Antarctica as a whole, there tends to be a net inflow of air in the upper troposphere (above about four kilometers) and a net outflow below.

Surface winds tend to be weakest in the interior and on the ice shelves around the continent, with annual mean values of about five meters per second (mps). Coastal winds in East Antarctica are strongest, with values of around 11 mps. During a year I spent at Mirny station, the peak wind gusts on seven occasions in the winter were over 50 mps.

These are the noteworthy katabatic winds over the steeply inclined slopes along the edge of the continent which are of relatively short duration, except as they may occur in conjunction with a storm from the sea. The wind speeds at Cape Denison were notorious for their ferocity. Records from 1912-13 show that 64 per cent of the days averaged greater than 17.9 mps, and 17 per cent averaged greater than 26.8 mps. Truly "the home of the blizzard" as Douglas Mawson called it. Only seven per cent of the days averaged below 8.9 mps.

Strong winds such as we have described, and the steady outflow winds, contribute much to the transport of snow from the continent, very often leaving only bare "blue ice" in some spots. Interior winds tend to be relatively constant, with small vector standard deviation. These show up in the snow surface undulations (sastrugi), which are good indicators of the prevailing surface wind direction.

STRATOSPHERIC CIRCULATION

In the stratosphere, the strong cooling at all polar latitudes strongly reinforces the meridional temperature gradient. This results in a circumpolar vortex of west winds which become stronger as the temperature falls (Fig. 2). This very strong vortex inhibits meridional exchanges; it persists all winter long and records to date show no case in which it has broken down before spring and the return of the sun. The reversal to summertime temperatures takes place within a period of only several weeks. Shrotly thereafter, the meridional temperature gradient in the lower stratosphere is reversed with the result that the west winds often completely disappear and east winds are observed. Generally the circulation is weak and variable.

In some years, the warming is slow and steady; in others it is rapid and extreme, even sometimes falling slightly to lower values after reaching an

early peak. Data are insufficient to delineate exactly the small-scale features of this warming, and
rocket data are not yet sufficiently widespread for
us to know whether the higher levels are involved.

The warming appears at first in the region of the
magnetic pole in East Antarctica, moving to the
geographic pole and thence to the Weddell Sea.
It seems to be associated with the progression of
a belt of strong winds in the stratosphere. At times
there is a temporary reversal of the warming, probably due to shifts in the stratospheric circulation
patterns. During the months of October and November, the net heat gain in the lower stratosphere
over Antarctica from both horizontal advection and
vertical motion is greater than in any other two-
month period. Radiation considerations indicate
that there should be a net loss of heat from this
layer; therefore it is evident that the warming is
primarily due to dynamic effects. These stratosphere warmings are also closely connected with an
increase in the total ozone content. Markedly different warming trends over several years coincided
with markedly different values of ozone at the same
time.

THE AGUNG EFFECT

The breakdown in the strong circumpolar vortex
and return to a summertime meridional circulation
over Antarctica was dramatically evidenced beginning in November 1963. By the middle of November, one month after the sun becomes visible from
an altitude of 20 kilometers above sea level, the
values of the direct solar radiation data received
on a surface normal to the sun's rays was about
at the value of the 1957-62 normal. After several
wide fluctuations in late November and early December 1963, the normal-incidence value began a
steady decline to a value only about 15 per cent
of the 1957-62 normal by mid-February 1964. Stu-

dies of trajectories at the 16-25 kilometer layer seem to indicate that the depletion was due to volcanic material put into the stratosphere in March 1963 by the eruption of Mt. Agung in Bali. Of great interest is the fact that although the direct solar beam was greatly reduced, the total of the direct and diffuse (solar and sky) radiation was only slightly below the normal for previous years. It appears that most of the decrease in the direct beam by the dust was due to scattering rather than to absorption. By the summer of 1964 (December), the value of the direct solar radiation had returned to about 75 per cent of the previous normal. In the summer of 1965, it had returned to about 91 per cent of the normal, and by 1968 it seemed to be normal again.

Because of the remoteness of Antarctica from other continents, its relative freedom from sources of pollution and its almost complete lack of vegetation, Antarctica can serve as a valuable "bench mark" against which to compare long-term trends in all significant atmospheric constituents and pollutants.

Total atmospheric ozone content has been measured in Antarctica since the IGY. The total remains low from fall through winter into October and, then, rises abruptly to a maximum in November, which is related to influx of air from lower latitudes, rise of pressure over the continent, sinking motion of air and an increase of ozone in the stratosphere. The increase seems to be strongest at 15 to 20 kilometers. The surface ozone variations do not follow the upper-air trends, but show a maximum outflow in winter. These conclusions are based on early data and thus warrant re-analysis and further study.

MAN-MADE POLLUTANTS

Carbon dioxide has been measured and sampled

since the IGY. No local vegetation is available to influence seasonal variations, so the variations would have to be due to horizontal exchanges. The trend of CO_2 concentration over the period 1958-63 is shown in Fig. 3, and is in close agreement with values at Mauna Loa in Hawaii. The antarctic mean value is about 0.6 parts per million less than Mauna Loa, perhaps indicating a gradient and suggesting the use of CO_2 as a tracer of atmospheric motions.

Analyses of the mineral content of snow as well as levels of radioactivity, both natural and artificial, in snow and air have been made; the interpretation of these data in terms of atmospheric motions has been little reported. The levels of artificial radioactivity have shown increases following northern hemisphere inputs, with time lags, of course, and at much lower levels of activity. From snow pit data it has been shown that during the period 1935-52 the gross gamma activity was of the order of 0.5 disintegrations per minute per kilogram of snow; this increased to 2.0 dpm for 1953-54, and 22.0 dpm for early 1955. For the period 1955-60, the value fell to 14.0 dpm. Long-lived strontium-90 values from air samples at the south pole were around 4.7 dpm per 1,000 standard cubic meters in 1964, an inactive period, compared with 59 dpm for Thule, Greenland.

Before 1940 the amount of lead in the antarctic ice sheets was undetectable. After 1940, it was found to be about 0.020 micrograms per kilogram of ice. This is about one-tenth the lead content of Greenland ice, yet still attests to the north-south atmospheric transport.

DDT and its residuals have appeared in the antarctic, mainly in the tissues of animals. Maximum residue values are about 0.44 ppm wet weight, well below those of northern hemisphere animals. It was thought that the method of transporting DDT

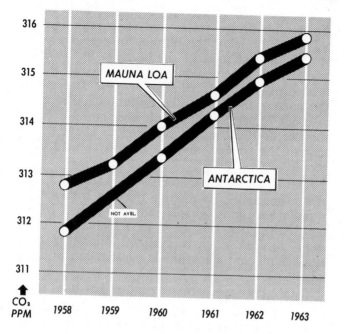

Fig. 3. Trend of annual average concentration of CO_2 (parts per million of dry air by volume).

from sources external to Antarctica is through the food chain. However, recent data indicate that there actually may be some transport by the atmosphere. Snow samples from the region of the high plateau of East Antarctica show values of 0.04 micrograms of DDT per kilogram of snow. This compares with values of up to 1.3 micrograms of DDT per kilogram of rain in Ohio.

The question of world-wide pollution is a pressing one at the moment and promises to become even more serious. The rise of CO_2, DDT and lead in Antarctica indicates that it is becoming contaminated by man-made pollutants. It is now time to establish stations to measure all aspects of this contamination in order to provide a base-line against which to compare future conditions.

The question of the gross or net amount of precipitation over Antarctica has been much studied and discussed. The several approaches — namely, direct measurement, pit-stratigraphic measurements, stake, isotope analysis, etc. — sometimes are at variance. However, it is agreed that the interior of Antarctica is a desert and that the pattern shown in Fig. 4 is essentially correct. The average value for snow accumulation over Antarctica is between about 15 and 19 grams per square centimeter per year. There is evidence to show that the high plateau receives a considerable portion of its precipitation in the form of snow crystals due to the slow eddy diffusion downward of some advected air above the temperature inversion. The question of ablation, sublimation, drifting and melting is still unresolved. Since the precipitation question relates to the heat budget through the latent heat term, which is thought to provide more than 10 per cent of the heat transport, it is of importance to resolve these questions.

CLOUDINESS

Cloudiness strongly influences the heat budget and surface temperatures. But clouds are difficult to observe and distinguish during the polar night. Even satellites are deficient in this regard since they sense infrared radiation and can confuse ice temperatures with cloud-top temperatures. Generally, cloudiness tends to be greatest along the coast and least in the interior; greatest in summer and least in winter. Sea level stations north of 65°S average about eight-tenths coverage for the year; coastal stations south of 65°S average about six-tenths coverage for the year; interior continental stations average five-tenths or less for the year.

TEMPERATURE

The general features of the surface and upper-air temperature regime are known in broad detail, both over the continent and over the ocean. Numerous mean maps have been drawn which show that the isotherms generally follow the surface contours over the continent, as one would expect, and are in close agreement with surface discontinuities (Fig. 5).

The small-scale variations are not well known, although they can be inferred on the basis of terrain, altitude, etc. Of great help in determining annual mean temperatures has been the clear relationship between the mean snow surface temperature and the temperature at about 10 to 12 meters

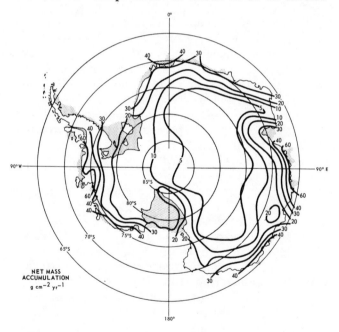

Fig. 4. Annual net mass accumulation of snow in grams per square centimeter per year (after Giovinetto).

below surface.

For the continental area, excluding the Antarctic Peninsula, the mean temperatures of the warmest months are around 0°C on the coast and from —20° to —35° C in the interior.

The mean temperatures of the coldest months are —20° to —30°C on the coast, and —40° to —70° C in the interior. The absolute minimum temperature was achieved at Vostok (—88.3°C) in August 1960. The minimum each year there tends to be in late August just before the return of the sun. In the region of the Antarctic Peninsula, the mean temperature of the warmest month ranges around 0° C, with the coldest month around —10° C. Absolute extremes there are about +15° C to —40° C.

The clear atmosphere, the strongly radiative snow surface and the long winter nights tend to produce very strong surface temperature inversions over Antarctica. This is a distinctive physical phenomenon that reaches its epitome on the high antarctic plateau, although it is frequently present and pronounced at most other locations in Antarctica. The depth of the temperature inversion averages from 300 to 700 meters depending on location and season, the lower values tending to occur in summer. The average value of the increase of temperature with height varies from about 5° C along the coast to about 25° C on the high plateau, and the maximum value never seems to exceed about 40° C. This limit probably exists because the backward long-wave radiation from the atmosphere, which is at a higher temperature than the snow surface, tends to balance that emitted by the surface. Other factors such as radiation from clouds or warm air at higher altitudes have the same inhibiting effect on the inversion.

Despite attempts to interpret temperature records, snow cores and other indirect data, it has

Most of Antarctic Lake Bonney is covered permanently by ice, but scientists have found water
temperature as high as 72°F under the ice in the
fresh water lake.

not been possible to determine any significant or
unambiguous long-term trend in temperature.

Some evidence exists for an increase in snow
accumulation in the interior of the continent and
possibly for a decrease in the coastal regions. This
amounts to an increase of mean annual precipitation of 5.4 grams per square centimeter from about
1780 to 1826, to about 7.5 grams per square centi-

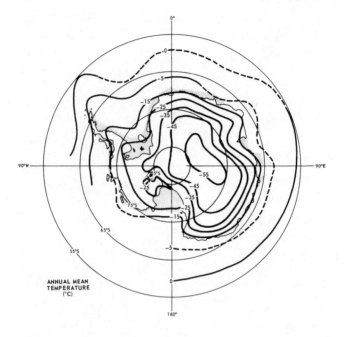

Fig. 5. Annual mean surface air temperature (°C).

meter from about 1890 to 1957 at the south pole.
Along the coast of East Antarctica, the ice sheet
seems to have thinned from between six meters to
22 meters in a 50-year period prior to 1957.

MUCH TO BE DONE

It might reasonably be claimed that we now have
a fairly complete understanding of the broad-scale
features of the climate and meteorological processes of the antarctic continent. But it is clear
that much more has yet to be done before we can
say that we can adequately describe, understand
and predict those phenomena of significance.

We should plan for future research activities
which will continue some of the present programs,

as well as for new programs which will help explain some of the original questions not yet answered, as well as those new questions which inevitably arise during the course of explaining previously incompletely understood phenomena. These developments should be in the direction of a more detailed analysis of those phenomena and conditions which until now have been only partially or grossly explained, and in the extension of our observational capabilities upward into the stratosphere, the mesosphere and outward over the ocean regions. In a general way, we can suggest the following:

1. Observations over the oceans by means of automatic stations, transosondes and satellites to couple Antarctica with the rest of the southern hemisphere and the northern hemisphere as well.

2. The extension of soundings by rockets to probe higher levels so as to estimate the role of the upper atmosphere and the mesosphere in the meteorological processes, particularly at times of rapid changes.

3. Continuation of stations with the longest records to establish references against which to measure future variations. New stations in other regions should be considered.

4. Continued measurement of ozone, carbon dioxide and improved measurements of water vapor to relate to circulation, heat budget and exchange studies.

5. Dust content, condensation nuclei, radioactivity, chemical and isotope observations and analysis to determine geographical and secular variations. These offer a valuable indirect method for determining large-scale atmospheric motions in regions where only intermittent observations are possible.

6. Local studies to determine reasons for such features as dry valleys and oases.

7. Improved methods of studying the age and

composition of the deep layers of snow in order to study the previous conditions as a guide to the future.

Antarctica continues to pose a great challenge to the meteorologists as well as to other scientists, and there remains much to be explained and related to the overall concepts we have concerning the meteorology of our planet. It still is a unique area, and one which well merits the exceptional efforts which have been expended there.

The Upper Atmosphere as Seen from Antarctica

ROBERT A. HELLIWELL

"The antarctic is unparalleled as a scientific laboratory for the study of the upper atmosphere. Its geographic location, its freedom from many of the limitations of civilization and the spirit of international cooperation fostered by the Antarctic Treaty combine to make this forbidding continent unique in the history of science." Robert A. Helliwell, one of pioneer investigators of upper atmosphere phenomena in the antarctic program, is professor of electrical engineering at the Stanford Electronics Laboratories. He has served as a consultant to the National Bureau of Standards and the National Aeronautics & Space Administration.

Study of the earth's atmosphere has long been motivated not only by the desire for more knowledge but also by practical applications, such as long distance radio communication via the ionosphere. In recent years additional practical problems such as air pollution and space radiation have been added to the list of those problems requiring more fundamental knowledge of atmospheric processes. For example, we are uneasy about the effect of pollution-stimulated changes in the composition of the lower atmosphere on the amount of ozone in the upper atmosphere. It is this ozone that absorbs deadly ultraviolet light before it can damage living organisms on the earth.

Led by the International Geophysical Year and the space program, the last decade has seen a remarkable expansion of our knowledge of the upper atmosphere and solar-terrestrial relations. We now have a much clearer picture of the ways in which the sun deposits energy in the atmosphere and the resulting response of the atmosphere to this input. With clarification of this picture has come a better appreciation of its extreme complexity and of the many questions that remain to be answered.

In all of this research, the importance and relationship of contributions from both the arctic and antarctic have come to be recognized. It is now clear that both polar regions will play an essential role in future research on the upper atmosphere.

One of the important energy inputs to the upper atmosphere is sunlight, which breaks down and ionizes the neutral particles of the air. As time passes the sunlit regions of the upper atmosphere eventually move into the shadow of the earth; there the ions tend to recombine to form neutral particles again. At middle and low latitude this sequence of events sets up a strong, 24-hour variation in the density of electrons in the ionosphere (60 to 1,000 km altitude). However, as we approach the poles an important change occurs. Because of the tilt of the earth's axis with respect to the plane of the earth's orbit about the sun, the seasonal effects, which are relatively small at low latitudes, begin to dominate the picture. At the poles there is one "day" and one "night," each six months long. Above 66.5° latitude and at the June and December solstices one end of the earth is entirely in darkness while the other is entirely in sunlight. Hence, as we would expect, there are marked changes in the temporal variations of the upper atmosphere with latitude. However, the observed changes often are as hard to explain as they are easy to detect. For example, the ionization at the south geographic pole not only does not disappear during the polar night, but shows a diurnal variation. Explaining this apparent anomaly will be one of the tasks of future research.

Superimposed on the effects of direct solar radiation (solar ultraviolet and x-rays) are other quite different effects that are connected with the earth's magnetic field. Like the ends of a giant bar magnet the polar regions of the earth draw in the lines of force of this field. Charged particles injected into this field from outside tend to be funneled into the polar regions. These particles, consisting mainly of electrons and protons covering a wide range of energies, may originate in the sun (the solar wind), the galaxy or the atmosphere of the earth. The fact that they have an electric charge causes them to travel in curved orbits, often tightly wrapped around a field line in the form of a spiral. Some of these particles are caught between "magnetic mirror" points in the earth's field, forming the Van Allen radiation belts of the magnetosphere. Others simply plow into the relatively dense lower regions of the ionosphere where they give up their energy in the form of ionization, heat and light (the aurorae).

These magnetically guided particles can produce important effects, such as ionization and radiation, in the polar regions. In fact, they are the dominant energy input to the auroral zone at night. Only recently (since the IGY), and with the aid of satellites, has the full range of fascinating phenomena connected with energetic particles in the polar regions been accessible to direct observation. Results of these new observations show the importance of coordinated ground and space vehicle measurements in the polar regions; they suggest that with improved understanding we can design ground-based experiments to do at least some of the work now done by satellites. They also show ways in which the polar magnetosphere can be used as a vast natural plasma physics laboratory in which experiments not possible on the ground can be performed.

ANTARCTIC vs. ARCTIC

It might be concluded that the upper atmospheres over the arctic and antarctic are alike except for the alternation of the seasons. It might then be further concluded that measurements made only in one hemisphere would suffice to study and monitor all high-latitude upper atmospheric phenomena. How convenient this would be. Many scientifically interesting locations in the arctic are accessible on a year-round basis and at far less cost than in the antarctic. Data show that there is indeed a close correspondence between the two polar regions for corresponding seasons. However, there are many surprising differences that must be explained if we are to reach a proper understanding of sun-earth interactions. For this reason alone it is necessary that research on the upper atmosphere be conducted in both the arctic and the antarctic. As we shall see, there are other factors that also attract us to Antarctica for upper atmosphere research.

The differences between the two polar regions with respect to upper atmosphere research can be classified as phenomenological, environmental or logistical. Phenomenological differences include (1) local effects that ought to be the same in the two polar regions and are not, and (2) the so-called conjugate-point phenomena. An example of the latter is the simultaneous observation of auroras at opposite ends of a field line. Sometimes conjugate auroras are the same and sometimes not, but the connections are not yet understood. It is therefore necessary to make observations at both ends of the path.

WHISTLERS

Environmental differences include both natural and man-made factors. In the study of whistlers and very-low-frequency (VLF) emissions, for example, the local atmospheric radio noise level in Antarctica is unusually low, thus enhancing the detectability of these phenomena. (A whistler is a VLF radio wave (1 to 30 kilohertz) excited by the electromagnetic impulse from a lightning stroke — often in the opposite hemisphere.) Furthermore, the lightning sources of whistlers observed in the Eights and Palmer Peninsula areas are unusually plentiful, because the conjugate area (in the northern hemisphere) is a region of high thunderstorm activity. Controlled experiments involving VLF whistler-mode transmissions are facilitated by the thick ice-cap of Antarctica which serves as a low-loss support for a long horizontal transmitting antenna. Furthermore, many scientifically desirable locations in Antarctica have readily accessible conjugate points in North America. This fact also serves to make existing VLF communication stations in North America useful in studies of artificially-stimulated VLF emissions.

Other environmental differences are associated with geographical features. The antarctic continent not only includes the south geographic pole, but it also includes a wide range of geomagnetic latitudes from the geomagnetic pole northward to 50° invariant latitude. Thus, it is possible in Antarctica to cover the south polar cap, the southern auroral and the subauroral zones. The location of the antarctic continent with respect to the earth's magnetic field fortuitously provides almost the maximum possible difference ($\sim 12°$) between geographic and geomagnetic latitudes over a wide range of latitudes. Thus, the effects of high geographic latitude (long nights or days) can be blended with magnetic field effects of lower geomagnetic latitude. For example, at Eights Station during certain parts of the year one can observe mid-latitude geomagnetically-controlled phenomena while the station is dark or sunlit 24 hours a day.

Logistically, many locations in the arctic are not suitable for year-round occupancy because of the uncertain availability of a permanent solid surface for a station. Thus, the north pole is not suitable for continuous observations whereas the south pole is. Maintenance of a fixed network of stations for synoptic studies is often more practical in the antarctic than in the arctic. There are, admittedly, certain disadvantages of manned stations in the antarctic, such as isolation, low temperatures, support cost and delay in receiving recorded data. These problems may be reduced in the future by the introduction of unmanned automatic observatories capable of transmitting data back to home base via communication satellite.

GROUND vs. SATELLITE

Because of their ability to scan large geographical areas, satellites might appear capable of replacing networks of ground observatories. This is not the case because of an essential difference between the two. Satellites (with the exception of a synchronous satellite at a geocentric distance of 6.6 earth radii) move rapidly '(7 kilometers per second for low altitude circular orbits) in an earth-based coordinate system, providing detailed data on spatial variations. It is true that to duplicate this feat from the ground would in many cases be impossible because of the localized nature of the satellite measurements. On the other hand, since the satellite cannot be made to stand still, there is often an ambiguity in the data resulting from the mixture of temporal and spatial variations. Sometimes this ambiguity can be resolved using the satellite data alone, by comparing results from different spacecraft or from successive orbits of the same spacecraft (90 minutes or more between data samples). More often the time changes are too fast or complex to be followed in this way. Then a continuous observation from the ground is essential to establish the time dependence.

In the short time since the IGY, Antarctica has already made many contributions to studies of the ionosphere, magnetosphere, geomagnetism and solar cosmic rays.

The ionosphere is the region between altitudes of 40 and 1,000 km, in which most of the upper atmosphere chemistry and ionization phenomena are centered. It interacts both with the lower atmosphere (e.g., gravity waves) and with the magnetosphere through electric and magnetic fields and particle fluxes. The ionosphere is usually divided into three regions: the D-region, 40 to 90 km; the E-region, 90 to 130 km; and the F-region, 130 to 1,000 km. In general, as height increases, the ionization density increases (up to about 300 km) and the collision frequency decreases. These quantities are important in the refraction and attenuation of radio waves. It is the ionosphere that gave birth, over half a century ago, to long distance radio communication. Even now, after the introduction of world-wide satellite communication circuits, the ionosphere continues to play a vital role in radio communication and navigation systems. Furthermore, it is a vital link in the complex and as yet incompletely understood relationship between the sun and the earth's atmosphere.

The D-region is ionized by energetic particle bombardment as well as by direct solar radiation. Particles may arrive in dense streams of relatively low energy particles which are associated with geomagnetic and auroral activity. They are found in and outside the auroral zone. Another type of corpuscular bombardment is a flux of high energy particles — solar protons, 30 to 1,000 million electron volts (mev) — which causes polar-cap absorption (PCA) at relatively low altitudes. Particle events can be detected by a riometer, an instrument for measuring the relative absorption of high-frequency galactic radiation. Another method for detecting the low-altitude ionization caused by particle bombardment is forward-scatter propagation, in which high-frequency waves scattered from below the E-region are attenuated by absorption at lower altitudes.

In riometer data from the south pole there is a diurnal variation of absorption activity with two peaks, one occurring just before magnetic midnight and the other just before magnetic noon. No seasonal variation of the diurnal variation is found. Energetic particle activity controlled by the earth's magnetic field is thought to be involved. Data from conjugate stations (e.g., south pole and Frobisher Bay) show differences in absorption that undergo seasonal and diurnal changes. Differences of a few minutes in the times of appearance of events at conjugate stations suggest that auroral

absorption may be connected with a hydromag-
netic wave. Another important result is that the
absorption tends to be greater in winter, when the
station is nearer the tail of the magnetosphere.
Movement of the conjugate points and hemispheric
asymmetries related to the source of the absorption

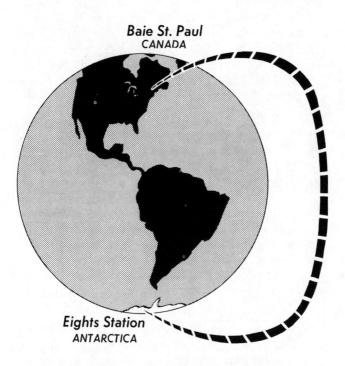

Baie St. Paul
CANADA

Eights Station
ANTARCTICA

**Conjugate points in the northern and southern
hemisphere are joined by magnetic lines of force.**

are thought to be connected with the differences
in absorption observed between conjugate points.
  Comparison of polar-cap absorption as measured
from the ground with the solar-proton flux as
measured by a satellite suggests that spatial varia-

Fig. 1. An aurora photographed at Byrd Station with forward-scatter antenna towers silhouetted in foreground. (Courtesy W. Burtis.)

tions can account for the enhancements observed both on the ground and by the satellite. These variations could be produced by the earth rotating under a pattern of precipitation or by the motion of the polar-cap field lines. There is some evidence to support the idea that field lines in the polar-cap regions may connect directly with the interplanetary field, causing asymmetry in the flux of protons reaching the two polar caps.

Like the D-region, the E-region is subject to both solar radiation and energetic particle bombardment. In addition to the normal solar-controlled E-layer, there is an enhancement of electron density at night which is caused by corpuscular radiation. By far the most dramatic aspect of the polar E-region is the colorful, dynamic aurora (Fig. 1). Auroras can be found all the way from 90 to 1,000 km, but appear most commonly between 90 and 120 km. Most of the light comes from the excitation of oxygen and nitrogen by electrons of around 10 kilo electron volt energy. Auroras at conjugate points often appear similar, but detailed studies indicate that significant differences can exist, probably reflecting the influence of local factors. The two auroral zones have different shapes and sizes, indicating important asymmetries in the earth's magnetic field. Recent studies have shown that auroral phenomena actually occur in an oval-shaped region which is eccentric with respect to the dipole poles. The auroral zone is simply the region of the oval where active auroras are most common.

For the F2-region, data from the south pole show that there is a 24-hour variation in electron density. Furthermore, F2-region ionization is somehow maintained through the antarctic winter. In fact, F2-ionization inside the auroral zone is mainly under Universal Time (UT) control, reaching a maximum at 0600 to 0700 UT. This leads to obvious anomalies. At Byrd Station, for example, the critical frequency in winter is a minimum near local noon and a maximum near midnight. These results show that in winter there is a major ionization input to the polar-cap region near 0600 UT. This source competes with photoionization in summer.

The source of the winter ionization is not yet known. It may involve horizontal transport of F2-ionization from middle latitudes driven by electric fields in the E-region. Diffusion of ionization along magnetospheric lines of force from the opposite hemisphere may also play an important role.

Another remarkable feature of the antarctic F2-region is that when the summer and winter diurnal

variations of peak electron density are very different, the transition between them occurs suddenly
(over the space of a few days) and at different dates
at different stations. There is some evidence that
this sudden change, involving an abrupt decrease
in electron density, is associated with the onset
of a polar stratospheric warming event. As yet
there is no accepted explanation of this association.
It has been suggested that the warming event
causes an increase in molecular concentration at
F2-heights which, in turn, increases the recombina-
tion coefficient, thus causing a lowering of the electron density. Clearly the behavior of the F2-region is
complex and the influence of both the magnetosphere and the lower atmosphere must be considered in its further study.

BETWEEN THE HEMISPHERES

We now turn to the magnetosphere (Fig. 2),
which extends from an altitude of 1,000 km out
to the magnetopause (about 10 earth radii in the
solar direction). Here the constituents are mainly
protons and electrons that are bound to the magnetic lines of force. Below the auroral zones these
lines tend to be "closed," providing effective conducting tubes in which charged particles and certain kinds of waves can flow between the hemispheres. Above the auroral zones the lines are
usually "open" extending into the tail of the magnetosphere or connecting with the interplanetary
field. It is the magnetosphere and its interaction
with the solar wind that accounts for much of the
interesting and complex phenomena in the polar-
cap region. Because of the primary role played by
the magnetic field it is convenient to use the "L"
coordinate instead of height when describing position in the magnetosphere. Roughly speaking, the
L value describes a particular magnetic shell on
which an energetic particle remains trapped. In

the dipole approximation, it is the geocentric distance to the top of the field line in earth radii. The corresponding latitude is called the "invariant latitude."

Thermal particles in the magnetosphere arise mainly through diffusion upward from the F2-region. Energetic particles are mostly fed in from the outside, either from the tail region of the magnetosphere or directly from the solar wind. Substantial acceleration of certain particles occurs within the magnetosphere by processes as yet unknown.

One of the unique contributions of the antarctic program to the study of the magnetosphere is the discovery of the plasmapause and its movements by means of whistlers. At Eights Station, because of the low local noise level and the high lightning activity in the conjugate region, it was possible to observe many well-defined whistlers. They are easily heard by connecting a high-gain audio amplifier to a loop or long-wire antenna in a quiet location. Some of this energy enters the ionosphere where it may be trapped in a field-aligned enhancement of ionization, called a whistler duct. It propagates to the conjugate point where it emerges as a whistling tone as a result of dispersion along the path. From the observed curve of frequency versus time the latitude of the path and the average electron density near the top of the path is obtained (Fig. 3). Many such paths are often excited by a single flash, providing data from which a map of electron density in the equatorial plane can be derived. Whistler data obtained at Eights and Byrd Stations revealed for the first time a surprising and totally unexpected sharp boundary (the plasmapause) in the equatorial ionization profile at about $L = 4$ (60° invariant latitude). Within this boundary the ionization is essentially in thermal equilibrium with the ionosphere, and the equatorial densities at L = 4 are around several hundred electrons per cubic centimeter. Outside the plasmapause the density typically drops to one electron per cc, more or less, and then may recover somewhat as the outer boundary of the magnetosphere is approached. The plasmapause moves to lower L-values with increasing magnetic disturbance, apparently as the result of erosion of the external plasma. During quiet times it may extend out to L = 6.

By observing the change in latitude of individual whistler ducts with time, the north-south drift of the plasma can be measured. Inward drifts during a polar substorm imply east-west electric fields of

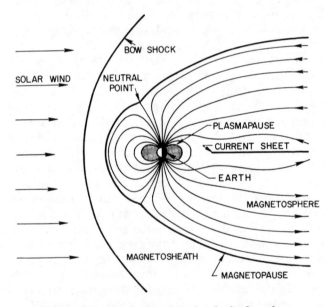

Fig. 2. Sketch of a model of principal regions of magnetosphere in noon to midnight meridional plane. From stations in the antarctic information can be obtained on most of the magnetosphere down to locations well inside the plasmapause.

about 0.3 millivolt per meter at 4 earth radii. These results provide a new technique for measuring electric fields deep in the magnetosphere on a more or less continuous basis. They also provide a unique tool for monitoring the convection patterns of the magnetospheric plasma, so essential to achieving a full understanding of magnetospheric dynamics.

The favorable location of certain antarctic stations (such as the new Siple Station) with respect to VLF transmitters on the east coast of the United States has led to another unique experiment. Along with VLF whistlers, an observer at middle and high latitudes can hear a variety of natural radio emissions, called chorus or hiss. Their sources are believed to be energetic electrons trapped in the earth's field, although the mechanisms of radiation are not yet fully understood. Certain discrete forms of chorus emission can be triggered reliably by signals from VLF transmitters. Morse code dashes (150 milliseconds) are most effective, while the dots (50 ms) seldom cause triggering. From data obtained in the antarctic and from satellites, the region of triggering has been placed near the equatorial plane. This is one of the first controlled experiments in the magnetosphere to be performed from the ground.

In the area of geomagnetism, the antarctic has made important contributions, both in supporting other types of measurements and in advancing our understanding of the external components of the earth's field. Generally speaking, geomagnetic variations are similar in the two polar regions. By comparing antarctic data with those from a low latitude station, it has been found that the first impulse of a sudden commencement occurs a few seconds earlier at the high latitudes. Comparison at conjugate points of the polarizations of the magnetic impulses of sudden commencements show that most are elliptical and of opposite sense. In general, the current systems deduced from magnetic measurements are mirror images of one another with respect to the geomagnetic equatorial plane.

In studies of micropulsations (period less than 10 seconds) of the geomagnetic field between Eights Station and its conjugate point (Baie St. Paul) in Canada, use was made of the tilt of the earth's dipole axis with respect to the geographic axis. Because Eights Station is near the meridian which passes through both geomagnetic poles and is above the Antarctic Circle, it is in darkness 24 hours a day at the June solstice, while the conjugate point cycles normally between day and night. Echoing micro-pulsations were observed under these conditions in the 0.5 to 1.0 hertz range, and their intensity was found to be reduced under the daytime ionosphere. The observed reduction was consistent with the assumption of propagation attenuation through the ionosphere.

In general, conjugacy has been established for micropulsations, but many exceptions are found. Movement of the conjugate points resulting from field-line distortion and the "opening" of field lines may both be involved in departures from conjugacy.

Geomagnetic variations are related to many other phenomena, such as auroras, particle precipitation and VLF emissions. It was found in conjugate studies between Byrd and Great Whale Stations, for example, that quasi-periodic variations in VLF emission ($\sim$ 1 kilohertz) intensity were often associated with geomagnetic pulsations in the period range 10 seconds to 2 minutes. One interesting suggestion advanced to explain this association is that the geomagnetic pulsations modulate a critical parameter in the VLF emission generation process, causing the VLF output to vary.

Another program of importance in the antarctic is the study of cosmic rays, principally those originating in the sun. Solar cosmic rays are nuclei generated in solar flares and have energies in the range 0.1 to 10^5 mev. Because of the shielding effect of the earth's magnetic field, it is only in the polar regions that the lower energy particles can reach the earth. Their directions of arrival and momentum spectra provide information on the magnetosphere and the interplanetary magnetic field. Comparison of balloon data from Mirny (antarctic) and Murmansk (arctic) has shown large north-south anisotropies. The same effect has been found in ground-based measurements with neutron monitors. It is thus clear that both polar regions must be involved in the continuing study of cosmic rays.

The brief period since the IGY might be called the exploratory or fact-finding phase of antarctic upper atmosphere research. From the wealth of data now in hand, many hypotheses have been generated and specific experiments are being devised, leading to what we might call the experimental phase of antarctic research. This does not mean that the exploratory phase has ended.

In designing upper atmosphere experiments we must resist the temptation to let a computer select our data for us. It is often better to record the raw data completely and, then, use the computer to select and process the data according to various strategies. Of course, some preprocessing of data in the field may be needed to speed up the analysis and, hence, useful changes in the experiment may be more obvious.

In planning future observational programs in the antarctic we can expect that many of the previous programs will continue but with different emphases. Perhaps the biggest change will be an increased emphasis on multi-discipline experiments in which recording methods, locations and scheduling of observing times are coordinated for maximum value in correlative studies. An example might be the

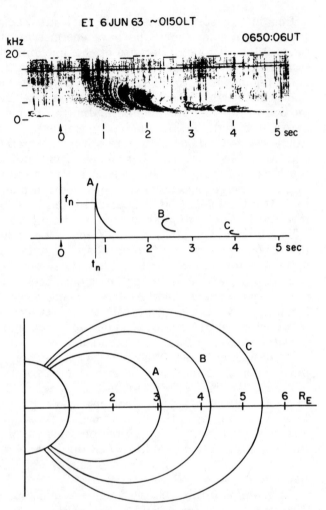

Fig. 3. Whistler spectra from Eights Station showing many separate components (upper panel). Three selected components (labeled A, B, and C) are traced in middle panel for greater clarity and corresponding magnetospheric paths are shown in lower panel. Path latitude is measured by the nose frequency f_n; electron content by nose delay t_n.

simultaneous recording at the same location of (1) strength of the earth's field, (2) micropulsations, (3) VLF emissions, (4) auroral light, (5) absorption (by riometer) and (6) x-ray events (observed in a balloon). In view of the increased interest in comparative data from different locations, it is more important than ever before that instruments and measurement methods be standardized. Certainly standard chart speeds should be used whenever possible together with accurate clocks.

An exciting future prospect for antarctic research is the development of controlled experiments. In the past we have depended mainly on our ability to isolate the effect of a given factor through statistical analysis of natural phenomena. Exceptions from the past are the Argus experiments of August-September 1958 in the Atlantic Ocean and the Johnston Island tests in the Pacific Ocean in which nuclear bombs were exploded in the upper atmosphere. These introduced known perturbations into the atmosphere, including both waves and particles, from which new knowledge was obtained. More recently, barium clouds released in the E-region and at high altitude in the magnetosphere have provided visible tracers by which drift effects can be studied.

An exciting new development is the successful creation of an artificial aurora by means of energetic electrons fired into the E-region from a rocket. Another type of controlled experiment is the injection of VLF wave packets to stimulate VLF emissions and modify the precipitation of energetic particles. (Preparations for a new controlled VLF experiment are now under way at Siple Station.) Repeatable controlled experiments should not only accelerate the solution of many problems but, more importantly, will elucidate effects that are either never produced naturally or are forever covered up by other effects.

As we look to the future we must recognize the role of new technology. Using space age circuitry and systems it now appears feasible to build an automatic multidiscipline station having remote programming control (Fig. 4). Such an observatory would be somewhat like an Orbiting Geophysical Observatory (OGO) satellite except that it would be geostationary at one earth radius. In the handling of data it appears that a big improvement is possible through the use of communication satellites. These would collect data from antarctic bases (including an automatic station) and transmit them to home laboratories in real time, thereby avoiding the costly and often frustrating delays (up to 18 months) presently encountered. In the area of sensors, new technology will also play a role. For example, the recent introduction of a TV camera for auroral studies has brought greatly increased sensitivity and time resolution to this field of study. This technique, combined with measurements of related phenomena, should aid in reaching a final understanding of the still enigmatic auroras. Another advance of considerable interest is the development at Byrd Station of a technique for vertical-incidence sounding of the D-region using a VLF sweep-frequency sounder.

Future upper atmosphere research in Antarctica should be extended upward to include more phenomena of the magnetosphere. This will require coordination between space measurements and ground measurements in the two polar regions. Thus measurements by a geostationary satellite should be coordinated with ground measurements made on the same line of force (e.g., Byrd and Great Whale).

More work is needed at the lower levels also, particularly in the D-region, where some of the most complex chemistry of the upper atmosphere takes place. A continuing challenge is to find and

Fig. 4. Prototype of the capsule (shown in right foreground) for an unmanned geophysical observatory located at Byrd Station for purpose of conducting environmental tests on the structure. A satellite telemetry dish appears in left background.

understand the connections between the lower levels of the atmosphere and the ionosphere as suggested by some of the antarctic data. Here the close co-operation of meteorologists and upper atmosphere physicists is required.

Drilling Through The Ice Cap

Probing Climate for a Thousand Centuries

C. C. LANGWAY, JR.
and B. LYLE HANSEN

One of the major questions of polar research has been whether climatic changes in the northern and southern hemispheres have occurred at the same time. It bears on theories of ice ages which range from local to solar-cosmic processes. One approach to the answer is the analysis of ice in deep cores taken out of the ice caps of Greenland and Antarctica by drilling rigs capable of perforating the great sheets. Stored within the ice is a record of climate, extending back into time for thousands of years. The record is now beginning to

*show that climate changes in the northern and south-
ern hemispheres are contemporaneous. B. Lyle Hansen,
a veteran antarctic driller, is chief, Technical Service
Division, and Chester C. Langway, Jr., is chief, Snow
and Ice Branch, of the U.S. Army's Cold Regions
Research and Engineering Laboratory (CRREL), Hanover, New Hampshire.*

Within the last few million years, up to one-third
of the earth's land surface was periodically inun-
dated by ice sheets, like those existing today in
Greenland and Antarctica. These remnants of a
past ice age play a very influential role in atmospheric circulation and contribute greatly to the
meteorological and climatological conditions of the
world, as did their former and more expansive counterparts.

Present-day glaciers permanently blanket about
12 per cent, or some six million square miles, of the
earth's land surface and are found on all continents
with the exception of Australia. Nearly 96 per cent
of this total ice mantle is located in the polar regions
of Antarctica (85 per cent) and Greenland (11 per
cent), which contain 78 per cent of the earth's fresh
water.

Although polar glaciers have been observed and
investigated since historical times and have been
the subject of numerous exploratory and scientific
expeditions, surprisingly enough, up until a few
years ago almost nothing was known of their internal nature and composition. The inner structure
of a polar glacier has always been of fundamental
interest to glaciologists; the problem was to obtain
suitable samples for study.

Attempts to bore mechanically into glaciers for
thickness measurements are reported to have begun
in Switzerland as early as 1842, but it was not until
1950 that even limited success was achieved. At

this time three major core-drilling projects were conducted by groups from France, the Scandinavian countries and the United States, almost simultaneously, on polar and temperate glaciers of the world. In all cases core diameter was small (5 to 8 centimeters), depth of penetration was shallow (100 to 150 meters) and core recovery was discontinuous and mainly of poor quality.

B. Lyle Hansen (left) and C.C. Langway, Jr., observing two pieces of the Greenland core.

The desire to develop a satisfactory method of continuous deep-core drilling in polar ice received considerable stimulus and support in the United States during the planning stages of the recent International Geophysical Year (IGY) and, in fact, was one of the principal study programs recommended by the National Academy of Sciences' Panel of Glaciology. Our laboratory, then called the Snow Ice and Permafrost Research Establishment, under the scientific leadership of H. Bader, accepted responsibility for implementing the entire program: designing and modifying drilling equipment, establishing techniques of ice core analysis and developing bore-hole instrumentation methods.

The deep-core drilling in ice program was initiated in Greenland during pre-IGY activities and was extended to Antarctica during the IGY. The results of these early projects were successful enough to justify post-IGY continuation in both Greenland and Antarctica. The drilling program produced eight deep ice cores (Table 1). Both the 1966 and 1968 cores penetrated through the ice sheets. During the 1966 Greenland operation 3.5 meters of sub-ice material was recovered.

Three basic drilling methods were used by the U.S. Army Cold Regions Research and Engineering Laboratory (USA CRREL) to obtain 10 to 13 centimeter diameter ice cores: (1) a conventional rotary system using a drill pipe to advance the tool and recover the core, and cooled, compressed air as the drilling fluid; (2) a thermal coring device using a hoist and an armored cable to transmit power and to lower and raise the tool, with the meltwater being removed by a vacuum system-storage tank device, and (3) a down bore-hole electromechanical boring tool which also uses a hoist-cable concept for delivery and power transmission with the chips being dissolved in an aqueous ethylene glycol solution and recovered in a bailer.

During the drilling program it was discovered that it was possible to "dry-bore" holes to depths of 400 meters below the glacier surfaces; for greater depths it was necessary to fill the bore hole with fluids (88 per cent trichloroethylene, 12 per cent arctic diesel oil) to prevent hole closure. The den-

TABLE 1
DEEP ICE CORE DRILLING IN GREENLAND AND ANTARCTICA

Year Drilled	Method of Drilling	Depth of Drilling (meters)	Location
1956	Rotary	305	Site 2, Greenland
1957	Rotary	411	Site 2, Greenland
1958	Rotary	308	Byrd Station, Antarctica
1959	Rotary	256	Little America V, Antarctica
1961	Thermal	185	Camp Century, Greenland
1962	Thermal	235	Camp Century, Greenland
1966	Thermal & Electromech.	1,375	Camp Century, Greenland
1968	Thermal & Electromech.	2,164	Byrd Station, Antarctica

sity of the fluid, 0.92 grams per cubic centimeter, compensates for the core removed by balancing the load.

Each method of core drilling has certain advantages and disadvantages in the quality of recovered core and depth of penetration. A fluid-filled hole is necessary for reaching depths greater than 400 meters but presents a contamination problem for certain ice-core studies. Because of the heat, the thermally-bored cores are physically and chemically altered over the depth of porous firn-surface to about 70 meters. Except for some fracturing between 200 and 900 meters, core recovery and quality is good to excellent using the electromechanical drill.

The recovery of these cores presented an opportunity that has not existed before. Never had the snow-ice mantle of high polar ice sheets been completely penetrated. Furthermore, since the cores were mainly obtained in dry-snow zones (that is, where surface air temperatures rarely, if ever, exceed the melting point), they contain entrapped within them all of the foreign material—organic, inorganic, soluble and insoluble—that falls upon the snow surface or serves as snow-crystal nuclei. At the high elevation, inland, dry-snow zones, each year's snowfall buries the previous accumulation deeper, increasing the density of the underlying firn by compaction and gradually, at about the 60 or 70 meter depth, the firn metamorphose into glacier ice. Atmospheric air between the ice crystals is trapped as bubbles in the ice. Dust, pollen and other small terrestrial and extraterrestrial particles are buried in the sequence in which they fall.

Since ice sheets are, in a sense, settling tanks for all atmospheric constituents and wind-transported debris, with ice cores we not only have a unique opportunity to examine systematically the physical and chemical nature of active ice sheets as a continuous function of depth, but also, once an age-depth relationship has been established, to investigate past climatological trends and even significant meteorological variations that have affected the world's atmosphere, such as volcanic disturbances.

It is possible to interpret annual layers from the upper 60 to 100 meters of polar ice sheets, with progressive difficulty as depth increases, in much the same manner as it is done in surface pit studies: by observing (1) such structural features as wind crusts, radiation crusts and grain size variations and (2) seasonal density changes. Generally, summer snows are lighter and less dense than the finer grained wind-packed winter snows. Below 100 meters megascopic features become obscure or disappear and density variations dampen to imperceptible differences.

Soon after the first deep cores were recovered it

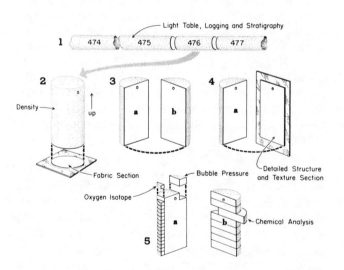

Fig. 1. A schematic diagram showing general plan and procedures of detailed investigations on deep ice core.

was realized that the classical method of stratigraphic analysis would not be appropriate for the deeper ice. A comprehensive and detailed study program was developed (Fig. 1) encompassing physical and chemical methods of analysis tailored to the limited amount of core available. A partial list of studies that have been or are being conducted on the deep cores is given in Table 2. These studies were or are being performed in the field or laboratory by USA CRREL scientists or by scientists from other laboratories, universities and institutes in the United States and foreign countries.

The most successful physical approach for determining seasonal variations from deep cores is by measuring the stable oxygen isotope ratio (O^{18}/O^{16}) of small vertical increments of melted samples of the core (Fig. 2). Summer snows contain more O^{18} than do winter snows. Deuterium is also a temperature indicator and parallels the O^{18}/O^{16} ratio data. Other natural and artificial radioactive isotope studies on the cores have provided measurements of the average annual accumulation over larger vertical profiles. Lead-210 with a half-life of 21.6 years allows us to obtain the average accumulation at a location for the last 100 to 150 years (60 to 80 meter depths). Silicon-32 with about a 500-year half-life and argon-39 with a 270-year half-life are still being tested.

Fission-product fallout (primarily strontium-90) from thermonuclear tests provides several excellent index horizons from 1954 to date. The levels of these index horizons differ for the Greenland and Antarctica ice sheets owing to the proximity of the testing sites and atmospheric residence times. Studies of the dissolved ionic constituents in melted ice-core samples indicate that very little material is present (averaging one milligram per liter in Greenland and about one-third or less that amount in Antarctica) and, in general, winter snows con-

TABLE 2

ACTIVE OR COMPLETED ICE CORE STUDIES
(AS A FUNCTION OF DEPTH)

ICE (PHYSICAL)	GAS	ISOTOPES (ACCUMULATION)
Density	Total composition	Stable
Stratigraphy	Trace gases	(oxygen, deuterium)
Structural features	Radiocarbon dating	Radioactive
Grain and crystal	Bubble	(tritium, Pb-210, Si-32,
(size, shape, texture)	(size, shape, pressures)	rare gases, Al-26,
Fabrics (orientation)	Ar-39	(fission products)
Elastic constants	0-18 content	
Densification		
Wave velocities		

FOREIGN PARTICLES (SOLIDS)	IONIC CHEMISTRY (DISSOLVED SOLIDS)	METEROLOGICAL AND CLIMATOLOGICAL INFERENCES
Cosmic dust	Na, K, Ca, Mg, SO_4, Cl	Accumulation rates
Volcanic dust	Trace constituents	Paleoclimates
Mineral fragments	Pollutants	Volcanic debris
Pollutants	Sea salts	Meteorological variations
Bacteria		
Microorganisms		
Microparticles		
Trace elements (Ag, Ni)		

tain more dissolved material than summer snows. A recent ionic chemistry study of the Camp Century (Greenland) core shows a three- to five-fold increase in the major ionic constituents during the late-Wisconsin glaciation (30,000 to 10,000 years

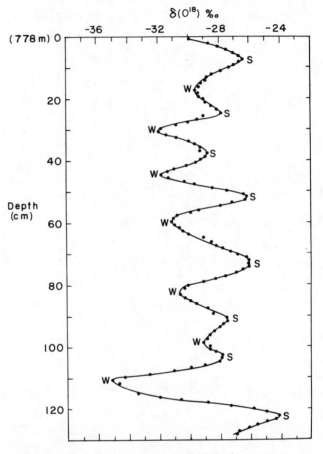

Fig. 2. Oxygen-18 variations ($\delta(O^{18})$ in parts per million) due to seasonal variations in a section of Camp Century core approximately 778 meters below 1966 surface. The maxima and minima indicate summer (S) and winter (W) snow respectively.

ago). Winter snows also appear to contain more sub-microscopic solid particles (0.3 to 5 micron diameters). Examination of microscopic insoluble particles, larger than one micron diameter, extracted from the cores show that the residue contains mineral fragments, glassy shards, magnetic particles and spherical micrometeorites.

Investigations of the composition and distribution of the black cosmic spherules show that they are mainly iron-rich (magnetite), that nickel is present but rare, and that greater spherule concentrations occur in summer snow. Three times as many spherules are found deposited in Greenland annual layers than are found in Antarctic firn layers. Rare gases and cosmic ray-induced radioactivities have been measured in bulk dust collections gathered from millions of liters of glacier meltwater at Camp Century, Greenland. The Byrd Station deep core shows several prominent volcanic ash layers which will be studied in an attempt to date the ice and establish deep-seated index horizons. The volcanic eruptions of Katmai (A.D. 1912) and Krakatoa (A.D. 1883) will be investigated in all the deep cores.

A new down-borehole gas extraction device is being perfected and tested in the Byrd Station deep bore-hole. The device was developed by the University of Bern and USA CRREL for shallow bore-hole studies in Greenland (Fig. 3). The tool was redesigned for the deep Byrd bore-hole and tested in the field during 1969 and 1970. In principle the procedure is to melt a volume of ice at the site and to separate with an ion exchange column the CO_2 component from the atmospheric gases in the air bubbles trapped in the ice. The exchange column is then brought to the surface. The carbon-14 activity is measured at the University of Bern. Preliminary results are promising but more testing is required before this equipment can be used in

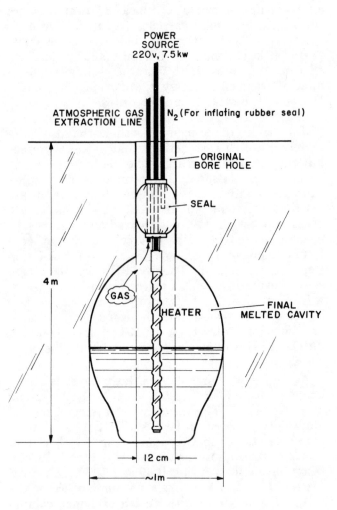

Fig. 3. Schematic diagram (Oeschger, *et al.*) of portable shallow borehole gas-extraction system used to extract atmospheric gases entrapped in glacier ice. It requires about 30 hours to melt approximately 1 metric ton of ice necessary to obtain enough CO_2 to make the C^{14} measurements for age-dating the ice.

deep fluid-filled holes.

Perhaps the most significant and scientifically rewarding studies that have been made on the ice cores to date are those related to the paleo-climatic interpretation of the stable isotope measurements. The seasonal variations of the O^{18}/O^{16} ratio gradually dampen with depth (age) by molecular diffusion, but long-term variations in the isotope ratios remain practically undisturbed for much greater lengths of time and depict climatic change. Recent measurements made at the University of Copenhagen on nearly 8,000 core samples, taken over the entire vertical profile of the Camp Century core, and about 3,000 samples from the Byrd Station core reveal a continuous temperature chronology from the present back more than a thousand centuries. As of this writing the Camp Century data have been more thoroughly analyzed (Fig. 4), but preliminary results of the stable isotope studies have been performed on the Byrd core at both the California Institute of Technology and the University of Copenhagen. The Danish study indicates that the Byrd Station region is extremely complicated, making it very difficult to interpret possible detailed climatic phase relationship for both hemispheres.

FLOWING ICE

Ice is a viscous material, and an ice sheet flows under the forces of gravity and shear stresses determined by the geometry of the ice sheet and the rock material upon which it rests. The rate of ice deformation increases exponentially with its thickness and as the temperature approaches the melting point. At the bottom of an ice sheet, movement may occur by viscous flow, with melting and refreezing processes allowing movement over small obstacles on the bedrock, or by a combination of

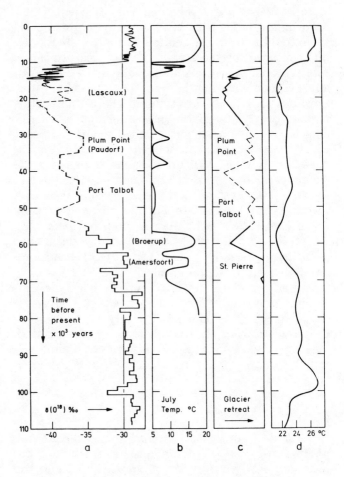

Climatic variations during last 80,000-110,000 years estimated by various methods (Dansgaard, *et al.*).

a, Oxygen isotope variations in Camp Century ice core;
b, A C[14]-dated pollen study from Holland;
c, A C[14]-dated stratigraphic study of Pleistocene deposits in Ontario and Erie basins showing measurements of edge of Laurentian ice sheet;
d, An oxygen isotope study on deep-sea cores showing part of a generalized temperature curve for surface waters of central Caribbean.

these mechanisms. If morainal rock material is embedded in the ice, the flow properties will be altered. To understand the basic mechanism of ice flow, it is necessary to measure the variations in temperature and movement of the ice with depth, as well as the deformation of the hole for a number of years afterwards.

From temperature measurements made in the bore-holes the calculated heat flow at Camp Century is 1.00 microcalories per square centimeter per second; at Byrd Station the value is 1.8 microcalories per square centimeter per second. Most of this is probably geothermal heat flux but some may be due to frictional heating. The ice/sub-ice interface temperature was found to be $-13°C$ at Camp Century and $-1.6°C$ (the pressure melting point) at Byrd Station. New bore-hole instruments are being developed, such as electrical property measuring probes, a camera to observe bottom bed-slip and remotely operated collection devices for solids, liquid or gases. The bore-hole studies make available the larger deep glacier samples that are necessary to supplement certain investigations that cannot be made with the limited amount of material available from the cores.

CHARTING GLOBAL POLLUTION

The value of investigating deep ice cores and bore-holes is far-reaching and has considerable scientific value. The results of the investigations have a bearing on many scientific disciplines: glaciology, meteorology, atmospheric chemistry, geochronology, hydrology, paleoclimatology, geothermometry, physical dynamics, ceramics, and rheology. From core studies one is able to investigate transporting processes of the atmosphere and the interaction between the hemispheres, to date ancient atmospheres, to study the changes in precipitation chemistry during historical times, to make compositional analyses of fossil atmospheric gases, to investigate high-latitude pollution and the effect of industrial wastes, to study the distribution of volcanic and cosmic dust as a function of time and to make climatological inferences from the resultant data.

The current studies by no means exhaust the avenues of search or the potential information that is sealed within the ice cores. It is hoped that this summary will stimulate further interest in core studies and allow continued progress to be made in the study of glacier ice.

The U.S. deep-core drilling in ice program is continuing in Antarctica. Considerable scientific interest has developed in this program and discussions are currently being held regarding an international cooperative program using the U.S. drilling rigs to bore intermediate and deep holes at selected sites over the entire antarctic continent. Presently the Canadians, Australians and a group from Ohio State University are boring or have bored into glaciers in the arctic and antarctic, using a thermal coring rig of USA CRREL design capable of penetrating to 500-meter depths. Several other countries in Europe and Africa are now planning ice core drilling projects in Antarctica.

A Survey of
Antarctic Biology

Life Below Freezing

GEORGE A. LLANO

To biologists, the animals of the antarctic seas are among the most fascinating on Earth. The Weddell Seal can dive 600 meters and remain submerged 43 minutes. A glycoprotein antifreeze has been found in the blood of Trematomus *fishes. It keeps them from freezing in seawater which is below the freezing point. Perhaps the glycoprotein interacts with the water to keep it from freezing. It may be useful as a refrigerant for red blood cells, sperm, tissue and other biological materials. George Llano is program manager, Polar Biology, the Polar Programs Office of the National Science Foundation. In this article, he discusses what kind of biological research is being done in Antarctica and what science is learning from it.*

205

Forty years after Captain Cook reported on the fabulous abundance of marine mammals in antarctic waters, British and American sealers had already depleted the principal seal stocks off the Antarctic Peninsula. The furtive exploitation by sealers and the rash of government-sponsored expeditions stimulated exploration in Antarctica but the lasting force was the rapidly developing natural sciences in the first half of the nineteenth century.

These events, coming at the end of the Revolutionary War when the United States suffered from lack of hard currency and foreign exchange credit, did not go unnoticed; and almost with the close of hostilities her Connecticut citizenry ventured into commercial sealing. Among the first revenues to the young nation, as recorded by the New York Customs House in 1795, were duties levied in excess of $75,000 on Chinese luxury goods obtained by trading in antarctic fur seal pelts. The antarctic peltry trade initiated New England to the profitable China trade, influenced the clipper ship era and, from all this Matthew Fontaine Maury gathered meterological and oceanographic data for his remarkable wind and current charts for improvement of sailing navigation. From information taken from logs of sealers and whalers, Maury concluded that a full knowledge of the antarctic region was essential for an accurate understanding of world climate. On the eve of the Civil War, he proposed an international assault on Antarctica through the cooperative effort of all nations, thus anticipating the International Geophysical Year (IGY) by 100 years.

In 1830, the Connecticut sealing captains, Edmund Fanning, Benjamin Pendleton and Nathaniel Palmer, under semi-government auspices, set out to the South Shetland Islands on a sealing and exploring expedition. Included in the party was naturalist James Eights of Albany, N. Y. Eights, the first American scientist and one of the first of any nation to visit the antarctic, published the earliest biological papers on antarctic fauna. The next American contributions were published 100 years later as reports of the Second Byrd Antarctic Expedition of 1934 by A. A. Lindsey and Paul A. Siple, and of the U.S. Antarctic Expedition of 1939 by H. M. Bryant. In general, the United States' role in early antarctic biological research is a modest one compared to that of Belgian, British, German, French and Swedish expeditions.

Antarctica's star role in the IGY is ascribed to its unparalleled interest for geophysics and geography. Nevertheless, the program committee of the pre-IGY symposium on antarctic science, held at the National Academy of Sciences in 1956, invited the views of two biologists. In the proceedings, "Antarctica in the Geophysical Year," Carl R. Eklund and I advocated complementary biological programs, thus presaging much of what is now supported under the national program for antarctic research. Eklund, as scientific leader at Wilkes Station during the IGY, initiated an international cooperative bird-banding study, carried out local observations on branded seals, conducted a census of seals while en route through the pack ice zone and applied telemetry techniques to monitor incubating skua egg temperatures for the first time in Antarctica.

The concurrence of 12 nations under the Antarctic Treaty to extend antarctic research at the close of the IGY to 1990 formally inaugurated international biological programs. American biological participation was endorsed as part of the U. S. Antarctic Research Program (USARP) by the National Science Foundation (NSF). As part of its responsibility to manage and fund the USARP, the Foundation has provided laboratories, instruments and other logistical support needed for modern biological research. It has supported biologists' de-

mands for winter programs and mid-winter flights
to extend the season for particular biological studies. In many cases, the facilities are better than
those found in the States, although instrument
maintenance and calibration are not easily accomplished.

MANY FIRSTS

The descriptive surveys so traditional to earlier
antarctic summer expeditionary work are now replaced by elaborate *in situ* studies, some of which
are conducted through the polar year, and rely on
the most modern logistic systems and techniques.
Updating of methodology has given the USARP
many "firsts" including scuba techniques for summer and winter studies in littoral marine ecology,
sub-ice observation chamber and underwater television for observing seal and penguin behavior and
telemetry to monitor and record the daily movements and internal physiological changes of seals
and penguins. Infrared and other aerial photographic techniques for avian and seal population
studies are now projected for satellite platforms.

McMurdo and Palmer Stations are coastal installations with different specific missions but both
have unique high-latitude marine biological laboratories. McMurdo lies in the continental zone where
the average monthly air temperature never rises
above 32°F (0°C) and in winter may fall below
–4°F (–20°C). This arid region is one of drying
winds, low precipitation, low humidity, meager flora
and fauna and brilliant austral summer sunlight as
high as 100,000 lux (lumens per square meter).
Seals, penguins and other marine organisms are
readily available for biological research which is
accomplished, without benefit of oceanographic
ships, through holes in the very stable plain of sea
ice that extends for miles across McMurdo Sound.

At Palmer Station, in the milder maritime zone

of Antarctica, winter temperatures rarely fall below 14°F (−10°C); summers are cool, with high precipitation (some as rain) and extensive overcast periods. The waters of the Antarctic Peninsula in the austral summer are + 2° to + 3°C higher than in McMurdo Sound; and since some of the same species occur in both areas, Palmer Station provides an excellent opportunity for comparative studies of the physiological functions and importance of temperature in biogeography of marine poikilotherms. By contrast with the rest of Antarctica, the vegetation of the Antarctic Peninsula is luxurant although not much developed beyond the moss-lichen stage.

Terrestrial research by Bruce Parker of the Virginia Polytechnic Institute and his graduate students on fresh water lakes in the Palmer Station area has been initiated into the processes of natural eutrophication. Among the several unique findings, they have shown that gaseous ammonia arising from penguin guano may enrich fresh water lakes located in other watersheds.

Marine research at Palmer Station and any work away from the station site requires the use of a ship. To meet this contingency, the station plans provide for a medium-sized research trawler which is appropriately named *Hero* after Nathaniel Palmer's sloop of 1820 fame. While designed fundamentally to serve as a floating laboratory for coastal oceanographic and land-based work in the Antarctic Peninsula, *Hero*'s service at other times of the year is projected for the study of whales, porpoises and seals, both at sea and in the inland waters of Tierra del Fuego. Deep-sea oceanographic studies are conducted by the naval ship *Eltanin*. She has worked continuously in the Southern Ocean since 1962 in 50- to 70-day cruises, averaging more than three-quarters of her time at sea. Her studies

on physical, geophysical and biological phenomena
of this vast oceanic region about the antarctic convergence increasingly rival the early contributions
of *Belgica, Discovery, Challenger, Pourquoi Pas?,*
and *Meteor.*

ANTARCTIC NEWS

Research activities and progress are reported bi-
monthly in the "Antarctic Journal of the United
States." While the majority of research papers appear in standard scientific journals, selections from
current studies are published in the expeditionary
series of the USARP, the "Antarctic Research
Series" (ARS) and the "Antarctic Map Folio
Series." In general, the dissemination of information about Antarctica has increased in the last decade and now requires a special "Antarctic Bibliography."

Against this background of history, geographical
exploration and logistics, the objectives of the national antarctic program are fairly easily identified. A primary one is the support of promising
areas of antarctic biologic research. This has
evolved as studies in ecological adaptation, physiology and ethology, and in systematics on both
marine and terrestrial organisms south of 60°S and
including the austral islands. A secondary objective
is designed to correct the imbalance in the nation's
scientific competence in polar specialties. To this
end, senior investigators use graduate assistants
both in the development of the field work and
preparation of data. Over the past 10 years, more
than 200 biologists have participated in antarctic
biological research, and of this number a third have
been young scientists who used the opportunity to
advance their scientific careers; most of the latter
are now independent and qualified researchers.
Consequently, this timely appraisal of the resources

and future prospects of USARP begins with the accomplishments of 10 years of national support, not the least of which is the development of a second generation of antarctic biologists. This is evidenced by the following partial summary of biological activities completed during the first decade of the U.S. Antarctic Research Program.

ACTIVITIES SUMMARIZED

Antarctic biological history began a new era in the austral summer of 1958 at McMurdo Sound with the construction of a laboratory, the first on the continent and for a number of years the only one south of 55°S, and the inception of year-round physiological studies by Donald E. Wohlschlag then of Stanford University. Wohlschlag began cold adaptation experiments with McMurdo Sound fish and found unexpectedly interesting ecological implications. The locality proved ideal because the relatively physical constancy of the seawater, with slight but important seasonal fluctuations, provided the proper environment for the study of cold-adapted organisms. As Wohlschlag said ("Biology of the Antarctic Seas I," ARS, 1964):

> Because the naturally cold-adapted marine organisms are at the extreme cold terminus of the adaptational spectrum and at naturally constant physical environmental conditions, there are obvious advantages in using both antarctic organisms and antarctic environment in ecological studies on animal populations.

His numerous publications report on the general level of cold adaptation and metabolic response to temperature increase, on sex growth and metabolic differences, and on metabolic requirements for swimming activity for species of nototheniiform antarctic fishes. He showed that seasonal cycles of one species of these antarctic cods in deep and shallow water can be related to seasonal differences in light penetration, slight temperature fluctuations, sexual differences and stage of gonadal development. Wohlschlag reported that, unlike temperate fish, antarctic species have their maximum swimming activity at the lowest temperature of the natural environment $-1.8°$ or $-1.9°C$. Suggesting that fishes from deep and permanently dark waters have lower metabolism than those from shallower waters influenced by light, he early advocated a thorough investigation of life in the dark sea beneath the Ross Ice Shelf.

Between 1959-65, Wohlschlag used eight graduate student assistants from Stanford to assist him in his antarctic research. These men—Arthur L. DeVries, George Somero, Jack Littlepage, John Pearse, Paul Dayton, John Dearborn, Hugh DeWitt and Gerald Kooyman) have all made critical and original scientific contributions of their own to polar ecology based on observations made during their winter and summer field tours at McMurdo Station.

DeVries' and Somero's interest in the physiological and biochemical mechanisms of cold adaptation in antarctic fishes began with observations of *Trematomus* fishes. Observing that species of this genus, commonly found in McMurdo Sound, often rested on masses of ice crystals in freezing seawater, they began to inquire into the metabolic bases of these highly cold-adapted fish. DeVries' and Wohlschlag's recent studies have shown that these fishes are extremely resistant to freezing because of their low blood-serum freezing points ($-1.9°C$ to $-2.0°C$) throughout the season. Sodium chloride, the most abundant salt in the blood of temperate water fishes, accounts for only 50 per cent of the serum freezing point depression in *Trematomus* fishes. Most of the remaining freezing-point depression is attributed to a glycoprotein.

The "antifreeze" discovery not only provides an

explanation as to why antarctic fish do not freeze but also poses a provocative question to biophysicists and physical chemists: How does this glycoprotein interact with water to prevent it from freezing? Carbohydrate chemists find the simplicity of the "antifreeze" glycoprotein an excellent model for studying other complex glycoproteins, and for elucidating the utility of several of the common chemical procedures and enzymatic techniques used in recognizing the structure of more compex glycoproteins, such as blood-group substances. There is the further possibility that the "antifreeze" may have some utility as a cryprotectant for storage of biological materials such as red blood cells, sperm and tissue.

Somero worked with *Trematomus* tissue in vitro to determine if the high level of metabolism was tissue or serum controlled. The results verify the extremely high metabolism of *Trematomus* tissues, suggesting that the relatively high enzymatic activity has been acquired through the course of evolution. DeVries and Somero also reported that *Trematomus* fishes resist only slight changes in temperature.

Littlepage, Dearborn, Pearse and Dayton have written about the pelagic and benthic invertebrate organisms found beneath the annual sea ice of McMurdo Sound, revealing oceanographic and biological peculiarities of the region.

BENEATH THE SEA ICE

Littlepage carried out oceanographic observations in McMurdo Sound from small field stations established on the floating sea ice; he also made one of the few comparative measurements ever taken under the Ross Ice Shelf. His reports showed that standard physical measurements in the sound had a remarkable seasonal consistency compared to antarctic ocean areas. Marked deviations were attributed to seasonal runoff from surrounding glacial systems. He also described the phytoplankton bloom phenomenon which in the sound lasts from mid-December to March. He sampled the zooplankton, reporting on the lipid content of a euphausiid and a calanoid copepod, the dominant members of the plankton community of McMurdo Sound.

Dearborn carried out detailed ecological and faunistic studies off Ross Island and surveyed and described the various bottom types of McMurdo Sound. His comprehensive listing of the organisms he obtained with grabs and dredges, working through holes in the sea ice, revealed an unexpected richness of invertebrate organisms in the shallow waters. His lists provided important base-line data for subsequent studies on the marine ecology of the region.

Pearse followed the reproductive and related changes in two populations of the common omnivorous antarctic asteroid over the course of one year. His findings indicated that increases in phytoplankton or slight changes in temperature or salinity may affect reproductive periodicities. He observed that ("Biology of the Antarctic Seas II," ARS, 1965): "The main reason that fewer data are available on reproductive periodicities of animals in the polar seas is the inaccessibility of these seas. Sea ice cover and the winter night have posed great obstacles. With the establishment of a laboratory at McMurdo Station, Antarctica, this problem has diminished and year-long studies can now be carried out in the Antarctic with little more trouble than at other marine biological stations."

Dayton examined the shallow water benthic communities, using scuba diving techniques. He and his graduate collaborators from the University of Washington made 178 dives of 40 minutes' duration to depths of 20 to 45 and, occasionally, 60 meters.

He obtained basic information about the patterns
of distribution and abundance of the dominant epi-
benthic fauna, much of it photographically recorded,
and he described the competitive interactions and
predation between sessile and motile organisms.
Dayton reported that sea ice had a scouring effect
to subtidal levels and that larger ice floes had the
same effect to 15 meters. He found that anchor
ice which forms on the bottom had a most marked
effect on the shallow water bottom fauna. Where
this form of ice breaks loose, it floats upward to
the underside of sea ice, lifting as much as 25 kilograms of substrate and attached benthes. Motile
and sessile organisms are entrapped in this manner.
Even *Trematomus* fishes may be caught but as
often escape unharmed. These physical stresses are
extremely important in the distribution of sessile
organisms in shallow water zones. In a paper given
at a symposium on polar ecology in Cambridge,
England, in 1968, Dayton noted that "the rich
antarctic fauna, high latitude, extreme physical stability and seasonally predictable primary productivity emphasize the potential important contribution investigations of antarctic marine communities may make to many ecological generalizations."
He postulated that an understanding of the biological and physical similarities of deep sea communities can come from data gained in the McMurdo
Sound studies of shallow water zones.

DE WITT'S STUDIES

Although DeWitt began his studies of the antarctic fish fauna at McMurdo Station almost all his
effort has been made from the *Eltanin*, conducting
open sea pelagic and benthic studies. He found that
in the Ross Sea the normal oceanic fish fauna of
the world ocean are absent and are replaced essentially by immature notothenoids with one exception. This discontinuity in distribution he attrib-

uted to the lowering of temperature due to ocean current patterns. His zoogeographic studies show that the surface current pattern of antarctic waters has had a great influence on the distribution of nototheniid fishes from Antarctica to isolated southern islands. Zoogeographic and ecological information on all antarctic benthic fishes will be reported by DeWitt in the "Antarctic Map Folio Series."

While assisting Wohlschlag at McMurdo Station in 1961-62, Kooyman began field observations on the Weddell seal, early suspecting that it was a deep diver. On returning to the United States, he started graduate studies at the University of Arizona on the diving behavior of *Leptonychotes weddelli*. His thesis work established that they can dive to 600 meters. Kooyman's observation of the Weddell seal's deep diving ability and that they could remain submerged up to 43 minutes led to a long series of experiments to elucidate mechanisms of adaptation to high pressure and rapid pressure changes, and the physiology of deep diving in general. Now with the Scripps Institution of Oceanography, Kooyman is continuing these experiments on the deep diving physiology and under-ice orientation of the Weddell seals. His physiological studies of Weddell seals brought back from Antarctica, as well as other species of seals, involve field and laboratory experiments utilizing pressure chambers. The physiological objectives have been estimates of pulmonary function, influence of high concentration of oxygen on breath-holding, and oxygen consumption in unrestrained Weddell seals. The orientation studies which seek to explain the method by which the Weddell seals navigate under the fast sea ice have involved late winter flights to McMurdo in order to observe diving seals during the polar nights. Using the emperor penguin, Kooyman is also seeking information on pressure effects in diving birds.

The Weddell seal is the epitome of all that is Antarctica. Among seals, no species lives at a higher latitude or exists under more severe environmental conditions; it has successfully adapted to an undersea ice environment during the polar winter. While seals generally are useful experimental animals in studies of cardiovascular physiology and in adaptation to high and rapid pressure changes, the Weddell offers additional advantages. It is indifferent to man and tractable, submitting to handling or treatment without show of hostility. It can be collected, by truck, in any number, weight or age class. It can be manipulated unrestrained, except for the simple expedient of isolating the seal by physically moving it to a part of the ice plain where it has only one access hole into the sea. The Weddell seal is cooperative in every respect and willingly exerts maximum effort in under-ice work. One couldn't design a better experimental animal or ask for more ideal field conditions than the stable ice platform off McMurdo Station.

Some aspects of the adaptive responses to diving in Weddell seals have been investigated by a team composed of Robert Elsner, Kooyman, and Douglas Hammond from Scripps Institution of Oceanography, University of California; Claude Lenfant, University of Washington; and Charles Drabek, University of Arizona. Their interest centered upon the special adjustments of pregnant and fetal seals to diving. Weddell seals tested in late pregnancy were found to be capable of diving for 60 minutes, and four out of five examined exceeded the earlier record of 43 minutes for a nonpregnant animal. The seal's blood oxygen storage was found to be very high, approximately five times that of a human being. This difference is accounted for by elevations in both blood volume and oxygen binding capacity. By using implanted blood-flow metering instruments, direct evidence was obtained for the

maintenance of maternal circulation to the uterus
of the pregnant seal during simulated diving. This
finding elaborates previously well-documented information regarding oxygen conservation by redis-
tribution of cardiac output in diving seals. Similar mechanisms were found by the Scripps group
to play a role in asphyxial adaptation of terrestrial
animals. Joining forces with Jay Shurley and
Robert Brooks of the University of Oklahoma, Elsner and Hammond demonstrated enhanced brain
tolerance to low blood oxygen content in Weddell
seals, as compared with other animals. Shurley,
who is studying the sleeping-waking patterns of
the South Pole station personnel, used the opportunity to obtain the first data on the neural physiology of sleep in the Weddell seal as well.

Obviously, a review of contemporary research on
antarctic seals would be incomplete without refer-

Female Weddell seal and south polar skua on sea
ice, McMurdo Sound.

ence to other anatomical, systematic behavioral and population studies which provide a better understanding of the sea mammal resources of Antarctica. Accounts of U. S. scientific contributions are being reported in the ARS volume, "Antarctic Pinnipedia." Jean Pierard's anatomical study in the classic style presents new information on the osteology and myology of the Weddell seal. The mystery of the mummified seals of the dry valleys, radiocarbon dated to about 1,400 years of age, has been stated in terms of histological structure and biochemical analysis by M. A. Marini and five associates. Bioacoustical recordings of the Weddell seal by W. Schevill and W. Watkins, and of the Juan Fernandez fur seal by Watkins and K. Norris give new information on underwater sounds. Two papers by C. Repenning, R. Peterson, C. Hubbs and K. Norris provide the most recent review on the systematics of the southern fur seals, *Arctocephalus*. A study of aspects of the population dynamics of antarctic seals by A. W. Erickson and D. B. Siniff includes the first reliable survey of any antarctic seals and the only one for the Weddell Sea. Work on snow blindness reported elsewhere by E. Hemmingsen and E. Douglas shows that while normally exposed to a very high level of ultraviolet radiation during the summer, the tolerance level of antarctic mammals, including seals, is approximately the same or even lower than those of other animals in regions of less intense solar radiation. An interesting underwater movie by Carleton Ray presents the behavior and social interactions of Weddell seals beneath the ice in McMurdo Sound.

COLD ADAPTATION

There are other equally interesting high-antarctic seals: The Ross is the least numerous, the most reclusive and, under the Antarctic Treaty, a specially protected species. The leopard seal, with the possible exception of killer whales, is the major predator in Antarctica. It is an efficient, relentless carnivore and it is questionable whether scuba divers can work leopard seal waters with impunity. However, the leopard is a fascinating subject for animal behaviorists. The crabeater is as ubiquitous to Antarctica as the ring of pack ice which it inhabits. These high-antarctic species, and the subantarctic elephant and southern fur seals, comprise one of the greatest concentrations of mammals on earth.

The work of Robert Feeney, University of California at Davis, which began in 1964 has also contributed important and interesting information on cold adaptation at the molecular level. With the assistance of graduate students, of whom 3 completed doctoral studies in antarctic biochemical research, he carried out two projects. One concerned the egg and blood proteins of penguins, the other the proteins and associated biochemical activity of tissues and sera of *Trematomus* and *Dissostichus* fishes. Both of these studies included evolutionary adaptations at the molecular level.

The second project emphasized the effect of cold adaptation on the molecular parameters of the purified proteins and enzymes. Specimens of *Dissostichus mawsoni* averaging 50 pounds were taken from Weddell seals as they surfaced on the ice. These, some still alive, were processed for muscle enzymes and blood proteins. Observations on fish blood based on electrophoretic patterns of six blood sera differed from each other so much as to suggest wide divergence in the same species or even different species. Studies on fish proteins have concerned the effect of temperature on the physical and chemical properties of four muscle enzymes from *Trematomus* and *Dissostichus* species. All four enzymes were shown to differ in their response to variations in temperature from responses of homologous enzymes from warmer water species. But

there was no "universal" original property characteristic of enzymes from cold-adapted species.
Feeney concluded that cold adaptation at the molecular level appears to take different routes. He
observed that the "antifreeze protein" of DeVries
and Wohlschlag is a result of adaptation to living
in ice waters and not an adaptation in the usual
sense of a constituent functioning at different temperatures. It is thus a very special case of molecular
adaptation.

Significant progress has also been made in other
specific fields of biological research. Studies in the
ethology of the Adelie penguin, south polar skua
and albatross of the West Wind Drift have provided
critical infromation about mating behavior, breeding habits, migration patterns, feeding habits, predation, age and mortality. Examples in point are
the studies of Dietland Muller-Schwarze on the
daily activity cycle in Adelie penguins and Weddell
seals during the continuous daylight of the austral
summer. At Hallett Station, where he began studies
in 1964, the light intensities range from about 300
lux at midnight to about 60,000 lux at noon during
midsummer. This amplitude is correlated with fluctuations of penguin activity. At the start of the
incubation period the following activities were observed: turning eggs over, preening, gathering
stones, walking, nest building, vocalizing and court-
ship displays. Later walking over the sea-ice, birds
swimming to and from the colony in search for food,
and activities of the chicks, such as running, preening, or demanding and consuming food, were investigated. All activities showed a mid-day minimum:
Between 0600 and 0900 U.T., when the light intensity is most rapidly increasing, most activities were
at a maximum (for example, ecstatic display of
the males, birds walking on the sea ice, and birds
swimming out for food). When experimentally confined in a hut under constant light Adelie penguins

showed a "free running rythm" of 20.5 hours. This demonstrates that normally the sunlight fluctuations keep these birds on a 24-hour schedule. Farther south at Cape Crozier more Adelie penguins were also found swimming between 0600 and 1200 than at other times of the day.

The activity of the Weddell seal was the reverse of that of the Adelie penguin. They were most active around 0200 after the light intensity's minimum one to two hours earlier. The leopard seal at Cape Crozier was also most active during the "night" between 2400 and 0600, which is the more remarkable as at that time the number of penguins in the water has not reached its maximum. These were the first studies of circadian rhythms of activity undertaken in the antarctic.

Dietland and Christine Muller-Schwarze worked on the behavioral predator-prey relationships between the leopard seal and south polar skua on the one hand and the Adelie penguin on the other. The penguin's prophylactic and defensive behaviors were described in detail: penguins avoid thin or slushy ice; when dispersed by a leopard seal attack, they remain motionless for long periods of time and at the same time more vigilant, as the increased rate of head turning indicates. Two-dimensional models of skuas and geometrical figures were moved over groups of penguins in order to determine recognition of predators and intensity of response over the season. The Adelie penguin responded to geometrical figures (disc and ellipse) as strongly as to skua models. At the time of the hatching of the chicks the intensity of response by the adults to skua dummies was highest.

The first biomedical program under the USARP was initiated by Jay Shurley of the Veterans Administration and the Oklahoma Medical Research Foundation. This was designed as a quantitative and qualitative study of the psychophysiology of

Adelie penguin and egg on stone nest.

sleep and dreaming of station personnel at the South Pole as the best approach to the biomedical and behavioral aspects of man's adaptation to an extreme environment.

One manifestation of overwintering stress, polar insomnia or the "Big Eye" was associated with a number of possible stressful factors. These Shurley cited as: disturbances in the synchronization of the biological circadian rhythm; anxiety from the continuous threat to survival posed by extreme cold and geographical isolation; depression and apathy engendered by the long period of unbroken social isolation; and physiological changes incident to the hyperbaric hypoxia of living and working under reduced oxygen of an equivalent altitude of 11,000 ft. above sea level, which gives rise to mountain sickness. His conclusion is that the partial, survivable deprivation of breathable oxygen in personnel living at the South Pole station is one of a number of significant deprivations which helps determine successful adaptation and adjustment of man to life on the South Polar Plateau. This report comprises one of a series of collected papers on human psychological and physiological problems in Antarctica appearing in a forthcoming volume of the "Antarctic Research Series." Shurley noted:

The simultaneous advent of the Space Age in October, 1957, may perhaps be blamed for the fact that the major increases in knowledge of the Antarctic which have been gained in the past decade have gone relatively unnoticed. Its potential as a fabulous laboratory in which to observe and measure the mechanisms, capabilities, and limitations for man's adaptation to an extremely alien environment has gone largely unrecognized and untapped. Consequently, it is a rare individual in our society and in our profession who has more than an elementary knowledge of Antarctica as it stands revealed today.

The usefulness of "Laboratory Antarctica" as a model for analyzing extraterrestrial environment was the object of cooperative research between Roy Cameron of the Jet Propulsion Laboratory and Robert Benoit of the Virginia Polytechnic Institute. Working with the relative simplicity of the ecology in the dry valley cold deserts, they studied the presence, numbers and distribution of surface and subsurface soil micro-organisms and relevant microclimatic and edaphic factors. Cameron's objectives were subordinate to his quest for information on how to detect microbial life under the most adverse conditions, such as on Mars. While not "Martian," the dry valleys of Victoria Land, Antarctica, approach expected conditions in terms of low magnetic field, comparatively high ultraviolet irradiation, desiccating winds and low humidities, similar temperature conditions ($-50°$ to $+20°C$ versus $\sim -70°$ to $+20°C$ for Mars), diurnal freeze-thaw cycles, permafrost, moisture-holding salts and surface or subsurface microbial life as the only possible life form. Some soil samples were collected from which no visible microorganisms could be obtained. A single population of bacteria was found in the harvested area. As the environment became more favorable, an ecologic sequence of micro-organisms could be shown. No other region on earth provides such an extreme, isolated situation.

Taxonomical and biogeographical studies have also progressed under USARP and much more reliable information is available about the kinds and distribution of terrestrial and marine organisms. This work is vital for ecologic, physiologic, biochemical and other disciplinary areas, because it is essential to know what one is working with and their relationship to other organisms. This activity is coordinated under the national antarctic programs with the Smithsonian Oceanographic Sorting Center for the efficient curating, identification and preservation of research collection essential to current ecosystem programs and broader studies on environmental, economic and conservation impact. Specialists are systematically assessing these collections and their monographic studies are reported in the "Antarctic Research Series."

In addition to these volumes, the series is presenting a long overdue guide to antarctic birds. Access to past and current biological specimens and data are also readily available in readout form from computerized data banks at the Smithsonian Oceanographic Sorting Center.

Despite the precipitous decline of baleen whale stocks and the almost complete loss of the southern fur seal herds, the probability is that the living resources of Antarctica are still a major natural resource. There is much speculation today on the utilization of krill, almost the only food of baleen whales and also basic food for fish, sea birds and seals—the total tonnage of which beguiles nutritionists and economists. *Euphausia superba*, the ubiquitous antarctic krill, is alone estimated well in excess of all fish harvested by man, which in 1968 was about 60.5 million tons annually. There is also con-

cern that if krill stock which forms the broad base
of the simple antarctic food pyramid is not harvested wisely, it may be dissipated like the baleen
whales and the whole ecosystem structure may be
drastically changed.

The task of harvesting, processing and otherwise
exploiting swarms of krill calls for as great an economic effort as is given to the Peruvian anchevetta
industry. In the context of their development, much
more basic biological information is needed on krill
life cycles, ecology and their interaction in the food
chain of the antarctic ecosystem. Termination of
whaling during two world wars demonstrated the
remarkable ability of whale populations to recover
from over exploitation and to increase to an appre-
ciable degree. With international accord to call a
moratorium on the taking of whales, it is conceivable that in 40 years whale stocks would be rein-
stated and, by wise harvesting, we could make the
most efficient use of krill without deranging the
simple but vital eons-old ecosystem.

The Soviets are already marketing the fish *Noto-
thenia rossi* for Russian markets. This fish, which
schools in large numbers, is presently collected while
feeding on swarms of krill. Antarctic seals, either
directly or indirectly, are dependent on krill and in
the aggregate comprise the most numerous of mammals in any region. Exploratory ventures to test
the possibilities for more expansive harvesting have
already begun, despite the fact that the population
dynamics of these animals is yet to be completely
understood.

Conservation of antarctic marine resources begins with an understanding of the primary productivity of antarctic waters and in estimating the net
trophic efficiency. Sayed El-Sayed's studies on
Eltanin which have taken him and his Texas A&M
assistants halfway around Antarctica are concerned
with the relationships between trophic levels and

the flow of energy through the antarctic ecosystem. In studying trophic relationships, it is imperative to know the amount of carbon fixed annually by the primary producer, the phytoplankton. This he has established for antarctic waters, exclusive of the pack ice, at 3.03 $\times$ 10^9 tons. His more recent studies on the *Glacier* in the Weddell Sea revealed an unexpectedly higher productivity rate in the pack ice than was hitherto believed in ice infested regions. In his most recent analysis, El-Sayed reported that "the proverbial richness of Antarctic waters is factual only with regard to coastal and inshore regions, and not with regard to the oceanic regions" ("Antarctic Ecology," 1970).

The present U.S. biological program in Antarctica is one of the largest among the Antarctic Treaty nations. This has been made possible because of superb logistic support, team cooperation and the presence of a greater number of biological scientists. Under the broad management of the National Science Foundation, biological research in the south polar regions has made impressive progress, when one considers the extraordinary breadth and depth of these investigations encompassing a region of continental proportions set in an ocean world. It is no exaggeration to state that our national antarctic program is the most comprehensive U.S. activity in the southern hemisphere, and one of the most effective effort on the frontiers of international biological research. The gains from this investment were evident in the development of international scientific cooperation by which Antarctica has been brought into context of contemporary world biological activities and in serving the needs of modelling terrestrial environmental problems.

With the success of the first decade of multidisciplinary effort, the prospects for future biological research are becoming increasingly more attractive. For reasons of biological, physical and geographical factors, Antarctica is the ideal region for studying short- and long-range effects of environmental alteration. The international apparatus for integration of effort and exchange of knowledge among scientists of all nations has been established. Terrestrial and marine ecosystem studies both have begun; with the great need for the wise use of antarctic living marine resources, the nucleus for ecosystem management is already seeded. While organized within severe physical parameters, the biology of the environment can involve all facets of biological interests. The essential operational know-how already exists as a result of the USARP management, and coordination experience has been tested in 15 years of antarctic logistic support.

McMurdo Station is the key site for staging biologic field studies throughout much of the continent since it is the logistic center for the most widespread of all antarctic expeditionary activities. This station is a logical focus for low temperature biology because of its locality and highly developed biological research facilities. Hallett Station has all-weather access to a 5,000 year old Adelie penguin colony, whose great numbers, indifference to man, and flightlessness make them ideal experimental animals for physiological and behavioral studies and population dynamics. Palmer Station is the gateway to the Antarctic Peninsula, a region of vast numbers of sea birds, marine mammals and a wealth of benthic organisms of the shallow continental shelf.

Opportunities for biomedical and biopsychological investigations will be tremendously enhanced with the completion of facilities for those special areas of research incorporated into the new South Pole Station. Participation by young scientists in the U. S. antarctic research program will enhance the international prestige of the United States in polar research, and acquaint the scientist with the fundamentals of planetary biological problems. The logistic and scientific investment at the south pole will also serve the esoteric requirements for training space scientists and for testing techniques and problems germane to extraterrestrial exploration and colonization.

MANAGEMENT
AND
DEVELOPMENT

Evolution of a Venture in Antarctic Science

Operation Tabarin and the British Antarctic Survey

SIR VIVIAN FUCHS

"At last, Antarctica had become an international laboratory, a far cry from the days when plans and movements were discussed in code or cypher lest someone else should forestall the next move." The development of the British Antarctic Survey from a paramilitary operation in World War II, and its present work, are described by its distinguished director, Sir Vivian Fuchs. The author, with Sir Edmund Hillary led the first, oversnow crossing of Antarctica during the International Geophysical Year.

After Aristotle had demonstrated that the world was round, the Greeks accepted the idea of a cold region at the southern end of the world corresponding to that in the north; but it was not until 2,000 years later that the adventurous voyages of early explorers gave some substance to this conception with the discovery of sub-antarctic islands such as Bouvet, South Georgia and Kerguelen during the first half of the eighteenth century. The next hundred years saw the unveiling of the continent itself, and numerous expeditions were engaged in geographical exploration of it. By the end of the nineteenth century scientific investigations had begun, and these gradually superseded geography as the sole object of journeys. Thus, during the early part of the twentieth century all expeditions had programs with a high scientific content. Nevertheless, they were only mounted irregularly and none lasted longer than two years.

Then in 1943, during the latter part of World War II, an expedition sailed from the United Kingdom to the antarctic. This was an unusual venture since it was of naval origin, designed to deny the use of certain sheltered points to enemy submarines or raiders, and at the same time to maintain United Kingdom sovereignty in the Falkland Islands Dependencies sector of Antarctica.

This expedition was given the code name "Operation Tabarin," and could well have served its purposes had it consisted entirely of military personnel. Fortunately, however, James M. Wordie (later Sir James) who had been Ernest Shackleton's Chief of Scientific Staff on the ill-fated Imperial Trans-Antarctic Expedition, 1914-16, was involved in the planning. It was Wordie who proposed that a number of surveyors, geologists, biologists and meteorologists should be included in the party so that some value, other than occupation of selected areas,

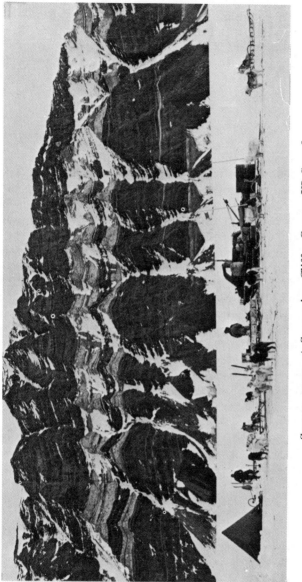

Survey camp at Succession Cliffs, George VI Sound

should come out of the enterprise. This was done, and so began the first continuous antarctic expedition, which is today in its twenty-seventh year. At the time this longevity was not envisaged, but the foresight of a scientist led to a military operation being turned to scientific account, and laid the ground for British antarctic work today.

THE FIDS

With the end of the war the military requirement ceased, but political considerations persisted and the United Kingdom decided to maintain a presence in Antarctica. To this end Operation Tabarin became a civilian organization known as the Falkland Islands Dependencies Survey (FIDS).

The way was now clear to place more emphasis on the scientific work and from the original small beginnings a gradual expansion took place. But political considerations continued to dictate such things as the number of occupied bases and their localities. Financial provision was included in the Colonial Office vote, for the Survey had been placed under that aegis, and although money was short and programs had necessarily to be held at a simple level, there was never any shortage of either scientists or support staff keen to spend two successive years in the antarctic.

Wisely, the Colonial Office allowed a considerable degree of autonomy in the prosecution of the work, and it was seldom that members of the Survey felt inhibited by the political aspects which, at this stage, provided the driving force enabling the work to continue. The men were dedicated to their studies, and only from time to time were they called upon to deliver or receive the official notes of protest which it was then customary for the nationals of different countries to exchange in support of disputed territorial claims. It is interesting that even on such occasions these political gestures, although faithfully performed, did not normally interrupt the friendly relations between the rival groups, all of which were engaged in fighting a common enemy—the environment. Their official duty done, it was usual for all to repair to ship or base hut, to exchange experiences and enjoy the local hospitality.

Such was the situation in the mid-1950s when planning for the International Geophysical Year (IGY) was in progress. Since this included global coverage in the physical sciences, and in particular called for the establishment of numerous stations in the polar regions, it was clear that national claims in Antarctica could prohibit the establishment of new stations and inhibit the necessary scientific cooperation. Fortunately, wisdom and forbearance on the part of some enabled the nations to agree that for the duration of the IGY the whole continent would be open to all for scientific work.

IGY STATIONS

In this climate 12 nations provided a total of 44 stations in the areas south of latitude 60°S. Of these, 11 were FIDS bases, another was specially built by the Royal Society and two more were established by the Commonwealth Trans-Antarctic Expedition. Although all these made some contribution to the IGY program, only two were fully equipped geophysical observatories; most of the British stations had been set up for work in disciplines not included in the IGY.

So successful was this international scientific cooperation that many governments saw the opportunity to perpetuate the spirit of mutuality which had developed. After long discussions an Antarctic Treaty was signed by all the nations actively engaged in antarctic research during the IGY. Under the terms of the treaty, which came into effect in 1961, military operations south of latitude 60°S were prohibited, territorial claims were frozen at the status quo and provision was made for the exchange of information on planning and the scientific results achieved. At this time the British sector lying within the treaty area was renamed British Antarctic Territory, and FIDS became known as the British Antarctic Survey (BAS).

At last, Antarctica had become an international laboratory, a far cry from the days when plans and movements were discussed in code or cypher lest someone else should forestall the next move.

Yet this posed another problem for those charged with executing Antarctic programs. The political reasons for financial support had disappeared, and scientific interests were exposed to the test of justifying continued expenditure on scientific grounds alone. In the United Kingdom it was not long before the very existence of the Survey was challenged. The case was brought before the Council for Scientific Policy, which carefully examined the many papers presented and interviewed experts in many fields. The Council finally came to the conclusion that science justified the continuation of the survey, and advised that it should be maintained at the existing level of activity. The government then decided to transfer responsibility for the Survey from the Colonial Office to the Department of Education and Science, which in turn directed that it should become a component body of the Natural Environment Research Council. At last the Survey had, so to speak, come of age and found itself associated with other bodies with similar interests in a compatible scientific environment.

Thus it can be seen that the early seed—a few scientists attached to a military venture in wartime —has evolved in a changing political environment to flower unchallenged in a world of science. In many aspects this sequence has been matched among other nations; the common thread being the way in which science has been able to prepare the way for political stability, and at the same time to achieve freedom for its work.

ONE SMALL SHIP

In the early 1940s British activities were restricted and unsophisticated. One small ship carried men and supplies south; there were no airplanes, no tractors—only dog teams. The general theme was reconnaissance: simple topographical mapping, a broad look at the geology, surface meteorological observations and preliminary collection of biological material. Today the scene is very different, even though the logistic means may still be small in comparison to some other nations. The greatest advance has come in the number and variety of scientific programs, and the equipment provided to promote them. Because of the relatively small size of the British effort, less than 100 men winter over each year. The aim has been to achieve efficiency by the careful selection of men and projects. Of the total number of men serving at the bases 50 per cent are scientifically productive, the other half being support personnel such as pilots, mechanics, divers and so on.

Experience has shown that there is little which a small group cannot achieve, given time and persistence. Although everyone is conscious that increased facilities would hasten the work, it is sometimes comforting to know that the very need to move slowly can be conducive to thorough and more detailed studies than might otherwise be the case. All main programs are planned on a progressive basis, and men are specially recruited to carry them out. For example, topographical and geological mapping is extended area by area, and the results are published as they become available. In addition to such systematic work, projects proposed by universities are adopted if facilities can be provided, and more especially if they are compatible with existing programs.

Today the Survey is active in atmospheric and ionospheric geophysics, solid earth geophysics, geology, glaciology, biology and human physiology. Because of the arrangements agreed to under the Antarctic Treaty, and the integration achieved by the Scientific Committee for Antarctic research (SCAR), the Survey feels itself to be not only a national endeavour, but part of a wider international program which is contributing its quota to the general understanding of global processes past and present.

TOPOGRAPHICAL SURVEY

Topographical survey is a basic requirement to most of the scientific disciplines, and for this reason a preliminary series of maps covering the Antarctic Peninsula area was produced by 1951, from all the material available at that time. More accurate mapping became possible with the first aerial photography which was flown in 1955-57, but some of the supporting ground control is still being produced today. The regular series of maps is being published at a scale of 1:200,000 and is designed to cover most of the British Antarctic Territory. A second series at 1:500,000 is compiled from the basic series. In recent years American aerial photography has overlapped the British work, and it is expected that the ground control now being completed will be useful in the final interpretation. Apart from these standard scales, special large-scale maps are produced for particular projects in other disciplines as the need arises.

Some programs, such as meteorology, ozone and radiation, are directed more particularly to accumulating long-term records which are lodged at appropriate data centers. They also provide material for short-term forecasting, the elucidation of seasonal variations and background for glaciological and biological studies.

The geomagnetic observations from the Survey's observatories at the Argentine Islands and Halley Bay take their place in the world network. There are also plans to start similar observations at South Georgia which, with the other stations, would form a regional unit of particular geophysical importance. This is because the magnetic and geographic latitudes in that longitudinal sector of the continent are extreme. Thus the distance between a given magnetic latitude and the same geographic latitude is approximately equivalent to 30 degrees of geographic latitude in the south, but the corresponding difference in the northern hemisphere is at most only 15 degrees, and more usually 5 degrees. It is therefore easier to interpret the effects of winds interacting with the magnetic field as well as the effects of particle precipitation which are also dependent on the field. Certainly these factors are more extreme in the antarctic region than in any other part of the world. Furthermore, with the advent of new techniques involving satellites, the importance of high quality observations is increasing, and the special geophysical situation has advantages for studies in magnetism, ionospherics, plasmapause and the magnetosphere.

WHISTLER STUDIES

For a number of years the Argentine Islands observatory maintained very-low-frequency (VLF) observations on behalf of workers at Dartmouth College, Hanover, New Hampshire. At Halley Bay a VLF direction finder (goniometer) is used to find the position at which whistlers penetrate the ionosphere. These are generated by the impulse emitted during a lightening flash. The high frequency components of this impulse travel faster than the low, due to dispersion in the ionized medium. Therefore the crack noise due to the original impulse is converted into a tone whose pitch drops smoothly with time. Some of the results have contributed to the interpretation of data recorded by the University of Sheffield experiment mounted in the satellite Ariel-3. This satellite receives whistlers when it is crossing the tube of force along which they are travelling. Thus the ground and satellite experiments are complementary. The ground observations show the area where the whistlers are being propagated, while the satellite provides the fine structure undisturbed by the reflection of emissions between the earth and the ionosphere.

Studies in this field have practical importance; for instance, the OMEGA navigational aid may be limited by signals received via the whistler path. It is considered that measurements on the 17.8 kilohertz transmissions from the state of Maine should indicate how important this effect may be.

The high rate of whistlers found at Halley Bay greatly aids synoptic measurements of the position of the plasmapause, and it is hoped to install a multi-band recorder for this purpose. The plasmapause marks the edge of the earth's regular dipole-type field and moves with changes in solar wind pressure; a synoptic study of this phenomenon is being planned in cooperation with U.S. workers. Halley Bay is at a convenient latitude for monitoring changes of the plasmapause with time of day and solar wind.

NIMBUS-4 SATELLITE

Twenty-two years ago the Survey began simple ionospheric soundings, and since then increasingly sophisticated studies have been made. With the establishment of the third observatory at South Georgia in 1970, and taking in the results from the British Radio and Space Research Station in the Falkland Islands, new programs will be possible. The intention is to investigate the properties of the winter anomaly in the D-region of the ionosphere and its relation to stratospheric and tropospheric phenomena. The data from these stations will also be valuable for comparison with that from the U.K.-4 satellite.

Recently United Kingdom infrared experiments in the Nimbus-4 satellite have made it possible to examine meteorological/ionospheric relations up to heights of 45 kilometers. By using the synoptic ionospheric soundings from the observatories the very large interactions between F-region winds and ionospheric parameters may lead to new methods of monitoring winds at heights between 200 and 500 kilometers.

MARINE SURVEYS

For a number of years the Survey has been examining the structure of the Scotia Ridge and its continuation into the Antarctic Peninsula. Whereas the work on land has been largely a Survey project, workers from the University of Birmingham have been given logistic support to carry out the marine aspect. Magnetic, seismic refraction and seismic reflection surveys, together with some ship-borne gravity profiles, have been achieved. As a result, the structure of some areas along the southern limits of the ridge is reasonably understood, and considerable progress has been made in interpreting the magnetic data, especially in the Drake Passage.

Recently the advent of satellite navigation has greatly improved the quality of the data.

Future work will be directed to correlating the results of the marine surveys with the geology of adjacent land areas. An attempt will also be made to confirm the presence of a mid-ocean ridge in the Drake Passage, and to establish its age, besides examining the large areas of anomalous ocean floor in the east Scotia Sea. When the structure of the ridge and the sea floor is known, it should be possible to reconstruct the history of the area, and determine its relationship to the ancient continent of Gondwanaland.

Geological field mapping on a regional scale has almost been completed in Graham Land and present work will continue systematically in Palmer Land, Alexander I Island and continental Antarctica. The remaining gaps in Graham Land and the islands of the Scotia Ridge will be filled as opportunities occur. Recently particular interest has been taken in Quaternary studies, and considerable work has been done on the nature and development of raised beaches and platforms, peat deposits and patterned ground. This work will continue in South Georgia and later be extended to the South Orkneys, the South Shetlands and the Antarctic Peninsula.

Recent volcanic eruptions at Deception Island have led to successive examinations of the island, for which isopach maps have been produced. Future events will be carefully watched, and the Survey is ready to mount immediate investigations if further eruptions occur. In the laboratory it has proved necessary to turn to KAr (potassium-argon) and RbSr (rubidium-strontium) radioisotope dating, since the provincial characteristics of the intrusive and volcanic rocks of the Antarctic Peninsula have precluded the interpretation of age relationships by the usual petrographic techniques and chemical analyses.

GLACIOLOGY

During the last four years the Survey has been placing increasing emphasis on glaciology. Clearly there are many interesting features of Antarctica's great ice sheet. The heat exchange with the atmosphere and water exchange with the ocean affect the world as a whole. The ice sheet provides comparable conditions to those which must have existed on other continents during former ice ages. It also provides a measure of precipitation for many thousands of years past, and incorporates extra-terrestrial and terrestrial contaminants which have been deposited upon it through the ages. Since local contaminants are almost absent, it contains a decipherable record of man-made contamination of the atmosphere. Finally, the glaciological factors of movement, temperature and surface form in the ice sheet may provide clues to the behavior of the Earth's upper mantle and ocean floor spreading.

Recent work has included studies of the budget and movement of the Brunt Ice Shelf and the enclosed ice shelf in George VI Sound. Airborne radio-echo sounding has been used to determine the main features of the subglacial topography and to measure ice depths where detailed work is to be undertaken on the surface. At present a project is in progress to determine the chemical composition of the snow at points along a 350-mile traverse extending directly inland from the coast at Halley Bay. By this means it is hoped to show the distance to which marine contaminants extend inland, and to obtain evidence regarding meteorological processes and progressive atmospheric contamination in recent years.

Another study in progress is designed to determine the heat, ice and water balance of a definable glacier on Alexander I island. This is regarded as a contribution to the International Hydrological

Decade program since it will provide a comparison between polar and temperate glaciers. Similar studies are to be promoted at South Georgia where the glaciers are representative of the sub-antarctic oceanic environment.

Studies of taxonomy, biogeography, habitats and seasonal cycles are a necessary basis for more detailed biological work. Although incomplete, much has been done in these fields, and the emphasis is now changing to quantitative research in ecology,

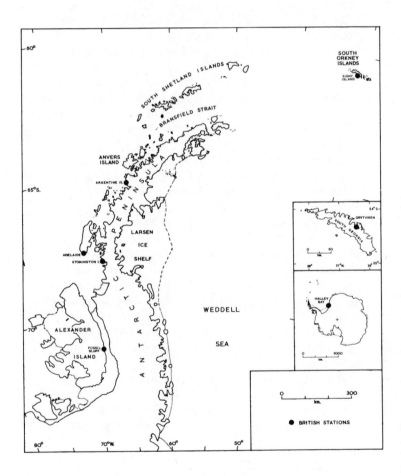

ethology, biochemistry and physiology. These studies are especially concerned with the extreme environmental conditions and the adaptation of plants
and animals to them.

"Antarctica has become a continent for science.
Let us hope that the scientists are allowed to continue their studies uninterrupted by outside influences from an over-populated world."

Future British work will concentrate upon eco-system studies at selected places, but the main effort will be based at the biological laboratories in the South Orkney Islands and at South Georgia. Investigations into the terrestrial ecosystem are, and will continue to be, concerned with the process-es of soil formation, nutrient release and uptake by plants and rates of primary production and decom-position. It is also intended to begin studies of the autecology, physiology and life-cycles of key plants and animals. Within the freshwater ecosystem in-vestigations of the phytoplankton and benthic algae are to be made in lakes for which the environmental parameters have been determined, and the abun-dance, life-cycles, feeding habits and secondary productivity of zooplankton will be examined.

Within the marine ecosystem British work has been chiefly concerned with inshore waters. It is of particular interest to determine whether the Scotia Ridge provides a dispersal route along which species are colonizing the antarctic. To this end a number of new sites are to be selected for a detailed examination of the composition and periodicity of inshore plankton and the effect of the ice regime. Later it is intended to investigate the general bi-ology of krill and the animals which feed upon it, for if it is to be harvested for the use of man, more must be known before the permissible catch can be determined.

From this brief look at the future trends which British work will follow it can be seen that full use will be made of the recently established freedom. Antarctica has become a continent for science. Let us hope that the scientists are allowed to continue their studies uninterrupted by outside influences from an over-populated world.

Developing
The U.S. Antarctic
Research Program

THOMAS O. JONES

The U.S. Antarctic Program pioneered management techniques in Big Science that worked. It demonstrated also that a partnership in this type of scientific exploration was feasible between the National Science Foundation and the U.S. Navy. The pattern of close cooperation was set by Laurence Gould and Admiral George Dufek in "Operation Deep Freeze" during the IGY. The National Academy of Sciences managed the science and the Navy provided transportation, food, shelter and medical care for the scientists. The author of this report, Thomas O. Jones, now deputy assistant director for National and International Programs, NSF continued this arrangement after the IGY with Admiral David M. Tyree.

The history of antarctic exploration has been stated, restated, reviewed and contested by explorers, would-be explorers, historians and politicians. I will try not to add to the confusion. The exploration of the antarctic has, until the International Geophysical Year (IGY), been basically no different than any other in history, except that it has been relatively slow primarily because of the very cold and hostile climate. Prior to the IGY, hoped-for resources, claims to territory and national interests, including security, dominated the activities. Granted that portions of the efforts of earlier explorers beginning with Charles Wilkes and including especially Robert Falcon Scott, Adrien de Gerlache, and Richard Byrd, included scientific observations to the extent they were able. But a concerted effort to gather information on such a large scale about such a large area and analyze it fully had, until the IGY, never been attempted. There is little need to review these efforts here. What is important is that the IGY work in Antarctica did establish a pattern for the pre-eminence of science in modern exploration.

As it drew to a close, the IGY was already showing signs of being a major scientific success, with data gathered by the many national groups freely deposited in the international data centers, and with much in preliminary results already analyzed and reported. That the polar regions have a strong influence on our oceans and climate was beginning to be understood. Furthermore, the polar areas proved to be unique for the study of certain geophysical phenomena including geomagnetism, cosmic rays and auroras. Machines and equipment, together with imagination and determination, had finally made the antarctic accessible. What had been considered formidable not 20 years earlier became "strictly routine." Admiral George Dufek and his men demonstrated that inland stations could be established and maintained throughout the year by air support, that snow landings and take-offs could generally be made as needed, and that over-snow traverses could be supplied and machinery could operate under such conditions. With this experience behind us, there was need only for a program worthy of the effort.

The IGY program was directed to worldwide or area-wide synoptic measurements of selected geophysical phenomena which would enhance our general understanding of our earth and its surrounding atmosphere. Important as scientific studies such as geology or biology may be, it was not intended that they be included in the IGY. Nor were there plans to produce the good maps so badly needed in the recording and analyses of data and to support safe operations. In the long run, if there were reasons to continue the programs, these activities had to be included.

Again in the IGY, we had committed ourselves to the establishment and maintenance of stations where uniform observations of selected geophysical phenomena were made in the same manner as at many other stations. The value of continuing to take such data tends to decrease as the measurement becomes less and less unique. The most elementary cost-effective considerations soon decreed that certain projects and even stations be phased out. Our own U.S. effort faced this issue by closing Little America V in 1958.

While certain university research scientists had been involved in many of the activities of the IGY, they joined the effort to help accomplish the particular programs of the IGY and not to do their own individual research projects—the strength of our American basic research capabilities. To build a program around the individual research initiative was essential if it were to be vigorous over a long period.

Largely through National Science Foundation
(NSF) support, the research capabilities of our universities were being greatly improved. As a consequence, NSF was in a position to extend this approach to the support of research in the antarctic.
Some synoptic observations started during the IGY
had to be maintained. These and other factors required that we adopt a modified program which included both the synoptic and the individual project.
The emphasis had to be on good science appropriate
to the area. And the evolution toward this combined
approach had to be achieved without losing the successes of the IGY. The taking of good and needed
data had to be continued while the new programs
were added, often without increasing the budget.

A MAJOR SUCCESS OF IGY

One of the major successes of the IGY was not in
science, but in international relations. Scientists
meeting in the absence of strict guidelines and
directives from their governments were able to
transcend many of the impediments to mutual operations which are so often encountered. Statesmen
and diplomats in many countries observed these
successes first with consternation, after which the
wiser saw the wisdom of taking advantage of and
capitalizing on the gains, of using the avenues
opened to accomplish in the political arena what
heretofore had been impossible. There had been
growing concern in many countries over the need
to settle the antarctic claims and other problems
of rivalry. The area of that continent is large and
its location in a modern world could make it a
source of controversy among great powers if these
problems were not settled. President Eisenhower
recognized the importance of dedicating the antarctic to the cause of peace and of finding ways of
preventing it from becoming an area of international conflict. In issuing a call for a conference

on the antarctic the President stated:

> The United States is dedicated to the principle that the vast uninhabited wastes of Antarctica shall be used only for peaceful purposes. We do not want Antarctica to become an object of political conflict. . . . We propose that Antarctica shall be open to all nations to conduct scientific or other peaceful activities there. We also propose that joint administrative arrangements be worked out to ensure the successful accomplishment of these and other peaceful purposes. . . . I am confident that our proposal will win wholehearted support of the peoples of all the nations directly concerned, and indeed of all other peoples of the world.

With stated objectives for an Antarctic Treaty under discussion, it became essential that we develop commensurate activities. Mechanisms had to be worked out to ensure that the efforts of the several agencies involved in the total U.S. antarctic effort be fully coordinated. During the IGY, many agencies such as the U.S. Weather Bureau, the U.S. Bureau of Standards, the U.S. Coast and Geodetic Survey and some of the military services had contributed to the scientific program. It was essential that many of these activities continue thereafter under the new arrangement—that their needs be heard and their capabilities be drawn upon. Each agency would also need to have funds to support the efforts of its scientists and their continuing work. A means to support the total antarctic effort was necessary if we were to avoid damaging fluctuations in the program.

To ensure that the scientific program was funded in all areas according to a given plan, single agency funding for the scientific research program was decided upon. This responsibility was assigned

to the NSF—not an unexpected decision, as NSF
had funded the IGY scientific effort and had already, in its enabling act, the authority to transfer
funds to other agencies and to make grants as necessary to institutions outside the government to support research investigations.

There existed only a general policy directive for
the effort but no overall management directive. It
was required, therefore, that NSF step into a new
arena, that of scientific program management. The
Antarctic Program became the Foundation's first
national research program effort. Later, the Office
of Antarctic Programs was established to undertake the responsibility. However, the extent and
involvement of NSF in this work was not pre-
determined and the staff found it necessary to experiment, as it were, in the degree of involvement
necessary to ensure a viable and operating program
while not interfering unnecessarily in the details
of the scientific projects. The art of the game (not
the science) was to venture into the unfamiliar and
unsure waters of science program management to
just the right depth.

Commensurate with the management program
was the need to determine, on a continuing basis,
the appropriate balance between federal agencies
and academic involvement in research. Here it was
soon realized that each had strengths in carrying
out field research. It was necessary to obtain the
best from each. As an experiment, it was decided
to have the agencies as well as the university scientists outline in proposals the work they intended
to carry out and thereafter have all proposals reviewed by working scientists in the field—plus re-
lying on the American tradition that free competition among the groups would encourage each to
consider the strengths of his competitors and put
forth his best efforts. It is my opinion that the

method has succeeded and that both agency and university scientists have benefitted. Both the agencies and the universities have been able to call upon the strengths of the other to improve their own programs. The complementary interplay of abilities becomes particularly evident out in the field when scientists are working side by side and the qualities and shortcomings of their programs are exposed, encouraging each to improve.

Beyond the need to plan and support the scientific work was the need to ensure an organized and safe operation for the total U.S. effort. For this duty, the Navy was assigned the responsibility. Such an activity supporting a program so large and involving such distances required ships, men, aircraft, supplies and experience in such operations. The experience of our Navy in such enterprises was unequaled anywhere, but to divide the assignment for science and for logistics between two agencies to run a single program was the cause for some concern. I believe events have shown such fears to be unfounded. In the first place, each agency was assigned duties in which it was most expert. The President gave no orders or operating plan beyond the clear but firm instruction that there was to be no "Donneybrook" over the arrangement and that we were "to get on with the job."

Some clarification of responsibilities had earlier been set by Dr. Laurence Gould and Admiral Dufek, who started their IGY efforts by agreeing that neither would get into the other man's area of responsibility, and that when they overlapped they would settle it between them. I inherited this arrangement and continued it with Admiral David M. Tyree and the other commanders of the Naval Support Force. It has continued to work well.

As the program became more complex and there was a need to plan for operations far in the future, there arose many management problems which required resolution. In conjunction with the Bureau of the Budget, a definition of responsibilities was agreed upon by all. This definition, later issued by direction of the President and known as Circular Number A-51, succinctly spelled out the division of funding and management responsibilities between the Navy and NSF, and set forth a concept of information and data management wherein the principle of a diversified system of centers rather than a central repository was established. Other provisions address responsibility for the safety and success of the field program and international planning. In each area, the delineation of the NSF role and the Navy role was quite clear. This arrangement has worked so well that it has produced the best and most flexible research program of any of the national programs in the antarctic. It would be misleading to deny that there have been moments of disagreement, but a wholesome spirit of give-and-take and mutual respect have always surmounted the difficulty.

In 1958, we needed also to use more efficiently available logistic capabilities. The cost of carrying a team of 20 to an antarctic outpost is not much greater than costs for transport of a team of three or four. Crew, fuel and other costs remain the same and only a few extra dollars for individual supplies and scientific costs are needed. These considerations led to a successful research expedition approach. Discussions of proposed projects throughout the scientific community served to stimulate ideas from scientists in different disciplines who saw possibilities for their work in the proposed area. This permitted the NSF staff to augment a smaller field project with additional but related projects on a time schedule which uses logistic operations at maximum efficiency.

A related management decision concerned the grant itself. Normally, NSF research grants include related logistic management and transportation costs of the research. In the Antarctic program, however, we found that with logistics operations available from the Navy, including transport to and from New Zealand, the similar needs of all scientists for certain items, often reusable, led us to withhold some funds from the grants and supply these items through a contract or through arrangements with the Navy. Such arrangements have produced benefits by making projects less expensive while ensuring tested equipment for each man. Knowledge of survival and safety in the field is generally not a requisite of most able scientists. What we wanted in the program were the best scientists available, so we decided to supply the field assistance and advice through an experienced staff who could arrange it. Today, the antarctic research grant consists of funds for the scientific expenses plus the assurance of the necessary related support for the field operations.

NSF, in its years of supporting research, has found invaluable the advice and guidance given by the National Academy of Sciences. Under the auspices of that organization, committees made up of distinguished working scientists selected from the total scientific community are brought together to consider scientific priorities. Their reports and advice are an essential input to our NSF planning and management decisions. For the antarctic, we "inherited" a committee originally established by the Academy as a part of the IGY. By continuing the committee under the leadership of Laurence Gould, who had chaired it in its first guise as the IGY Antarctic Committee, we started from a position of strength. The committee required new blood, however, since the scope of the research program had grown so considerably. With some pain at the start, a rotation system was established for the committee and its panels so that the new technical expertise required could be brought to our advisory body.

The growth and development of science depends upon the rapid and full availability of the results of research. Publication, dissemination, and international exchange of results became a necessary part of a science program. From our already assigned responsibility from the Congress for scientific information, the Foundation launched a special antarctic information program to ensure that our scientists learn about one another's work. We began by circulating information only to the scientists engaged in antarctic work but soon found that the interested audience was much larger, both at home and abroad. A journal reporting on future program plans and program summaries as well as logistic activities became a necessity. Our "Antarctic Journal of the United States" has fulfilled this need. It now has a circulation of 7,000 to 8,000 copies on a bi-monthly basis.

Publication of antarctic research results in scientific journals directed to the individual disciplinary fields is the best way to ensure that the information is available to those most interested. As the literature grew, there became a need to abstract and index for rapid dissemination the total world literature on antarctic sciences. This is now done and summary volumes of this information are published regularly.

The clarity of statements in Articles I, II and III of the Antarctic Treaty setting aside Antarctica "for peaceful purposes only," assuring the "freedom of scientific investigation" and promoting "international cooperation in scientific investigations in Antarctica" has done much to ensure the international success of these programs. Furthermore, the attitudes and actions of the representatives of governments who meet regularly (Article IX) "for the purpose of exchanging information, consulting together on matters of common interests pertaining to Antarctica, and formulating and considering, and recommending to their Governments, measures in furtherance of the principles and objectives of the Treaty" has done much. There have been recommendations made and approved by governments which have facilitated these programs and have given backing and substance to the exchange of information, logistic assistance and conservation.

While the governments themselves have done much to assist, their representatives have understood from the IGY experience that much in the nature of international science could better be done by the scientific community itself. Thus, the activities of the Scientific Committee on Antarctic Research (SCAR) and the separate scientific agencies were encouraged to produce politically feasible ways and means and to plan and mount scientific programs. The operating groups handling the scientific programs have worked directly with one another and in conjunction with SCAR to plan and arrange international cooperative programs, exchanges of personnel between expeditions and international scientific conferences to exchange ideas.

The U.S. program has adopted key concepts aimed at maintaining a strong and vigorous program. First, we decided to include any and all sciences and studies for which Antarctica was a unique place to carry out such work and to exclude work which could just as well be done elsewhere. As stated earlier, we saw the need immediately to include work in biology, geology and oceanography as well as cartography. We have also ventured into medical studies of cold adaptation and are considering certain astronomical studies for which the location may be unique. We have suported necessary reconnaissance work on the ice as well as in the oceans as forerunners to more detailed studies. We have tried to maintain a reasonable level of operations by carefully reviewing program elements in terms of value and costs, as measured against the need to venture into new operations and studies. We decided early on having a program constantly in flux with new studies being undertaken while others are phasing out. We have discontinued stations in order to have funds to establish new ones in places more profitable scientifically. In the same manner, we have phased research projects out of the program to make space and funds for new ones.

An administration is frequently required to make difficult decisions regarding the assignment of responsibilities for new programs and effecting better management of existing ones where the expertise for parts of them lie in many agencies. The easy way out is often to reassemble bureaus or to create coordinating committees. I believe the success gained in the Antarctic Program through centralized management and single agency funding of programs, which involve planning the responsibilities of many agencies, bears examination for further application in the conduct of broad-scale multidisciplinary research efforts.

Perhaps the most important lesson is that scientific programs can be the trail blazer in new areas of foreign relations, in ways in which the political diplomat cannot act. If science is to be successful as a channel for foreign relations, however, it must not be encumbered or made an obvious tool of the diplomat. The science involved must not be contrived nor shallow. If it is, the work becomes suspect and can be no more successful than many of the military, commercial or political moves we have seen fail. Given a free and honest trial, science has shown it can succeed as an instrument of international cooperation and should be given additional opportunities in that area. But it cannot even try without adequate support. Our country has spent billions on commercial, military and political activities in the international arena, many of which have been colossal failures, while we have allowed only a pittance for our international cooperative scientific activities which have put science to work for peaceful purposes. Perhaps the U.S. program in Antarctica, and the programs of the other Antarctic treaty signatories will demonstrate the greater achievements and security that can come from the adequate support of international scientific cooperation.

Antarctic Research

A Pattern
of Science Management

WILLIAM D. McELROY

"The period of history we are now entering will put science to a test unprecedented in man's long struggle to learn about his environment and himself. . . . In order to continue to live productively on this very finite planet, man must continue to increase his knowledge of it." Dr. McElroy is director of the National Science Foundation.

A dozen years of sustained, intensive scientific research in the antarctic has generated a by-product of managerial lessons applicable to specific new initiatives of the National Science Foundation.

The U.S. program in Antarctica, started by the National Academy of Sciences for the International Geophysical Year (IGY) and conducted by the National Science Foundation with the support of the Navy since 1958, has mobilized and employed in a closely coordinated effort a multi-disciplinary, multi-institutional and multi-national array of scientific talent and technical support. The experience has provided insights into the otherwise unforeseeable complications of such massive research efforts, enabled us to develop techniques of coordination and joint support, and given us confidence for the design and conduct of scientific investigations of still greater size and complexity.

These lessons have almost immediate application, general and specific. The period of history we are now entering will put science to a test unprecedented in man's long struggle to learn and control his environment and himself. To continue to live productively on this finite planet, man must continue to increase his knowledge of it. The search for knowledge, the investigation of the planet itself and its atmospheric veil, becomes more and more complex, more and more costly, and more and more demanding of talent beyond the capability of any single individual. In the antarctic we have learned about teams of scientists working on a variety of projects, but all sharing, as it were, the same laboratory.

Most "big science" nowadays is strictly a team effort, but most of our team experience has been in finely targeted, one-shot efforts — regardless of the spread of talent and resources required — or in tool-oriented research such as that conducted with a large accelerator, a high-power nuclear reactor, or a great telescope. The antarctic program has been channelized only by the obvious limitations of what we like to call the "bottom" segment of the earth. The opportunities for research and the range of investigations offered are limited only by the imagination of the investigators. Adapting investigative techniques to the hostile environment is as much a challenge to ingenuity as to teamwork.

The lessons learned in Antarctica since IGY are broader than just managerial. They include a de-

monstration of foreign policy formulation which
can't help but be a productive precedent for problems we can foresee in studies of the oceans, the
seabed, the environment (since pollution recognizes
no national boundaries) and possibly in the care
and development of land resources shared by more
than one nation. The bottom of the earth may be
a well of both inspiration and information that will
help the nations cooperate for survival.

Science has provided both the objective and the
momentum for the creation of a special foreign
policy for the United States and, in varying degrees,
for the other 11 nations participating in the scientific investigation of that frozen continent. Since
the beginning of the IGY, U.S. policies on Antarctica have recognized the importance of science. Our
considerable success, I think it is fair to say, led
to the Antarctic Treaty. National policies formulated at the time the Treaty was under consideration have shaped the U.S. Antarctic Research Program through the 1960s. Those policies have been
reviewed at the highest government level, and on
October 13, 1970, President Nixon announced the
results of this re-examination of policy.

U.S. POLICY OBJECTIVES

The President reaffirmed a continuing U.S. interest in Antarctica and in the scientific work undertaken in cooperation with the other 11 nations
signatory to the Antarctic Treaty. The President
noted that U.S. policy in Antarctica includes several
objectives:

1. To maintain the Antarctic Treaty and ensure
that this continent will continue to be used only
for peaceful purposes and shall not become an area
or object of international discord.

2. To foster cooperative scientific research for
the solution of worldwide and regional problems,

including environmental monitoring and prediction and assessment of resources.

3. To protect the antarctic environment and develop appropriate measures to ensure the equitable and wide use of living and non-living resources.

The research program funded and managed by the National Science Foundation will, of course, be responsive to these key elements for our national policies toward Antarctica. Both the research and the management of the program will continue to demonstrate the interaction of science and foreign policy.

Our successful antarctic experience has been instrumental in the formulation of plans for two new National Science Foundation (NSF) national programs — the Arctic Research Program and the International Decade of Oceanographic Exploration (IDOE). NSF has been designated the lead agency for both programs by the Vice President in his capacity as Chairman of the National Council on Marine Resources and Engineering Development. Since receiving the assignment in October 1969, program plans for both the IDOE and the Arctic Research Program have developed rapidly, and when appropriations for new programs in fiscal year 1971 are received, the program offices will be ready to support research in both areas. To capitalize upon the antarctic program experience and management abilities existing in NSF, the antarctic program office was reorganized into a polar office so that both the arctic and antarctic programs would be handled by the same group of administrators.

The Foundation's Arctic Research Program will support broad interdisciplinary research efforts important to the understanding of the harsh environment of this region. The program's goals are: (1) to support and coordinate the federal research effort in the arctic; (2) to stimulate the agencies concerned with arctic operational and administrative functions to conduct research required for the technological development of the area and to share logistic facilities where possible, and (3) to facilitate international research cooperation in the arctic, through the exchange of information and cooperative field projects.

Accelerated research focusing on the following six areas is planned: (1) Marine research, including sea-ice studies; (2) terrestrial physiography and ecology; (3) permafrost, snow and ice; (4) atmospheric phenomena, including geomagnetic phenomena; (5) geology and geophysics of the land and sea floor, and (6) environmental biology.

Like the antarctic program, our arctic activities will be interdisciplinary, interinstitutional and international in character. Of course, the antarctic is not a template with 100 per cent application to any other national research program, even the arctic. There are surprising differences. The arctic, for example, has a comparatively large population. Most important, all of the landmass is sovereign territory and therefore international relationships are complex indeed. Nonetheless, the management experience gained by the 13 years of our antarctic program clearly has useful application in the arctic.

GOALS OF THE IDOE

The International Decade of Ocean Exploration is an international effort by the United States and other participating nations to apply their combined resources to expand knowledge of the earth's marine environment. The long-term goals of the IDOE are: (1) to preserve the ocean environment by accelerating scientific observations of the natural state of the ocean and its interactions with the coastal margin; (2) to improve environmental forecasting, thereby reducing hazards to life and property and permitting more efficient use of marine resources; (3) to expand seabed assessment activities, permitting better management of ocean mineral exploration and exploitation; (4) to develop an ocean monitoring system, facilitating prediction of oceanographic and atmospheric conditions; (5) to improve worldwide data exchange, and (6) to increase opportunities for international sharing of responsibilities and costs for ocean exploration, assuring better use of limited exploration resources.

Projects selected to inaugurate the IDOE will emphasize specific problems or specific geographic areas which are needed to advance marine science and technology and to promote more effective use of the marine environment.

To maximize initial effectiveness, the first year support for the IDOE activities will be concentrated in three major efforts:

1. Identification of physical, chemical, and biological indicators and establishment of "baselines" to provide a basis for assessing and predicting modifications of the oceans, caused either naturally or by man, and to identify and ultimately control and manage pollutant concentration and waste disposal.

2. Studies of the physical, chemical and biological dynamics of convective systems such as regions of upwelling or deep-water formation.

3. Geophysical and geological studies of selected areas of the outer continental shelf and continental margin, certain small ocean basins and deep sea anomalies, to facilitate identification of resource areas and increase knowledge of ocean floor structure and dynamics.

These areas of effort are of immediate interest to investigators and are essential to the future development of IDOE goals. Other nations are also interested in these areas of investigation and for this reason offer opportunities for international cooperation. With a bit of luck, hard work and much money, these studies promise to increase

NSF *Hero,* tied at dock, Palmer Station

knowledge and understanding of the alterations of the environment resulting from technology, and will contribute to man's ability to predict and to minimize further undesirable technological effects. These investigations will initiate a process of technological assessment with respect to man and his effect upon the marine environment, one of the fundamental requirements of the IDOE.

Although I expect IDOE will increase international cooperation, I would be overly optimistic to hope for any early solution to the complex political and legal problems related to the world ocean. Here, leadership on the part of scientists working through programs such as IDOE can make a substantial contribution. In the antarctic program scientists demonstrated their sensitivity to problems of the world outside their own field of research. If scientists participating in IDOE relate their studies to societal problems, science may again influence international foreign policy.

Although the antarctic program has been distinguished by its interdisciplinary research, other NSF national programs have also fostered such research. Our record is not one of unblemished success, but we have learned that interinstitutional relationships or interdisciplinary research seldom just happen; usually a considerable management effort must be made by the funding organizations and by the participants to achieve success.

A more difficult challenge involves breaking down those virtually inviolate barriers separating one kind of science-performing institution from another. Governmental, university and industrial laboratories exist side by side, often performing related work, using similar talents and sometimes serving identical masters. Yet, in the way they see their function — despite the fact that each is enormously dependent on the work of the other — there seems so far to be little commonality among them. The scientific disciplines are coming to recognize their dependence on each other in a truly symbiotic sense, but the various institutions that house science have not quite reached that state. If we are to concentrate maximum scientific resources on the problems of our times, we must develop a new way of articulating, and of using, all of the talents we have at hand. Rather than wait and see what ideas develop almost randomly at governmental, university and industrial laboratories, we have to build deliberate bridges among these separate kinds of institutions, bridges stronger and more lasting than those interim ones we have used in the past.

The management experience of our antarctic program has given us confidence that we can attack those more difficult and complex societal problems. After all, if 12 nations can cooperate in research, it should be only slightly more difficult to get our departments — even one university laboratory and one industrial laboratory — to work to-

gether on a single problem. To test this theory, NSF
has begun a program called Interdisciplinary Research Relevant to the Problems of Our Society
(IRRPOS). In view of the complexity of societal
problems, the nation needs special efforts to encourage the formation of interdisciplinary scientific
research teams which will study specific problems
and provide data that may lead to their resolution.

The scope of the problem may require the combined efforts of physical, biological, engineering and
social scientists, as well as contributions from non-
scientists and other experienced practitioners or
professional personnel. An approach similar to
IRRPOS could lead to improved technology assessment and mechanisms to meet emerging problems
through a new kind of problem-oriented research
center, combining the talents and resources of the
social, the life and the physical sciences.

On a global scale the problems of technological
assessment in the developed countries and technological assistance to the underdeveloped countries
are major issues of our time. Historically these
have not been normal concerns of NSF. But these
are abnormal times, and the Foundation must be
concerned.

Science and Logistics in Antarctica

GORDON de Q. ROBIN

In the second half of this century, the Heroic Age of antarctic exploration when men pitted all their strength and courage against an unyielding environment gave way to the Techno-Scientific Age. Modern explorer-scientists rely heavily on machines and electronic tools in polar investigations. One of the great investigations marking this transition was the Norwegian-British-Swedish Antarctic Expedition of 1949-52 in Queen Maud Land. It was the first to apply the resources of postwar technology to the problem of traversing the region and sounding the depth of the ice. Gordon de Q. Robin, who led the ice sounding traverse on that expedition, has been asked what distinguished it from the general trend of expeditions over the preceding 50 years. Dr. Robin is director of the Scott Polar Research Institute, Cambridge, England, and since August 1970, president of the Scientific Committee on Antarctic Research.

The main point of antarctic research is to increase our understanding of the world in which we live. Our ability to do this depends not only on being able to visit any corner of Antarctica we wish, but also to perceive what is taking place at any location. Much can be done with the human senses, but for objective measurements instruments are needed. In order to study the terrain beneath the ice cover or the nature of the outer layers of the earth's atmosphere quite sophisticated instruments must be used, and the importance of matching the techniques of science to those of logistics increases as the costs and complexity on both sides grow.

The Norwegian-British-Swedish Antarctic Expedition (1949-52) to Queen Maud Land, which helped to open a technical era of polar research, was certainly fortunate in its timing. It took greater advantage than contemporary expeditions of the considerable advances in electronic and scientific techniques of the war years from 1939 to 1945. Furthermore, our experience was gained just in time to be transmitted to the many new antarctic expeditions that took place during the International Geophysical Year (IGY). The expedition did of course establish its base over 1,000 miles distant from any previous over-wintering headquarters on the antarctic continent. A combination of tracked vehicles and dogs was used for inland transport, while aircraft provided air reconnaissance to locate a suitable base site and photogrammetric coverage of inland mountains. The members of the small seismic traverse party in a "caboose" were the first people to sleep on spring bunks on the high plateau of East Antarctica — perhaps a retrograde step to old antarctic hands. However, it is doing no injustice to my companions to say that the logistics work of this expedition, while it reflected sound judgment and experience, was not revolutionary.

SCIENTIFIC RESULTS

The reason why our expedition may have been considered to have opened a technical era of polar research lay in the systematic and successful character of the scientific results of the expedition, rather than in the various "firsts" achieved by the party. Thus we were not the first to send radiosondes aloft to measure upper air temperatures, but we did show that it was possible to make such measurements on a regular daily basis. Our glaciologists showed how the net accumulation of snow and mean snow temperatures varied systematically over the region which was studied. In measuring the ice thickness along a profile from the coast to the inland plateau, we concentrated on obtaining results that would be convincing when seen by experts and laymen at home, rather than on making as long a journey as possible into new territory.

This change of emphasis does not imply any less dependence on logistic facilities than was the case on earlier expeditions. Rather, the reverse is true. We took it for granted that our logistic facilities could do all that was expected for normal expeditions with sufficient ease to ensure that there was a considerable reserve in hand to let men devote more time and skill to scientific investigations.

We can see the logic of this argument if we briefly review the history of science and logistics in Antarctica. Nothing can be achieved until the logistics can be provided to take men to the region designated for exploration or study. The whole history of exploration supports this view. First come the intrepid travellers or voyagers who, usually after considerable personal hardship, take back verbal and written accounts of what they have seen. Then the exploiters of the new discoveries arrive, usually with the intent of opening up new human or economic horizons. Economic horizons in the antarctic started with the exploitation of seals and

whales, but are now tending towards exploitation
of the oceanic fish and krill populations. On the
ice-covered continent, exploitation is directed at
providing new scientific knowledge of our planet.

EARLY ACHIEVEMENTS

Let us look more closely at this sequence of discovery and scientific exploitation on the antarctic
continent. Omitting the earlier voyages, the first
wintering expeditions were those of Adrian de Gerlache in his ship *Belgica*, and Carsten Borchgrevink
whose party wintered on land at Cape Adare. The
primary achievement of these expeditions was to
show that man could safely spend the winter months
in Antarctica. Once this had been shown, there
followed a rich harvest of scientific results from the
expeditions of 1900 to 1915. These results came
mainly from antarctic coastal stations and their
vicinity. Scientific results from far inland were confined to laboriously gained descriptions in log books,
from photographs and sketches, and by a few geological specimens. The effort of travel and survival
inland in Antarctica was such that man had little
time or energy for intensive scientific studies. However, the internal combustion engine revolutionized
world transport to such an extent that eventually
it opened up the antarctic interior to detailed study.

FIRST TRACTORS

Ernest Shackleton introduced the first motor car
in 1907, then Robert Scott the first tractors in 1910.
In 1912 Douglas Mawson tried wireless communication from the antarctic to Australia via Macquarie
Island, but with little success. Still less successful
was his attempt to introduce aircraft to the antarctic in 1912. The plane crashed during trials outside
Adelaide before the expedition, but the salvaged
remains, minus the broken wings, were taken to the
antarctic to serve as a propellor-driven sledge. This

was a forerunner to similar vehicles used by Alfred Wegener in Greenland in 1932, and of propeller driven sledges in use today.

The first two decades of this century were the era when machines were introduced but failed to perform effectively. It was largely due to the expeditions of Richard E. Byrd, during the two decades up to 1940, that a gradual evolution to the successful use of machines took place, especially of tractors and aircraft. The potential of these techniques was shown, although results of the first flights were difficult to interpret and were even misleading at times, as shown by erroneous reports of channels through the Antarctic Peninsula.

The following decades from 1940 to 1960 saw the successful coupling of scientific investigations to the capabilities of the internal combustion engine. The new ability to place scientific stations at any inland location on the continent by use of tractor and aircraft transport opened up an era from 1956 when inland studies were carried out in great detail in much the same way as the coastal studies carried out from 1900 to 1915. These studies were not confined solely to static inland stations, but ranged widely over the inland ice by use of efficient tractors. Possibly the era of 1940-1960, in which the first reconnaissance exploration of the continent can be considered to have been completed, should be extended to 1970, but we are too close to assess the answer. Certainly the changes over the period 1960-80, resulting from the greater general interest in the systematic study of this planet, are causing a new approach. The shift is to more professional long-term management of programs on a basis of scientific and cost effectiveness. Coupled with this is the effect of improved communications and the introduction of computers and other techniques to speed the analysis of data.

IMPROVED LOGISTICS

These improvements on the scientific front have taken place at around the same time as important improvements in logistic technique. Although there have been no drastic changes in antarctic ship design, comparable to the nuclear submarine capable of crossing the Arctic Ocean under its ice cover, understanding of the problems involved in shipping has considerably improved reliability. Mechanical surface transport has become more reliable and adaptable, with vehicles ranging from the lightweight motor toboggan which has replaced dog teams through tractors of various sizes up to the huge Soviet machines weighing 35 tons, which can make unsupported journeys of 2,000 miles over the antarctic plateau.

In the air, much experience has been gained with aircraft, but two types stand out as major contributors to antarctic studies during the 1960s. One is the helicopter, which has supplied a new capability for putting geologists, botanists, surveyors and others down at the precise locality where they wish to carry out their work. Whether operating from a ship steaming off a little known coast, or using turbine-powered helicopters for landing on the highest mountains in Antarctica, the helicopter has made many difficult locations accessible to scientists.

The other major development in air transport in the last decade is the advent of the large, long-range aircraft on the antarctic scene, of which the ski-equipped C-130 Hercules aircraft (U.S. Navy) is outstanding. Introduction of this aircraft followed the use of other less suitable four-engine planes which were used for flying people into the antarctic from New Zealand and for dropping supplies to inland stations. Contributions of twin-engine (ski-equipped) planes such as the DC-3 and Soviet Il-14 should not be overlooked; but it is the ski-equipped C-130 aircraft, with a gross weight of around 70 tons, that has opened up Antarctica most effectively in the last decade. It can carry 40 or 50 people from New Zealand to McMurdo Sound in nine hours. It can take 11 tons of stores from McMurdo to the south pole. Its ability to land on unprepared surfaces enables it to take a Tucker Sno-Cat tractor 1,450 miles out into Byrd Land ready for a traverse, a turbine-powered helicopter to the head of Beardmore Glacier to provide close air support to a geological party, or to fly across the continent from McMurdo Sound to Halley Bay to support operations from that base or pick up an injured man.

Use of long-range aircraft, serviced to high standards, requires a vast and expensive logistic support of its own. The major part of a staff of about 1,000 at McMurdo during summer, and 150 in the winter months, are involved directly or indirectly in seeing that five C-130 aircraft, two Super Constellation aircraft and seven helicopters are kept running. A 35,000-ton tanker in January 1970 supplied McMurdo station with some seven million gallons of fuel, the major part being for aircraft. In addition two 10,000-ton cargo ships were necessary to bring in supplies of food and general cargo. This shipping is of course the first and basic requirement of the whole operation.

BASIC TRANSPORT

Ships have also shown how the basic transport system can be used as an effective platform for scientific research. A good example is the systematic work of the *Discovery II* in studying the southern ocean at all depths during all weathers and seasons throughout the 1930s. Similar use of oversnow vehicles for studying inland Antarctica took place two decades later, while efficient use of aircraft as a platform for research is still evolving.

The basic change which was needed in developing this use of oversnow transport was to forget about length of a journey as a prime factor. During the IGY many traverse parties used a routine of traveling one day and stopping for research investigations the next. Radio communications often made possible resupply or evacuation of parties by aircraft. When one has 10 or 20 tons of fuel, a few pounds more or less of food for the men is not the major importance that it was to early travelers in Antarctica. Consequently food supplies can be attractive and interesting. In planning, it is important to watch the time taken up by cooking and camping rather than the weight of food.

Weight considerations become important when planning the scientific program. For example, for

The helicopter has supplied a new capability for putting Antarctic researchers down at precise localities.

a seismic shooting traverse on the antarctic plateau, it is known that explosives should be placed at a depth of 50 meters or more in the ice for good results. It is quite possible to drill to this depth using lightweight gear weighing 100 or 200 pounds, but this may take two days. A mechanically powered drill weighing half a ton will do the task in a couple of hours, so the latter alternative is chosen, even though it may reduce the range of the party by 100 miles or necessitate an extra air supply operation.

Time considerations become still more critical when aircraft are used as platforms for scientific investigations. Development of the joint program of the Scott Polar Research Institute and National Science Foundation for radio-echo sounding of the antarctic ice sheet from long-range aircraft has shown the importance of many factors. These long-range flights provide an effective method of mapping the sub-ice relief of Antarctica on a reasonable time scale. One flight of eight or 12 hours provides a profile which it would take a ground party a whole season to complete. However, each flight costs hundreds of dollars an hour for fuel alone, and employs some 20 highly trained men in the aircraft and 10 times that number in ground support.

Such operations are only justified if the importance and quantity of results are considerable. Breakdown of scientific equipment in the air would be inexcusable. Like the aircraft systems which are duplicated or triplicated for safety, scientific systems are triplicated so that plug-in replacement units are available during flight.

With radio-echo systems for sounding ice depths, most efficient operation is obtained by flying close to the surface of the ice, but the C-130 aircraft operates most effectively at high altitude. By spending some thousands of dollars, it might be possible to increase the efficiency of the radio-echo

equipment so as to obtain equivalent results from
high altitudes, where fuel consumption is lower and
hence longer-range flights are possible. Such a
change in the radio-echo technique is clearly desirable in some cases, if it can be achieved, and it
illustrates the trade-off between specific scientific
and logistic factors.

Balancing expenditures between science and logistics is not the only problem in developing an airborne program. For scientific effectiveness one must
know the precise location of the aircraft at any
instant, but sophisticated navigation systems are
very expensive, though essential to all studies made
in an airborne laboratory. The effectiveness of
aircraft data is further enhanced if different techniques are employed at the same time. Photogram-
metry enhances the navigational accuracy as well
as the scientific value of radio-echo sounding of the
ice, and again high altitudes are necessary for the
best photographs. Simultaneous magnetic and
radio-echo profiling from aircraft will be very valuable, but magnetic profiles give most detail if obtained at low altitudes. Similarly airborne gravity
profiling — if it becomes effective — will be desirable from low rather than high altitudes, although the aircraft will provide a steadier and better platform for such work at high altitudes. The
complexity of the operation of an airborne laboratory is really comparable to the operation of a well-
equipped scientific spacecraft.

ENGINEERING PROBLEM

Obviously, problems of similar complexity crop
up in various fields. Does one consider the great
engineering problems of obtaining ice cores from
the surface of the ice sheet down to bedrock as a
scientific or a logistic problem? The two are in-
distinguishable until, say, the sample is back in a
home laboratory — when the problem is labeled

scientific. In meteorology, in studying the ocean or the upper atmosphere, science and logistics are merged into what may be called an engineering problem. Where, then, is this broad field of science and logistics leading during the next few years?

First, it must be clear that major surveys tend to have small beginnings, and very many problems will remain to be tackled by individuals and small teams as in the past, but with more efficient transport and in comparative comfort. Such problems abound in biology, geology and in the early stages of new developments in the physical sciences. The need for surface studies and surface traverse parties will remain: It is not possible at present to make precise measurements necessary to measure the movement of the ice sheet of a few meters a year from an aircraft. Precise surveys are needed for this — and they are most economically run by tractor parties, although helicopters would be more rapid and, in some areas, safer.

In the case of geophysical observatories in Antarctica, improved communications via satellites may revolutionize the study of results. Instead of waiting for the annual relief operations to bring home antarctic records of cosmic radiation or of earthquakes during the past year, senior investigators may expect to have detailed records on their desks almost as soon as any untoward geophysical events take place. Recording instruments in Antarctica, which may be looked after by technicians on the spot or may be fully automatic, will generate signals which will be beamed at a communications satellite for retransmission to the home country. There the data will be decoded for scientists who may receive corresponding data at the same time from other locations around the world. They can therefore study geophysical phenomena immediately after the event, rather than as some distant occurrence that happened 11 months earlier. These projected improvements are not vague hopes — they are the subject of design studies by a group at Stanford University, working under contract for the National Science Foundation.

AUTOMATED OBSERVATION

Such new developments will intensify the data explosion, which is in fact already with us. This has come not so much from surface stations, traverses and airborne instruments in Antarctica, but from satellites orbiting over the poles to measure the structure of the ionosphere, characteristics of the atmosphere at lower levels, distribution of cloud cover, oceanic surface temperatures, sea ice and a host of other parameters that will be added in future. How much of this data can be absorbed and understood in time to be useful to man, either to improve his living standards or to improve his general knowledge of this planet?

The meteorologists aim to put this data explosion to good effect in planning their World Weather Watch. Information from surface and upper air stations around the world together with satellite data will be fed rapidly to major centers in Moscow, Washington and Melbourne by worldwide radio networks now being constructed. Analyses will then be fed back to users over the world such as airports, ships, agriculture, etc. One can imagine similar systems being set up to exchange data on the ionosphere, the state and level of ocean surfaces and earthquake disturbances. Computers can then quickly determine the state of the ionosphere and hence direct the use of channels for radio communication. They can predict the state of the sea and so direct ships clear of areas of waves and swell and into regions of favorable seas and ocean currents, as well as produce rapid warnings of tsunamis or tidal waves. Earthquake epicenters may be accurately determined in a matter of hours instead of years, and earthquake prediction may become practical.

The end product of all these efforts will be a current awareness of what is happening on our planet, so that, understanding it better, we can take action to avoid the worst consequences of natural disasters.

THE NEXT DECADES

The Antarctic

Any Economic Future?

NEAL POTTER

"Antarctic research is particularly fraught with possibilities of fundamental value, since the area has so much of the previously unknown. Its geology and geophysics may be opening a new era in theories of the Earth's development; its meteorology is a key factor, if for no other reason than because it is the Earth's greatest heat sink; biological studies offer great challenges and instruction because of unique evolutionary and physiological adaptations which have occurred here. Thus scientific discovery in the antarctic may well be much more important than the economic potential of that area." Neal Potter, research associate with Resources for the Future, Inc., in Washington D.C., is the author of "Natural Resource Potentials of the Antarctic."

287

As exploration of the antarctic region proceeds, and as knowledge of the geology and the seas advances, speculation increases as to the possibilities of developing the resources commercially. What are the chances for economic exploitation of this "new" continent or the seas around it?

There have been a number of shimmering visions of the antarctic in the twenty-first century. Even the staid "New York Times" has printed articles with such headings as "Antarctic Abounds in Rich Ores, Big Tourist Industry Envisioned." Dr. Phillip G. Law, former head of Australia's antarctic office, once foresaw whole mining towns being hollowed out of the rock to escape the rigors of the climate and to permit the miners to bring their families. A Reuters dispatch datelined Wellington, N.Z., was headlined "Vast stores of diamonds, gold, platinum, and oil believed awaiting prospectors of icy wasteland" by the "Christian Science Monitor" of June 8, 1970.

The historical and scientific facts are, however, that the antarctic has already been through its lush period of exploiting readily available resources. The fur sealers, pressing southward after despoiling the Falklands and the Juan Fernandez islands, discovered the continent as they ravaged the seal colonies on the South Shetland Islands. Reckless slaughter all but eliminated the species within a single decade, and the antarctic fur sealing business has been of no importance since about 1828. Partial recoveries of the seal colonies were met by new hunting forays which nearly eliminated the species in 1872-74 and 1892, since when no fur seals of any value have been taken. The hair seals have attracted some attention in recent years, however, and in 1968 the Fifth Consultative Meeting under the Antarctic Treaty proposed tentative catch limits of 200,000 for crabeater seals, 15,000 for leopard seals and 10,000 for Weddell seals. The

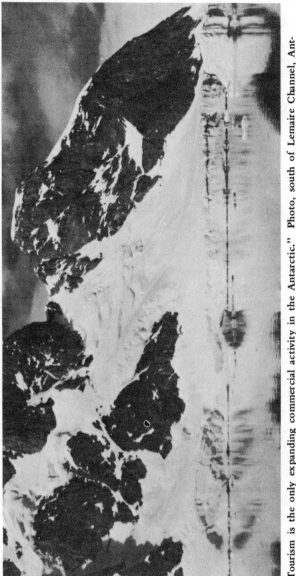

Tourism is the only expanding commercial activity in the Antarctic." Photo, south of Lemaire Channel, Antarctic Peninsula.

value of the 225,000 pelts might be $2 million an-
nually.

Early in the twentieth century exploitation of
the antarctic's second important resource — whales
— was begun. Stations for cutting up the carcasses
and rendering the blubber into whale oil were
established on South Georgia, the South Shetlands and the South Orkneys. As long as they were
dependent on these land bases, the whaling fleets
could not seriously exceed the catch which natural
reproduction rates could sustain, for much of the
best whaling area was far removed from these
bases, and towing the carcasses long distances was
prohibitively costly. Even so, the need for restric-
tion became apparent, and a system of licensing
the number of catcher boats was established among
the island stations.

In 1925 the situation was altered by Norwegian
development of a "factory ship" which winched
whale carcasses up onto the deck through a large
slipway in the bow. Within five years 41 such
factory ships had been launched, accompanied by
a fleet of catcher boats numbering 232, and the
size of the catch had more than quadrupled.

Catastrophe was postponed by the depression
of the 1930s and by World War II, which reduced
the catch considerably. By the 1950s, however, a
fleet of 19 factory ships and 250 catcher boats
was operating, and the great decline in whaling
began. By 1967-68, catching of the large and profitable blue whales had at last been stopped by
international agreement, though there is doubt
whether this species — the largest animal that ever
lived on earth — will survive the 99 per cent reduction in its numbers. Output, meanwhile, had declined by more than 80 per cent, and the industry
had become so unprofitable that all nations but
two — Russia and Japan — had ceased participating in antarctic whaling (see table).

Thus overkill, due to lack of effective international regulation, had brought about the destruction of the principal antarctic resources. At least some decades of drastically reduced catching will be required to permit either the fur seals or the whales to recover to a level permitting maximum sustainable yield. If this is done, the production could be worth $100 million annually.

Clearly, economic development of these antarctic resources is dependent on effective international institutions for their protection. Freedom of the seas leads only to destruction of the industry which the seas might sustain. Anarchy is not only dangerous; it is also impoverishing.

If the resources of the past have been pressed to the point of economic extinction, may new resources attract a new commercial interest in the artarctic?

The possibilities of mineral riches in this wholly untouched continent have stirred the most fabulous hopes. Geologic studies thus far tend to confirm the likelihood that vast stores of mineral deposits do exist in the antarctic. The continent is larger than Europe and over half the size of North America. Scientists are becoming convinced that in earlier geologic epochs it adjoined Africa, India, Australia and South America in the Gondwanaland protocontinent. Since each of these "related" continents has produced numerous rich mineral deposits, and since similar mineral-forming geologic processes have been at work in the antarctic, it seems likely that the minerals are there.

The chances of discovering them, however, are poor. The exposed area of rock in the antarctic continent is very different from that of its geologic relatives. Exact figures have not yet been developed, but probably no more than two per cent of the area of East Antarctica (the major portion

of the continent, located mostly in the eastern
hemisphere) is free of ice cover. The rest is covered
by glaciers, several thousand feet thick, moving
over the rock at speeds varying from a few inches
to hundreds of feet each year. West Antarctica
offers exposed rock probably less than 10 per cent
of that of the geologically related Andes Mountains.
Taken together, the rocks which are accessible
(many with great difficulty) in the antarctic have
an area less than the exposed area of Greenland.
And it is worth noting that Greenland, though considerably more accessible, has never produced minerals of significant value except for cryolite (from
a mine now exhausted).

In addition to the lack of exposed area, Antarctica suffers from another serious handicap to the
discovery of minerals — a population. Many of
the great mineral discoveries of the past have been
made by persons noting small outcroppings or unusual rocks; most of the antarctic will never receive
this coverage.

Newer geophysical and geochemical techniques
provide means of surveying large areas for anomalies with the use of only a few men, but these
techniques have very limited usability in the antarctic because the ice cover stands in the way. The
new techniques will also increase the supplies of
minerals from other continents, thus postponing or
preventing price increases which might make it possible to cover the high antarctic costs of discovery,
production and transportation. Thus hopes for
discovery of workable minerals in the antarctic
appear quite dim.

If found, mineral deposits will have value only if
price exceeds costs of mining, refining and shipment.
Data on the costs of operating a mine or an ore
concentrator in the antarctic are nonexistent, of
course. But we can get some idea of the level of
such costs from a study of the costs of operating

Whaling in the Antarctic[a]

Year	Species of Whale Caught							Oil production (000 bbl.)
	Blue	Fin	Hump-back	Sei	Sperm	Others	Total	
1920-21	2,617	5,491	260	36	31	13	8,448	391
1925-26	4,697	8,916	364	195	37	10	14,219	783
1930-31	29,410	10,017	576	145	51	2	40,201	3,608
1935-36	17,731	9,697	3,162	2	399	—	30,991	2,436
1940-41	4,943	7,831	2,675	110	804	—	16,363	1,100
1942-43	125	776	—	73	24	—	998	51
1945-46	3,606	9,185	238	85	273	—	13,387	819
1950-51	7,048	19,456	1,638	886	4,968	1	33,997	2,304
1955-56	1,614	27,958	1,432	560	6,974	42	38,580	2,307
1960-61	1,744	28,761	718	5,102	4,800	164	41,289	2,233
1961-62	1,118	27,099	309	5,196	4,829	4	38,555	2,052
1962-63	947	18,668	270	5,503	4,771	23	30,182	1,496
1963-64	112	14,422	2	8,695	6,711	—	29,942	1,341
1964-65	20	7,811	—	20,380	4,352	—	32,563	1,063
1965-66	1	2,536	1	17,583	6,121	—	26,246	689
1966-67	4	2,893	—	12,368	4,960	—	20,225	601
1967-68	—	2,155	—	10,357	2,568	—	15,080	426

Sources: 1920-1963, "International Whaling Statistics," vol. 52, p. 14; 1963-64 to 1964-65, *ibid.*, vol. 56, p. 13; 1965-66, "Norwegian Whaling Gazette," July 1966, p. 141; 1966-67, *ibid.*, May-June 1968, pp. 68-69; and 1967-68, *ibid.*, July-August 1968, p. 88.

[a] From Potter, "Natural Resource Potentials of the Antarctic" (American Geographical Society, 1969).

the scientific stations now located at various points on and around the continent.

At spots where ships can readily approach the shore, as at the U.S. stations on Anvers Island and Ross Island (McMurdo), costs appear to run from 2 to 10 times as high as in accessible areas of continental United States. The wide range in costs is due to the variety of conditions of the sea ice (and icebergs) encountered in different areas and in different years. Wherever fast ice or pack ice must be removed, either to gain access to the shore or to lengthen the shipping season, icebreakers must be used, at costs which exceed by severalfold the costs of the freighters. The handicap of ice-bound areas can be reduced to a considerable extent, however, if the operation is a large one, so that the costs of icebreakers can be spread over many tons of freight. Thus the highest costs are estimated for small operations and for coastal areas which are rarely free of ice. The lowest costs can be expected in the case of a large operation on a coast with a long (10 weeks) and dependable ice-free season.

Wages required to secure labor for antarctic operations have not thus far been out of line with those at home; but it should be noted that most of the labor at existing stations stays only for the summer season of four or five months. Experience of Alaskan and Siberian operations indicate that labor costs are likely to be quite high because of turnover rates of 100 per cent or more per year, and because of the need to provide living quarters, large food and fuel needs, medical care, entertainment, etc., under conditions of severe cold, lack of light in the winter, high shipping costs and heavy expenditures for storage and for protection against fire, plant failures and other emergencies. Even a large operation with easy access to shipping by sea would face labor costs two to four times as high as in milder climates and in less isolated areas.

Costs of operations inland, beyond the immediate coastal areas, are much higher. While tractor-trains equipped with crawler treads can be used for trips up to 100 miles, long distances are most economically traversed by air. U.S. stations at the south pole and other points inland are served by special ski-equipped Hercules planes, which deliver freight to these distant points at costs about three to five times commercial air freight rates in the United States. This high cost imposed by antarctic

Geologists examine wall of "coal mine" excavated in the mountains of the continental interior.

conditions is in addition to the costs of building
and operating the airfields and of bringing the
freight by sea to the point of transshipment (Mc-
Murdo Station). Taken together, the costs of delivering fuel oil at inland stations is about $3 per
gallon — in addition to the costs of the "overhead"
of airfields and icebreakers required to make the
whole operation possible.

Could rich finds of high-value minerals surmount
antarctic costs? It is not possible to say with absolute certainty, because data on costs of mining are
not publicly available. The U.S. Census of Mineral
Industries in 1963 seems to indicate, however, that
if labor costs alone had been just twice as high as
they were in that year, most if not all of the U.S.
gold mines would have ceased operation. In South
Africa, whence two-thirds of the world's gold supply
now comes, we find reported costs of about $6 per
ton of ore mined, yielding an average of around
half an ounce of gold, worth roughly $18. If such
ores were found in the antarctic, at a location and
under conditions in which costs would not be over
three times the South African level, gold mining
could be economically feasible. However, this is an
extremely improbable event because of the difficulties of discovery and operation noted above. The
chance appears near zero when we take into account
the facts that South Africa is far richer in gold
than any other part of the world and that South
African costs are exceptionally low, in part because
of the low wages paid the blacks who provide most
of the labor.

Diamonds have been suggested as a mineral
which could easily pay the high costs of antarctic
transportation. Gem diamonds are currently worth
about $100 per carat, and industrial diamonds
about $5. Even the lesser price is equal to $25,000
per kilogram, so the idea seems attractive. The im-
probability of a profitable find appears, however,

from the facts that (1) the occurrence of diamonds is a very rare phenomenon: 85 per cent of the world's gem diamonds come from Africa, principally from South Africa and Southwest Africa; (2) in the diamond-bearing areas, only one kimberlite pipe in 26 has enough diamond-bearing material to be workable, and (3) in the workable pipes, only one part in 15 million is diamond, so a massive collection of machinery and much energy is required to extract the diamond from the matrix material.

NEW INDUSTRIES?

Uranium sounds attractive for the future, but the outlook for antarctic mines is discouraging. Ore prices are currently around $15 per ton, and the complexity of producing concentrates containing even one per cent of U_3O_8 (tri-uranium oxide) is great. The price which the U.S. Atomic Energy Commission offers for such concentrates ranges only up to $9 per pound of U_3O_8. The price of one per cent concentrates might thus be as high as $160 per ton, from which would have to be subtracted antarctic shipping costs ranging from $30 to as high as $300 per ton or more, depending on location and size of the operation. It is true that the development of atomic energy has only begun, so prices may rise; but as the market grows, the sources of supply in easily accessible areas seem likely to expand, as they have for all other minerals.

Perhaps we are too narrow in our vision if we look only to the possibilities of traditional industries in an area that is so different from all others.

May the unique properties of the antarctic — low temperatures, large ice accumulation, remoteness — serve as bases for new industries? This line of thought has led to a number of suggestions which are superficially appealing. But few seem able to meet the cost test.

One of these ideas is to use the natural cold-

storage capacity of the antarctic continent. Foods
left behind by the Scott expedition are still in good
condition after 60 years of natural deep-freeze. Why
not put surplus agricultural commodities here,
avoiding costs for refrigeration and protection from
rodents, weevils and thieves? The answer is three-
fold:

1. The costs of transporting foods to the antarctic are large. The trip down and back would
run to at least $60 per ton, under the most opti-
mistic calculations with respect to a very large operation. This is equal to 16 years of storage charges
for grains at current costs in the United States. If
we deal with meats or butterfat, the minimum
transportation costs are still higher; but the cost
of refrigerated storage is higher by an even wider
margin, so that the costs of transportation would
be no more than the costs of six to eight years of
storage in the United States.

2. The cost of storage in the antarctic is not zero.
Wind erosion is a serious problem for many materials, as is the penetration of snow and the formation of permafrost, from which materials are extracted only at significant cost. If protective structures are built, most of the cost advantages of antarctic storage are lost.

3. Economic factors, including interest charges
and fluctuations in market prices, make it too unlikely that storage would prove economic. The interest factor requires that the price of the stored
commodities rise during the period of storage by
at least enough to cover interest charges in addition to transportation and storage charges. Any
smaller rise in price would make the venture a
losing one. Thus butter stored at 60 cents a pound
must have an expectation of rising to $1.60 per
pound in eight years if transportation to the antarctic, storage and interest charges at five per cent
are to be covered. This is obviously a catastrophic

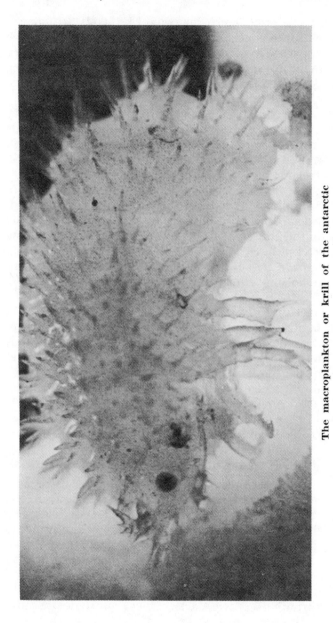

The macroplankton or krill of the antarctic

rise in price which few would be likely to forecast with the slightest degree of confidence. And if the rise were to occur in a shorter time period, the shipment to the antarctic would have been a losing venture compared to the cost of cold storage in the United States.

Some interest has been directed to the possibility of towing enormous antarctic icebergs to provide fresh water to needy areas. Icebergs, measuring half a mile square or more and perhaps 500 feet thick, are frequently seen in antarctic waters. A berg of these dimensions contains fresh water worth over $4 million if we value it at five cents per ton, approximately the price paid by residential water users in the United States. However, the costs of moving such a berg to even the nearest water-short coasts appear to be considerably higher than even this handsome sum. In 1966 three icebreakers in Mc-Murdo Sound succeeded in pushing a berg about one-fiftieth as large as this only 2.5 miles in 12 hours. If and when a big berg approached a harbor, it would become grounded, for bergs draw hundreds of feet, while harbors rarely offer more than 40 feet of depth. The berg would thus have to be broken up into smaller pieces or melted and brought in by ship or pipeline from a position many miles at sea. It appears that desalination of seawater — still too costly for most purposes — is likely to prove more economical than importing icebergs, especially as it would be a more reliable and continuous process.

The economically important resource of the antarctic in the foreseeable future will come from the sea, as did the great resources of the past. The difference will be that the resource of the future is likely to be a step higher on the food chain: Men will use the food of the whale and the seal instead of the mammals themselves. The macroplankton or krill of the antarctic — similar to very small shrimp — provide a rich diet for whales because they swim in dense schools, enabling a whale to scoop them in by the million, straining them out of the water with his built-in net of whalebone. Man-made nets and ships can do the same job — an experiment conducted by the USSR ship *Ob* some years ago yielded 300 kilograms of catch in a five-minute pass with a net.

The value of the krill is still open to much question, since no plankton of any kind have yet been utilized commercially. However, the quantities consumed by the whales have been estimated at figures ranging from over half to several times the size of the entire world's present catch of fish. Such a large sustainable yield could make an important contribution to the world's supply of scarce animal protein, and methods have been developed for making dried krill "flakes" which are reasonably palatable. Perhaps a more likely use in the nearer future will be use of dried meal from krill as a protein feed for the chicken broiler industry which has grown so rapidly in the last three decades. This use could make a large contribution to growing more meat in "chicken factories," and might also release for human consumption the half of the world's fish catch which now goes into animal feed. Thus the krill must be rated as a resource which may soon be economically exploitable, and which can be of great significance to the world when it is used.

TOURIST TRADE

With sealing having been destroyed and whaling nearly so, Antarctica's chief private enterprises in the next few years seem likely to be those based on its attraction for adventurous travelers. This is the most remote and unknown area of the world. Its heroic explorers belong to recent history, some of them still living. Few people have seen the antarctic, and its exploration and mapping are still going on. It is an area of extremes, in climate, geology and biology. It has great scenic beauty, particularly in the relatively accessible peninsula area. An index of the high public interest is the number of newspaper and magazine articles about the new continent — 16 in the "National Geographic" in the past 20 years alone, each with numerous full-color photographs.

The earliest test of potential tourist demand was a pair of expeditions organized by the Argentine Naval Transport Command in 1958. This enterprise recorded 400 applications for the 194 berths available on a nine-day and a twelve-day trip to the Antarctic Peninsula. The first private, commercial tour sailed into the peninsula area in 1966. Since then, two or more cruises have been made into the antarctic each year. In 1967 the U.S. Antarctic Policy Group issued a general policy governing visits of tourists to U.S. stations.

It appears that this will be an expanding business despite price tags running upward of $3,000 per berth. Lindblad Travel, Inc., the principal tour organizer, has made long-term plans to use a Finnish-built ship of 2,300 tons, with which it may accommodate as many as 400 tourists per year. Potential demand could easily run several times this figure, even at fares running to several thousand dollars. U.S. tourist trips to the Far East, Australia and Africa run in the neighborhood of 50,000 annually, and citizens of other countries might easily double this figure. Tourist trips into the far northern parts of Alaska and Canada are well into the thousands annually; all of these high-cost trips have been increasing rapidly. At $3,000 per ticket, an annual flow of just 1,000 tourists to the antarctic would finance a $3 million business.

Though private enterprise (or state bureaus, as in the case of the USSR) may develop significant industries around the tourist attractions and the krill, it seems most probable that science will be the chief industry of Antarctica for a good many years. In common with most research, its value to mankind cannot readily be translated into dollars, but probably far exceeds its money costs. Antarctic research is particularly fraught with possibilities of fundamental value, since the area has so much of the previously unknown. Its geology and geophysics may be opening a new era in theories of the Earth's development; its meteorology is a key factor, if for no other reason than because it is the Earth's greatest heat sink; biological studies offer great challenges and instruction because of unique evolutionary and physiological adaptations which have occurred here. Thus scientific discovery in the antarctic may well be much more important than the economic potential of that area.

Of possibly even greater value could be the patterns of international cooperation being developed under the Antarctic Treaty. This agreement, signed in 1959, permits free travel all over the continent and its surrounding seas without regard to various national claims. It provides for visits, by nationals of any of the signatories, to the scientific stations of any of the others and for accommodating foreign personnel at summer or year-around stations for scientific research. It has secured a full exchange of information developed by the research work of the signatories, and regular meetings are held by scientific and diplomatic personnel of the signatory nations to exchange ideas and make new arrangements for cooperation. If this cooperative venture could lead to reduction of suspicions and to new fields of cooperation, the new continent could be the doorway to a new world. The economic values of such a development would be almost infinite, for war is the great destroyer as well as the world's most expensive enterprise.

The Long Look Ahead

A. P. CRARY

"I do not think the problems are so different in Antarctica that the science policy in that region can be isolated. I would like therefore to discuss two, new thrusts for science in the future. . . . First, scientists must learn to participate in the solution of problems and, second, scientists must help to demonstrate the value of international science."

Albert P. Crary, now division director of Environmental Sciences, National Science Foundation, was senior geophysicist, deputy chief scientist and chief scientist of the U.S. Antarctic Research Program during the International Geophysical Year and in the post-IGY period that followed. He led expeditions which circumnavigated for the first time the 210,000 square-mile Ross Ice Shelf and plunged deep into the great, high plateau of Victoria Land. His traverses ranged across the polar plateau to Amundsen-Scott Station at the geographic south pole. He has also worked as an explorer-geophysicist in the Arctic Ocean Basin.

Forecasting the role of science for the next few decades in a world in the midst of revolution and discord is a formidable task. Predicting the future of Antarctica, a region primarily dedicated to science, might seem to be mainly a task of extending the existing patterns; but the world consists of the sum of all its parts. It should not be assumed that even remote areas such as Antarctica do not or should not play some part in the shaping of the future of mankind. Remote and without an indigenous population, Antarctica should be able to provide a unique contribution.

The people of this planet appear to be precipitously approaching crises of all types; and, whether justified or not, a large share of the blame accrues to science and technology, which have contributed so greatly to the attainment of the present level of civilization. The Industrial Revolution, starting about two centuries ago, created a great middle class in the Western world and forever broke the stranglehold of the master-serf system. This middle class was nurtured by the utilization of the world's resources through the exploitation of colonialism. In more recent years, the practitioners of war have used science and technology to a fine degree, bringing about a great upswing of industrial development, which has benefited and further uplifted the middle class of the privileged nations. A small percentage of the people, mainly those in the United States and Canada, Europe, Japan and Australia, has reached an ultimate degree of material development and "small conveniences" that have provided an unequaled general elevation of the standard of living. To maintain this elevated living standard, however, a minor percentage of the world's population is absorbing a major share of the world's energy resources.

Science and technology are inescapably woven into this great industrial complex. Regardless of

where the blame is put, and at present it is on the
military (defense) machines, we delude ourselves
if we think it is a temporary condition which can
easily be altered. This condition is the backbone
of our Gross National Product, the creator of our
high standard of living. The great space effort,
introduced partly as a way to keep from losing
ground when the military machine slowed, was a
successful scientific and technological venture, but
the timing was poor: the military machine did not
slow down, and the problems were augmented. Such
operations, whether military or space, are carried
out by the federal government, and expenditures
by and large represent salaries—any retreat means
loss of salaries and jobs which is an unpopular political move. Our Congressional hawks are not war-
mongers; they only are trying to help their constituents to maintain their high standard of living.

The exponential increase in the population of the
world has resulted from increases in medical knowledge and medical skills. Perhaps these same skills
can also stem the increase, but it is unlikely that
they will be brought to bear equitably throughout
the divided world. There is at present too great a
contrast in living standards for us to expect that
programs of the wealthy will be accepted by the
poor. Any disproportion of the application will only
increase the chasm between the developed and less
developed nations. And in the midst of this number
one problem of the present and future—population
increases—we are spending great sums of money
to minimize the equalizers: the hurricanes, tornados,
earthquakes and floods.

The tremendous advances in agriculture are
viewed as triumphs for science. Yet the present
urban crises, the sprawling cities with their ghettos,
pollution, overcrowding, crime and unrest, are all
primarily the outcome of the successes of agriculture, which allowed one man to produce food for

many, and so the country boys flocked to the factories in millions to build the great urban communities.

Transportation and communications are examples of major industries that derive directly from science and technology and from our twentieth century industrial revolution. Mobility combined with the successes of agriculture moved millions to promises of better lives. Communications—radio, television, telephone, the rapid transfer of information, with the practitioners of Madison Avenue taking full advantage of their opportunities—have brought solidly home to millions the great inequities in the distribution of material goods. And the news media have provided a means to nurture the class and national struggles for wealth and power.

DECISIONS QUESTIONED

Science and technology have provided, along with the benefits, a deteriorating quality of our environment. This is a by-product of overpopulation, concentrated agriculture, transportation and industry: a by-product which can be diminished, though not without a tremendous cost. In a way, the system itself is self-correcting and in the end would right itself. Overpopulation and overindulgence lead to conflicts, both within and outside the system, that will bring change. We, of course, are reluctant to accept any solution that will lower our standards of living, but hard choices must soon be made. Science and technology can and must play an important part in the cure, but how this can be done is another matter. There must be a revolution in science practice—away from being a tool for changes; back to the contemplative science of the naturalist, long ago left in a minor role. The science and scientists of today are unfortunately no longer trusted, and it may be up to future generations to effect properly the necessary changes.

Where does science in the antarctic, the first truly international community, fit into this rather dismal view of the present predicament of the people of the world? It would be possible to plan antarctic science on an optimistic basis, with a fixed inflation rate increase of expenditures annually, at the least, but this could hardly be considered a challenge. Looking back at the progress and the mistakes we have made in Antarctica in the past dozen years, perhaps we should ask ourselves: Have we done too much? What was the big hurry? Must we continue to entice hundreds of scientists to the continent each year? How will future generations of scientists view our work, with those from only a few decades getting the real opportunities? What have been the criteria for justifying the budget figures? Could we have done all that was really needed to be done at half the cost?

I would say that our decisions on Antarctica have the same basis as that of many other national budget decisions over the years. Starting at any level, the trend continues up and up. Like all facets of American life, there is no hint of retreat. Every added project, each additional scientist, represents something to build on. Civil servants succeed best if they can in some manner get budget increases. This is the way of life in Washington, and one need only follow the budgets of the major agencies to see how reluctant either the recipients or the promoters are to reduce a budget, regardless of the changing needs of the agency. Obviously, the well-being of the people involved is at stake. For science, there is another subtle difficulty. The real breakthroughs in science generally come from the young scientists, but it is extremely difficult for a young scientist to get a start in the system. The old ones do not fade away fast enough. Neither, of course, do the civil servants who have nurtured these same scientists through the years. Obviously, the system has many inequities.

I have sometimes thought that the proper way to handle the antarctic effort would be to have one three-year expedition every decade, with no repeat performers permitted from one decade to the next. This would allow each scientific team the time to collect adequate data and to work it up thoroughly so that the next group could absorb the information and adequately plan its expedition.

PRESENT SYSTEM INFLEXIBLE

If we look closely at this scheme, we soon discover just how inflexible our present system really is. We are dealing with many people, each adding his own inertia and inflexibility. Logistics compound the problems in many ways. When we deal with ships and planes and helicopters and nuclear power plants, we introduce a further inflexibility. Plans for major facilities take a long time to materialize, and no one can predict at the time the need arises when a given facility will be ready, or if there will still be a need when it is ready. Once it is available, no choice is left, it must be used and used fully to justify the expense. So we are caught up in an ever-increasing rigidity of operations.

What about our international allies? I believe that there is a little more flexibility in their programs: the small countries have not built inflexibility into the system, primarily because they could not afford such luxuries. I expect that for most countries it has been a challenge to "follow the leader." On the other hand, nothing is quite as monotonous as yearly expeditions planned to do the same things over and over again. The United States has had opportunities to revise the science considerably from year to year, a tremendous asset in a continuous system, and perhaps the salvation of the U.S. antarctic budget.

Three icebreakers push a small iceberg near McMurdo Station. Their combined efforts moved the berg 2.5 miles in 12 hours.

What are the priority areas in the antarctic and how can these be determined? Let us look at a few fields of science very generally and briefly. The rationale for the present division of funds among the various fields is quite simple: last year's funds determine this year's funds. Biology and geology came in late, following the International Geophysical Year (IGY), and consequently have had a hard time catching up, if in fact they have ever caught up. Oceanography was brought in first with the ship, *Eltanin*, then later with the recently launched *Hero*, and now is a fixed inflexible cost. Innovations, badly needed in any program, and particularly in the antarctic, require flexibility. In an inflexible system these innovations are not universally welcomed, because they require that something old give way to something new.

What about the resources of the solid Earth? Over the years, many people have justified their expeditions to the antarctic by the wealth that obviously was underground. But how much difference would it make if these treasures were never used? The world will be desperately needing new sources of energy in a few decades anyway, and our best chances are not to seek such sources from traditional coal, oil, gas or uranium-235, but to find them in newer developments such as fusion reactors, solar energy, tidal power or geothermal energy.

We have reached the point where we must learn to preserve and not exploit our natural resources. And I do not believe there is a desperate need to assess the reserves of nonrenewable energy resources. If there are other types of resources to be discovered in the solid earth of Antarctica, wouldn't it be best to let them remain for a generation that could more easily study them, more equitably distribute them, and more usefully employ them? We should instead direct our attention to the unresolved global problems of a geological and geo-

physical nature where antarctic studies would contribute to the total picture. And there is no hurry.
The rocks are not apt to weather appreciably in a
few decades.

What about the environment above us? I do not
think that there is a single facet of antarctic operations that has bothered the staff more through the
years than the decisions relating to extensive work
on the antarctic atmosphere. Why are we really
concerned? Is it for better understanding for better
forecasting, or for eventual modification and control of the weather, the ionosphere, and the solar
wind?

No one will argue the point that if we fly planes
we must know enough about the weather to fly
them safely. But other than for transportation
safety, are better global forecasts really important?
If so, who is benefited? Is it the farmer? I hardly
think that better weather forecasting plays a major
role in agriculture. Just how much is it going to
cost to increase our weather forecasting assurance
by a few per cent or to add an additional day of
forecast with the same percentage assurance? I am
afraid that larger and larger federal expenditures
are going into better weather forecasts without a
thorough examination of how much better the forecasts will be and who will really benefit. Perhaps
the atmospheric physicist should turn his attention
instead to methods of harnessing the great energy
sources of the atmosphere. He should increase the
efforts on the monitoring of carbon dioxide, and the
determination of its distribution among air, oceans
and biomass. Also, to combat pollution problems
there is a need to monitor the gases and fine particles of the atmosphere.

Monitoring the man-made influences on the atmosphere will not solve the problems, however. One
of the most damaging trends appearing in the public
approach to pollution is the general confidence that

science can somehow settle our problems, a confidence not discouraged by the scientists. Science is hardly prepared to tackle the monitoring problem adequately, not knowing quite what the problem is. The solution is a scientific-social-economic-political problem. Atmosphere scientists can only be prepared to put up warning signals when certain limits have been reached.

How about the untapped resources of the antarctic oceans, about which there is considerable history and knowledge? If the past records of whaling and sealing provide us with the best examples of the use of ocean resources, then our efforts should be directed against the exploitation of these resources. With respect to food for the expanding populations of the world, the facts are that only one-half of the earth's potentially arable land is under cultivation, that food from the sea could only at best comprise a few per cent of total requirements and that aquaculture, even in our own backyards, is in its infancy. The antarctic is a very unlikely area of exploitation.

Further, when we consider our limited knowledge of the basic information on the food chains in the oceans, the types and speeds of the actions and interactions and the energy flow, there are more reasons to leave these biological resources alone than to tamper with them. The forecasted needs of the coming populations and the problems of pollution have finally elevated the ecologist to a more appropriate niche in the world of science, and there is much to be said for taking up this type of study in the antarctic, where there are apt to be fewer elements to deal with.

The glaciologists have, naturally enough, found a bonanza in Antarctica, a proving ground for their theories and a fertile field for new ideas and developments. They started out a dozen years ago by stressing the importance of the study of an ice cap which, if melted, would raise sea level about 200 feet and disastrously inundate the great seacoast cities—as though in some manner the glaciologists would heroically plug the dikes. It was as foolish to promote this idea a dozen years ago as it is to look at the appealing prospects today of a new continent of Antarctica replacing these coastal cities. Fortunately or unfortunately, the glaciologists do not hold the fate of the world in their hands: they are unable even to combat effectively the avalanches of the Alps and Andes.

KEY TO WEATHER FORECASTING

The big ice caps of Antarctica and Greenland and the vast areas of the oceans surrounding the continent, on the other hand, do hold the key to long-range weather forecasting. Meteorologists may deny this, but it is my firm conviction that weather forecasting has nearly reached its peak effectiveness until more is learned about the ice caps and the frozen seas, either of which have the potential for major changes with periods of a year or more. The present art of meteorology developed from military and air traffic needs. No such need has ever arisen for comparable knowledge of the dynamics of the oceans and the continental ice. Nor is a need apt to appear that would justify the tremendous expense of monitoring these time-dependent, three-dimensional movements in the manner that is now being done in the atmosphere. Such monitoring is not years away; it is decades away. It is so far in the future that the best that could be done at present is to monitor the antarctic ice for major fluctuations that may develop from regional surges and to monitor the extent of the sea-ice cover over the polar oceans.

I do not think that the problems are so different

in Antarctica that the science policy in that region can be isolated. I would like therefore to discuss two new thrusts for science in the future—thrusts which we must strive to make if science is to regain the ground it has lost. First, scientists must learn to participate in the solution of problems and, second, scientists must help to demonstrate the value of international science. In each of those areas science has much to gain and indeed, without such successes, much to lose.

SOLUTION OF PROBLEMS

When I speak of the solution of problems, I speak of a broad complex of social, economic and/or scientific problems. For each problem, certain steps must be taken to assure results. First, we need a concise definition of the objectives, what is wanted, the end products. Second, we must develop, in some manner not yet completely clear, a plan to meet the objectives. This plan will contain many subsystems or elements, such as an automobile being built in Detroit with presumably no parts missing and all parts in some way essential. To do this we need an insight into results of the past and into present efforts. Through some miracle, a management team, with the help of systems analysts, will produce a master plan. It is clear that scientists alone cannot develop a plan which involves social or economic facets; but in Antarctica, for programs like the ecology of the dry valleys, the glaciological project in East Antarctica, or a hole through the Ross Ice Shelf, scientists should be able to recognize all the essential parts. They must learn, however, to think about the whole system and not just the parts on which they would like to work individually. The third step is to execute the various stages with the correct timing, accounting for each subsystem either by teams of scientists or, where gaps still remain, by contract teams. The dovetailing of the various projects, the transmission and coordination of data eventually to make mathematical models would be done by the management team.

This concept has two serious weaknesses. First, scientists are against it, arguing that successful science comes from dedicated individuals and subjugation to a system will destroy scientific initiative, the foundation of all good science. It is true that problem-solving will to some extent subjugate the individual, but this is the proven method of industry and of many federal laboratories. And there will always be, in any system, a mix of the individual's work and teamwork. In addition, many individualistic, dedicated scientists, such as those who worked in the pre-World War II days, should be left to continue their individual projects. No easy solution presents itself, however, for those dedicated scientists who require "big science" where only the rate of work retains any degree of flexibility.

Second, in the problem-solving method, the planning and management issues are emphasized. There are so few good science managers that their rewards are out of proportion to those received by the scientists that they manage. Many people view the problem-oriented science, therefore, with some alarm in cases other than military or space efforts, where such expensive overbalance is less a problem. For every dollar available, they feel that the management will take the lion's share. This is indeed a serious matter that must be faced in the broad areas of societal problems, where university scientists are expected to be major contributors and where, unlike industry, there are no profit-and-loss sheets to curtail overmanagement.

The average antarctic scientist, however, is already a mixture of individual and team member. The antarctic staff has, by necessity, worked closely with the scientists, from the submission of a given proposal to the final technical paper. The antarctic staff also has the information aspects well in hand, and there are not the inter-agency responsibilities that one finds elsewhere in federal support. In other words, the office is well organized to initiate a management of problem-oriented studies.

VALUE OF INTERNATIONAL SCIENCE

International science is an enigma. There are many ways in which cooperation is practiced internationally, and some that have been tried have worked well while others have been failures. In general, the difficulty lies in the reluctance of the U.S. scientists to become involved where they do not clearly see the advantage to themselves. If scientists from different departments or different universities in the United States have difficulty working together, why should we expect scientists from different countries to form a cooperative team? For the U.S. scientist who wants to study in a foreign land, cooperation is not truly reciprocal but really means that the foreign people with whom he deals will cooperate with him. For international science to prosper, a situation must be found in which the nations and the scientists on both sides will benefit.

One major drawback is the language barrier. Except for a few scientists who still have ties to a foreign country this remains a glaring U.S. weakness. It is true that the English language is spoken widely throughout the world, but I see no reason for this trend to continue. For two centuries, English has travelled the world, first with the British, then with the United States; but the power of the former abroad has become minimal and the power of the other is fast declining. Any scant hope of an international language now seems more remote than ever. For too long some of our potential allies have been very tolerant of the United States on the language problem. A Texas oil driller in the 1930s

gave me a clue to the language problem when I
first arrived in South America: "You have to shout
at these people; they don't hear so good."

Opportunities are excellent for scientists to demonstrate the value of international cooperation in
the antarctic. Though progress has been slow, it
has been steady. If international cooperation were
correlated with major problem-solving efforts, I
believe that this cooperation would be greatly
strengthened. Foreign scientists can undoubtedly
help us to understand how to add up many small
efforts to solve a problem.

U.S. INVOLVEMENT

Most arguments against U.S. involvement in the
polar regions can be fended off by reference to the
acquisition of Alaska a century ago. The lesson is
that the apparent folly of one era can become an
advantage in another era. The whole system of values, determined by economics and international
policies, changes measurably through the years.
The present is a very propitious time for arctic
science. How should arctic science be modeled, and
how can we learn from the antarctic program what
the policies in the arctic should be? No greater
opportunities exist for polar science than the ones
which challenge us in the northern areas. Here is
a region receiving emphasis at present, and science
progress will be monitored very closely, much more
so than has ever been the case in the antarctic.
The two requirements of science that I have out-
lined for the antarctic are much more relevant in
the arctic. Projects like AIDJEX (Arctic Ice Deformation Joint Experiment) and the tundra biome
of IBP (International Biological Program) are perfect examples of problem-solving science programs.
International science will also be very visible, and
the best way to accomplish results here is to work
together with our foreign friends on such projects

as AIDJEX, the tundra biome, or one of their projects.

Over the next few decades, there must come a revolution in science, if science is to survive and be a viable tool to help solve the ills of the world without in the process creating more problems than solutions. And, in the solution of these problems, scientists must be prepared for international efforts, both to help solve the problems and, at the same time, to bring mutual benefits. The revolution in science will not be an easy transition and to be successful may need to await a new system of rewards and a new generation of scientists. While the scientific problems in the antarctic are not as pressing as problems elsewhere, the methods of solving the problems are as important as the solutions themselves. And science in Antarctica is already being directed along the right path.

PART TWO

Report on
International Scientific
and Operational Activities
in the Antarctic as Reported
in the "Antarctic Journal
of the United States"

[The articles that follow in Part II appeared originally in *Antarctic Journal of the United States*, published by the National Science Foundation. Some of them have been shortened slightly and, in a few cases, tenses have been changed to reflect the passage of time since they were written.]

Late Cenozoic Glaciation in Antarctica

The Record in the McMurdo Sound Region

GEORGE H. DENTON,
RICHARD L. ARMSTRONG,
and
MINZE STUIVER

More than 50 years of antarctic research have provided numerous observations and diverse ideas, along with many unanswered questions about the long history of antarctic glaciation. What is the history of the Antarctic Ice Sheet? When and why did it form? Has the Ice Sheet existed continuously since its origin, or has it ever partly or wholly disappeared? Has the Ice Sheet undergone changes in area and volume and, if so, were the changes contemporaneous with world-wide Quaternary glaciations? Has the Antarctic Ice Sheet experienced catastrophic surges (Wilson, 1964), or has it merely reacted passively to sea-level changes induced by Northern Hemisphere Quaternary ice sheets (Hollin, 1962), or has it fluc-

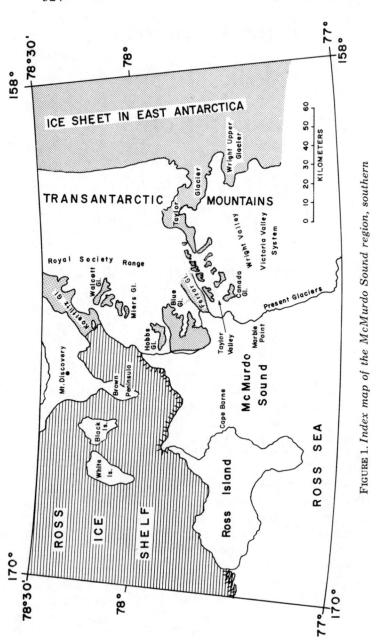

FIGURE 1. *Index map of the McMurdo Sound region, southern Victoria Land, Antarctica.*

tuated out of phase with worldwide Quaternary glaciations as a result of increased accumulation during interglacial ages (Scott, 1905; Markov, 1969)? Will the future behavior of the Ice Sheet involve large-scale surges, widespread melting, continuation of present growth, or stability? Finally, have any areas remained free of ice to serve as possible biologic refugia throughout the long history of antarctic refrigeration?

Some of these questions can be answered partially by examining the glacial history of ice-free areas in the McMurdo Sound region of southern Victoria Land. Here is preserved a unique and datable record of the history of the three major glacier systems in the region (Fig. 1). First, the huge ice sheet of East Antarctica is dammed west of the Transantarctic Mountains, which in this region trend nearly north-south along the coast. Taylor and Wright Upper Glaciers, which are small tongues of the ice sheet, spill over bedrock thresholds and occupy the western ends of Taylor and Wright Valleys—glacially carved valleys that cross the mountains from the ice sheet on the west to McMurdo Sound on the east. Second, the Ross Ice Shelf floats on the surface of the Ross Sea to the east of the Transantarctic Mountains. The Ross Ice Shelf is nourished by direct accumulation of snow, by discharge both from the ice sheet in West Antarctica and from outlet glaciers draining the ice sheet in East Antarctica, and perhaps by bottom freezing. Finally, independent alpine glaciers occur throughout the Transantarctic Mountains in the McMurdo Sound area. A few of these glaciers are shown in Fig. 1.

Past fluctuations of the three major glacier systems of the McMurdo Sound region were not synchronous. Therefore, the history and chronology of each system must be considered independently. Taylor Glacier drains the ice sheet in East Antarctica

Frozen Future

Taylor Glaciations (Ice Sheet in East Antarctica West of Taylor and Wright Valleys)	Ross Sea Glaciations (Ross Ice Shelf)	Alpine Glaciations
	4450 yrs. B.P. (L–627; Marble Point)[1]	
	5900 yrs. B.P. (L–462; Hobbs Glacier)[2]	
	6100 yrs. B.P. (Y–2401; Hobbs Glacier)	
	9490 yrs. B.P. (Y–2399; Hobbs Glacier)	
Taylor I		*Alpine I*
		12,200 yrs. B.P. (I–3019; Hobbs Glacier)[3]
	Ross I	
	34,800 yrs. B.P. (no laboratory number given; Cape Barne)[4]	*Alpine II*
	>47,000 yrs. B.P. (Y–2641; Cape Barne; same locality as sample dated 34,800 yrs. B.P.)	K/Ar dates; 2.1 to ~0.4 m.y. (Walcott Glacier area)
	>49,000 yrs. B.P. (Y–2642; Cape Barne)	
	Ross II	
Taylor II	*Ross III*	

Ross IV

K/Ar dates; 3.1 to 1.2 m.y. (Walcott Glacier area)

Alpine III

K/Ar dates; 2.1 m.y. (Taylor Valley)

K/Ar dates; 3.5 m.y. (Taylor Valley)

Taylor III

K/Ar dates; 1.6 to 2.1 m.y. (Taylor Valley)

Taylor IV

K/Ar dates; 2.7 to 3.5 m.y. (Taylor Valley) and 3.7 m.y. (Wright Valley)

Taylor(s) V

[1] Nichols (1968, p. 471); Olson *and* Broecker (1961, p. 150). The C^{14} date given in the chart and text is corrected. The uncorrected date is 5650 ± 150 yrs. B.P. (L–627).

[2] Péwé (1961).

[3] Black *and* Bowser (1969).

[4] Wilson (in press).

FIGURE 2. *Schematic correlation chart and chronology of glacial events in the McMurdo Sound region. The K/Ar dates given here are rough averages of numerous age determinations made over a period of several years. The dating is still in progress; thus, the averages given here have changed and will change slightly as new data becomes available.*

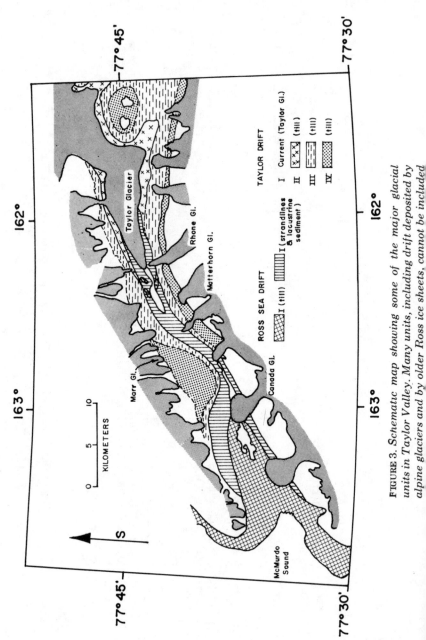

FIGURE 3. Schematic map showing some of the major glacial units in Taylor Valley. Many units, including drift deposited by alpine glaciers and by older Ross ice sheets, cannot be included

and, at the present time, spills over a bedrock threshold to occupy the western 70 km of Taylor Valley. The eastern half of the valley is now free of ice except for small alpine glaciers on the valley walls. However, on at least five occasions in the past, increases in the surface level of the ice sheet in East Antarctica have caused major advances of Taylor Glacier (Fig. 3).[1]

The drift sheets or erosional features of all five Taylor advances are related to the ice sheet in East Antarctica and are not associated with local alpine glaciers or intermontane ice sheets. During Taylor Glaciation(s) V, which probably was multiple, ice tongues reached McMurdo Sound and carved all the major features of glacial erosion in the valley, including truncated spurs, riegels, hanging valleys, and over-steepened walls. Taylor and Wright Valleys thus attained their present profiles during Taylor Glaciation (s) V. Subsequent glaciations of Taylor Valley have caused very little erosion, suggesting that the ice tongues that carved the valleys were wet-based, whereas subsequent ice tongues were dry-based.

Ice of Taylor Glaciations V, IV, and III also reached McMurdo Sound. However, the advance of Taylor Glaciation II was relatively minor and extended only about 4 km downvalley from the present terminus of Taylor Glacier. Taylor Glaciation I, as will be detailed in a later section, is current; and Taylor Glacier, Wright Upper Glacier, and the edge of the ice sheet in this area now occupy their maximum positions since before the beginning of the Wisconsin (Würm) Glaciation as defined elsewhere in the world.

---

[1] Péwé was the first to discover multiple glaciation in Antarctica and to describe advances of Taylor Glacier. Similar advances have been recognized in Wright Valley and in the Victoria Valley system.

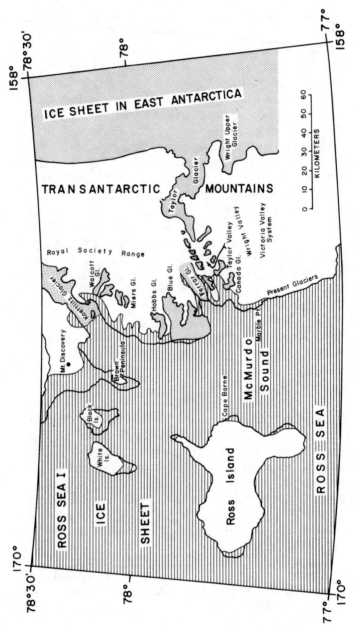

FIGURE 4. *Schematic map showing the extent of the Ross Sea I ice sheet. In places, the thickness of this ice sheet exceeded 1000 m. The present-day configuration is shown for the ice*

Considerable ice recession separated each Taylor Glaciation. Lava flows deposited in Taylor Valley between Glaciations V and IV provided potassium/ argon dates that range from 2.7 to 3.5 m.y.; volcanic cones in a similar stratigraphic position in nearby Wright Valley are about 3.7 m.y. old. Lava flows separating drifts of Taylor Glaciations IV and III are between 1.6 and 2.1 m.y. old.

On at least four occasions, the Ross Ice Shelf expanded into an ice sheet grounded on the floor of the Ross Sea (Fig. 4). During these Ross Glaciations, ice sheets in the Ross Sea and McMurdo Sound reached high on the flanks of Mount Discovery, Brown Peninsula, and Black, White, and Ross Islands. Glacier tongues from these ice sheets pushed westward up Taylor Valley and the valleys fronting the Royal Society Rar ge, leaving well-preserved moraines on the valley floors and along the coast.

Several potassium/argon and carbon 14 dates place limits on the ages of Ross Sea Glaciations, although carbon 14 dates in Antarctica must be interpreted with caution. The base for the age determinations given here is 0.95 percent of the C^{14} activity of oxalic acid. Because the waters of McMurdo Sound are deficient in C^{14}, dates calculated in this manner are too old and must be adjusted by 600 to 1300 years (Broecker *and* Olson, 1961, p. 200; Marini *et al.*, 1967). Likewise, samples of algae from hard-water lakes also may be too old in some cases; this problem is not restricted to Antarctica but is encountered in numerous areas throughout the world. Unless otherwise indicated, the dates given here are not corrected.

In the vicinity of Walcott Glacier, lava flows dated at 1.2 m.y. underlie drift of Ross Sea Glaciation IV, thus placing a maximum age on all recognized Ross Sea Glaciations. At two localities on Cape Barne, Ross Island (Debenham, 1921; Wilson, in press), raised marine beds containing numerous shells occur immediately beneath erratics or drift presumably deposited during Ross Sea Glaciation I. On this stratigraphic basis, the marine beds are assigned to the interval between Ross Sea Glaciations I and II, when McMurdo Sound was free of grounded glacier ice. However, the shells may possibly date from an earlier interval of ice recession. Shells from one of the marine deposits, located at 59–63 m above the present sea level, gave an age of >49,000 yrs. B.P. (Y–2642). Shells from the other deposit, located at 28.5 to 31.7 m above present sea level, gave conflicting results. A. T. Wilson reports a date of 34,800± 2300 yrs. B.P. (no laboratory number given) for these shells. However, another sample collected by the writers from the same locality gave an age of >47,000 yrs. B.P. (Y–2641).

Several carbon 14 dates afford minimum ages of recession of the Ross Sea I ice sheet from coastal areas back into McMurdo Sound. Most of these samples consist of fresh-water algae buried in, or resting on, ice-cored moraines deposited along the west coast of McMurdo Sound by the Ross Sea I ice sheet. The algae originally grew in small kettle lakes, which formed on ice-cored moraine and which were destroyed by shifting of moraine due to melting of ice cores. In the area of the present Hobbs Glacier, algae samples provide minimum dates for initial retreat from the outer portion of Ross Sea I drift of 5900 yrs. B.P. (L–462) (Olson and Broecker, 1961, Péwé, 1960, 6100 yrs. B.P. (Y–2401), and 9490 yrs. B.P. (Y–2399). Another carbon 14 date from this area indicates that ice had receded from the present coastline prior to 3930 yrs. B.P. (Y–2401). An algae sample resting on Ross Sea I drift at an altitude of 65 m on Cape Barne, Ross Island, gives a minimum date for ice recession of 2760 yrs. B.P. (Y–2623). Finally, based on the corrected age of an elephant seal buried in a raised beach at Marble Point, ice recession had proceeded sufficiently for seasonal open water to exist there prior to 4450 yrs. B.P. (L–627) (Nichols, 1968).

The ages and distribution of mummified seals resting on ice-free surfaces in the McMurdo Sound region give information about the withdrawal of the Ross Sea I ice sheet from McMurdo Sound, since nearby open water was necessary for seal immigration. The corrected ages of the oldest mummified seals in the ice-free areas range from about 900 yrs. B.P. to about 3000 yrs. B.P. (Barwick and Balham, 1967; Siegel and Dort, 1968). Furthermore, mummified seals are common in ice-free areas only as far south as Miers Valley, which fronts the Royal Society Range and trends eastward from Miers Glacier to the Ross Ice Shelf. Extensive search by the writers revealed only one mummified seal south of Miers Valley. This distribution seems to rule out a recent retreat of the Ross Ice Shelf, for such retreat would have opened ice-free areas south of Miers Valley to extensive seal immigration.

Two parameters relate recent Ross Sea and Taylor Glaciations, and allow comparison of their relative chronologies. First, the present tongue of Taylor Glacier is in physical contact with deposits of Ross Sea I and Ross Sea II ages, which in turn are related to the C^{14} dates mentioned above. During Ross Sea II and Ross Sea I Glaciations, ice tongues from Ross Sea ice sheets pushed westward up Taylor Valley to the vicinity of the present Canada Glacier (Fig. 3). These tongues dammed large lakes in Taylor Valley. The resulting strandlines are common throughout the eastern half of the valley; those of Ross Sea I age occur up to about 310 m in altitude and those of Ross Sea II age reach 400 m. Subsequent to recession of Ross Sea I ice and concomitant draining of lake water from Taylor Valley, Taylor Glacier advanced across Ross Sea I strandlines, across moraines deposited by alpine glaciers during the Ross Sea II/I interval of ice recession, and across Ross Sea II strandlines (Fig. 3). The geometric relation of Taylor Glacier to these features shows that the glacier presently occupies its maximum position since before Ross Sea Glaciation II. Second, a vast difference in weathering exists between Ross Sea I drift and Taylor II drift, which borders Taylor Glacier. Granite boulders on Ross Sea I glacial deposits are very little weathered. In sharp contrast, granite boulders on Taylor II deposits immediately bordering Taylor Glacier are in an advanced state of cavernous weathering and some are weathered to ground level. Highly weathered drift also borders Wright Upper Glacier and the adjoining edge of the ice sheet where it abuts against the Transantarctic Mountains. The sharp weathering difference between Ross Sea and Taylor drifts indicates that these ice bodies presently occupy their maximum positions since before the Ross Sea Glaciation I. These data are consistent and, taken as a whole, indicate that Taylor Glacier, Wright Upper Glacier, and the adjoining ice sheet were smaller than at present during Ross Sea I time, that they have since expanded, and that they now occupy their maximum positions since before Ross Sea Glaciations I and II. In view of the C^{14} ages of young Ross Sea events, Ross Sea Glaciation II must have occurred during or prior to the Early Wisconsin (Würm) Glaciation as defined elsewhere in the world. Thus it follows that the ice sheet west of Taylor and Wright Valleys probably occupies its maximum surface level since before Wisconsin (Würm) time. These data are in complete accord with the conclusion previously reached by Wilson from geochemical data that Taylor and Wright Upper Glaciers did not advance eastward through the valleys during Wisconsin (Würm) time.

The fluctuations of alpine glaciers have been discussed by Denton and others (1969). All three recognized alpine glacier fluctuations were minor. The youngest two occurred in opposite phase to Ross Sea Glaciations, probably reflecting the presence or absence of a precipitation source in the Ross Sea due to opening or closing of that water body by ice sheets. In addition, a slight change in shape of alpine glaciers has occurred within the last several thousand years, and may record a relatively recent change from a warmer, moister climate to a cooler, drier climate.

CONCLUSIONS

1. The huge ice sheet in East Antarctica had attained a full-bodied stage more than 4 m.y. ago. The buildup of this ice sheet and the accompanying fall of sea level through about 55 m thus occurred during or before the Pliocene Epoch. Rutford and others (1968) have shown that a large ice sheet occupied much of West Antarctica by the late Miocene. Since it was largely grounded below sea level, this ice sheet in West Antarctica must have been preceded by ice shelves, which in turn required polar conditions and snowlines very close to sea level. Considering the conditions in West Antarctica, it may be reasonable to assume that an ice sheet in East Antarctica also existed during late Miocene time, especially in view of the probable long history of glaciation that occurred in Taylor and Wright Valleys prior to 4 m.y. ago. Supporting evidence for the existence of late Miocene ice sheets in polar regions is given by a plot of Tertiary sea level, which shows that eustatic sea level began a rapid decline during the Miocene (Tanner, 1968). Finally, data from deep-sea sediment cores indicate that calving glacier ice has existed in

Antarctica continuously for more than 5 m.y. without major interglacials (Goodell *et al.*, 1968).

Whether large glaciers existed in Antarctica prior to the Miocene remains an open question. Tertiary sea-level data provide no evidence for polar ice sheets prior to the Miocene (Tanner, 1968). Furthermore, Australia and East Antarctica were contiguous during the early Tertiary. About 40 m.y. ago, the continents separated, and sea-floor spreading has since moved them to their present positions. Lack of evidence for glaciation in the early Tertiary stratigraphic sections of southern Australia suggests that the East Antarctic-Australian land mass did not support large ice sheets prior to about 40 m.y. ago. In accord with this, Adie (1964), Cranwell and others (1960), McIntyre and Wilson (1966), and Wilson (1967) have reported temperate floras and faunas in rocks of Eocene, Oligocene, and early Miocene age on the Antarctic Peninsula and in the Ross Sea area. On the other hand, the presence of quartz grains with glacial surface textures in Eocene sediments from deep-sea cores taken in the southern oceans suggests that glaciers may have existed on Antarctica during the early Tertiary (Geitzenauer *et al.*, 1968). Whether these quartz grains represent local calving glaciers in coastal mountains, or whether they represent large ice sheets, is unknown.

2. The ice sheet to the west of Taylor and Wright Valleys in East Antarctica has undergone several changes in surface level during the last 4 m.y. The latest increase in level is current, in accord with the present large positive mass budgets for this drainage system of the ice sheet in East Antarctica (Giovinetto *et al.*, 1966). Radiometric dates and geologic relations indicate, in fact, that the ice sheet in this area is now at its maximum height since before the Wisconsin (Würm) Glaciation as defined elsewhere

in the world (Denton *et al.*, 1969). The recorded changes in surface level of the ice sheet in East Antarctica were not synchronous with worldwide glaciations.

3. All four recognized Ross Sea Glaciations were confined to the last 1.2 m.y. The withdrawal phase of Ross Sea Glaciation I coincided closely with the rapid rise of sea level during Late Wisconsin (Würm) time. The most probable explanation for this apparent correlation is provided by Hollin's (1962) model of alternate grounding and floating of the Ross Ice Shelf due to sea-level changes caused by Northern Hemisphere ice sheets. It is unlikely that the fluctuations were climatically controlled, because alpine glaciers in the area diminished in size during Ross Sea Glaciations. A third alternative, which is unlikely but which cannot be dismissed at the present time, is that ice surges from West Antarctica caused Ross Sea Glaciations.

In addition to the major Ross Sea Glaciations, which were not synchronous with surface-level changes of the ice sheet in East Antarctica, minor fluctuations of the Ross Sea Shell may have resulted from variations in discharge of outlet glaciers which drain into the Ross Ice Shelf from East Antarctica. Such discharge variations could have resulted from the surface-level changes of the ice sheet in East Antarctica recorded by Taylor Glaciations.

4. Extensive ice-free areas have existed in the McMurdo Sound region throughout the last 4 m.y., and perhaps throughout the long history of Cenozoic glaciation in Antarctica. These ice-free areas may have served as biologic refugia.

REFERENCES

Adie, R. J. 1964. Geologic history. In: *Antarctic Research*. Butterworths, London, p. 118–162.

American Commission on Stratigraphic Nomenclature. 1961. Code of stratigraphic nomenclature. *American Association of Petroleum Geologists. Bulletin,* 45: 645–665.

Barwick, R. E. *and* R. W. Balham. 1967. Mummified seal carcasses in a deglaciated region of south Victoria Land, Antarctica. *Tuatara,* 15: 165–180.

Black, R. F. *and* C. J. Bowser. 1969. Salts and associated phenomena of the termini of the Hobbs and Taylor Glaciers, Victoria Land, Antarctica. *International Union of Geology and Geophysics. Commission on Snow and Ice. Publication* 79: 226–238.

Broecker, W. S. *and* E. A. Olson. 1961. Lamont radiocarbon measurements VIII. *Radiocarbon,* 3: 176–204.

Bull, C., B. C. McKelvey, *and* P. N. Webb. 1962. Quaternary glaciations in southern Victoria Land, Antarctica. *Journal of Glaciology,* 4(31): 63–78.

Calkin, P. E. 1964. *Geomorphology and Glacial Geology of the Victoria Valley System, Southern Victoria Land, Antarctica.* Ohio State University. Institute of Polar Studies. Report no. 10. 66 p.

Cranwell, L. M., H. J. Harrington, *and* I. G. Speden. 1960. Lower Tertiary microfossils from McMurdo Sound, Antarctica. *Nature,* 186: 700–702.

Debenham, F. 1921. Recent and local deposits of McMurdo Sound region. *British Antarctic (Terra Nova) Expedition. Natural History Reports. Geology,* 1: 63–100.

Denton, G. H. *and* R. L. Armstrong. 1968. Glacial geology and chronology of the McMurdo Sound region. *Antarctic Journal of the U.S.,* III (4): 99–101.

Denton, G. H., R. L. Armstrong, *and* M. Stuiver. 1969. Histoire glaciaire et chronologie de la région du détroit de McMurdo, sud de la Terre Victoria, Antarctide; note préliminaire. *Revue de Géographie Physique et de Géologie Dynamique,* 11: 265–278.

Geitzenauer, K. R., S. V. Margolis, *and* D. S. Edwards. 1968. Evidence consistent with Eocene glaciation in a South Pacific deep-sea sedimentary core. *Earth and Planetary Science Letters,* 4 (2): 173–177.

Giovinetto, M. B., E. S. Robinson, *and* C. W. M. Swithinbank. 1966. The regime of the western part of the Ross Ice Shelf drainage system. *Journal of Glaciology,* 6 (43): 55–68.

Goodell, H. G., N. O. Watkins, T. T. Mather, *and* S. Koster. 1968. The antarctic glacial history recorded in sediments of the Southern Ocean. *Palaeogeography, Palaeoclimatology, Palaeoecology,* 5 (1) : 41–62.

Hollin, J. T. 1962. On the glacial history of Antarctica. *Journal of Glaciology,* 4 (32) : 173–195.

Marini, M. A., M. F. Orr, *and* E. L. Coe. 1967. Surviving macromolecules in antarctic seal mummies. *Antarctic Journal of the U.S.,* II (5) : 190–191.

Markov, K. K. 1969. The Pleistocene history of Antarctica. In: *The Periglacial Environment.* McGill-Queen's University Press, Canada, pp. 263–269.

McIntyre, O. J. *and* G. J. Wilson. 1966. Preliminary palynology of some antarctic Tertiary erratics. *New Zealand Journal of Botany,* 4 : 315–321.

Nichols, R. L. 1961. Multiple glaciation in the Wright Valley, McMurdo Sound, Antarctica. *Tenth Pacific Science Congress. Abstracts of Papers Presented,* p. 317.

Nichols, R. L. 1968. Coastal geomorphology, McMurdo Sound, Antarctica. *Journal of Glaciology,* 7 (51) : 449–478.

Olson, E. A. *and* W. S. Broecker. 1961. Lamont natural radiocarbon measurements VII. *Radiocarbon,* 3 : 141–175.

Péwé, T. L. 1960. Multiple glaciation in the McMurdo Sound region, Antarctica; a progress report. *Journal of Geology,* 68 : 498–514.

Rutford, R. H., C. Craddock, *and* T. W. Bastien. 1968. Late Tertiary glaciation and sea-level changes in Antarctica. *Palaeogeography, Palaeoclimatology, Palaeoecology,* 5 : (1) 15–39.

Scott, R. F. 1905. Results of the National Antarctic Expedition, I. *Geographical Journal,* 25 : 353–372.

Siegel, F. R. *and* W. Dort, Jr. 1968. Mirabilite and associated seal bones, southern Victoria Land, Antarctica. *Antarctic Journal of the U.S.,* III (5) : 173–175.

Tanner, W. F. 1968. Tertiary Sea Level Symposium: Introduction. *Palaeogeography, Palaeoclimatology, Palaeoecology,* 5 (1) : 7–14.

Wilson, A. T. 1964. Origin of ice ages: an ice shelf theory for Pleistocene glaciation. *Nature,* 201 : 147–149.

Wilson, A. T. 1967. The lakes of the McMurdo dry valleys. *Tuatara,* 15 : 152–164.

Wilson, A. T. In press. Radiocarbon age of a raised ma-
    rine deposit on Cape Barne, Ross Island, Antarctica.
Wilson, G. J. 1967. Some new species of lower Tertiary
    dinoflagellates from McMurdo Sound, Antartica. *New
    Zealand Journal of Botany*, 5 (1) : 57–83.

U.S.-Soviet
Exchange Program
at Vostok

F. MICHAEL MAISH

Vostok Station, Antarctica, is the coldest place on earth inhabited by man, at one time having recorded a temperature of −88.3°C. The smallest and most remote of the three inland stations in Antarctica (the others are Byrd and Pole), Vostok is located near the earth's geomagnetic pole at 78°27′48″S. 106°48′24″E., at an altitude of 3,488 m on approximately 3,700 m of ice. The air is perpetually drier than in the world's worst deserts. During the polar night, temperatures drop so low that they would normally freeze carbon dioxide out of the atmosphere (CO_2 condenses at −78.5°C.). The altitude starves lungs of oxygen, and the normal rate of heartbeats nearly doubles. Here, 15 to 25 men winter over each year, isolated from contact with the world for more than nine months, half of this time in utter darkness.

Vostok's climate is beautiful, monotonous, hostile, and calm. The sky overhead fades to space blue, while the horizon stretches to incredible distances owing to the purity of the air and to surface-temperature inversions. The purity of the snow is reflected in shim-

mering whiteness in all dimensions. The generally calm wind, low humidity and atmospheric pressure diminish the chilling effects of the bitter cold, and well-designed clothing enables the personnel to work in even the coldest temperatures. Precipitation rarely occurs; rather, water vapor condenses to fine crystals which the wind can blow into sizeable drifts.

Traditionally, Vostok has been the Soviet station with the highest international complement. It has thrice been the home of U.S. Exchange Scientists. In 1969, the station was manned by 16 Soviets, one East German (Dr. Manfred Schneider), and one American (the author). In addition, a five-man group of French glaciologists was present during the 1969 austral summer. At that time, four flags flew over Vostok, testifying to the peaceful use of Antarctica under the Antarctic Treaty—the world's most harmonious international relations at the site of the world's most discordant climate!

Russian antarctic exploration dates back to the expedition of Admirals Bellingauzen and Lazarev in their notable circumnavigation of the Continent in 1820–1821, which greatly supplemented the delineation of the probable coast drawn by Captain Cook on the basis of his voyages of 1772–1785. Undoubtedly,

PHOTO BY AUTHOR

Bellingauzen was among the first to sight the ice-shrouded Antarctic Continent.

During the Second International Polar Year, 1932–1933, a modest Soviet antarctic expedition was planned, but it never materialized. However, since February 13, 1956, the date that the Soviet flag was first hoisted over Mirnyy Station, the U.S.S.R. has carried out an elaborate scientific program in Antarctica. At present, it maintains five wintering stations: Bellingauzen, at 62°12′S. 58°56′W. (opened February 22, 1968); Mirnyy, at 66°33′05″S. 93°00′ 58″E. (February 13, 1956); Molodezhnaya, at 67°40′03″S. 45°50′41″E. (January 14, 1963); Novolazarevskaya, at 70°46′S. 11°50′E. (February 18, 1961); and Vostok (opened December 16, 1957, and closed temporarily January 21, 1962—January 23, 1963). In the 1970–1971 austral summer, the 16th Soviet Antarctic Expedition (SAE) intended to open a sixth station—Leningradskaya—at 69°30′S. 154° 23′E.

In addition to the research on the Continent, the Soviets engage in oceanographic and meteorological work on board their resupply vessels *Professor Vize* and her sister ship *Professor Zubov,* both specially designed and constructed in 1967 for polar operations. *Professor Vize* is a substantial ship of 6,934 tons and 124 m length, with reinforced hull for ice work. She is a fully equipped scientific vessel with many specialized laboratories and luxurious accommodations for perhaps 200 scientists and crew, reflecting her use as the main transport for expedition members to and from Antarctica. Oceanographic projects are carried out primarily while in antarctic and near-antarctic waters. Meteorological work, including radiosonde launchings, is carried out throughout the voyage. There is a modern Minsk-22 computer aboard for reduction of the data. The ship is also equipped to launch rockets of modest scientific payload.

The U.S.-U.S.S.R. exchange of scientists is part of the implementation of Article 3 of the Antarctic Treaty. Scores of Americans have been involved with the antarctic expeditions of other nations in Antarctica; since the IGY, 12 Americans have wintered over at Soviet stations. In addition to accommodating the U.S. scientists and equipment at Vostok, the Arctic and Antarctic Institute in Leningrad has cooperated with the ESSA Research Laboratories (ERL), Boulder, Colorado, in maintaining continuously several programs of geophysical research at the station. Since the inauguration of these programs in the austral summer of 1964, American and Soviet investigators have basically alternated as operators of the equipment during the winter seasons.

These cooperative programs include a complex micropulsation system sponsored by ERL with the Geophysical Institute of the University of Alaska and the Arctic and Antarctic Institute in Leningrad (for the Institute of Physics of the Earth, Moscow). A standard riometer station is operated at 30 MHz and 50 MHz, and VLF hiss is being recorded. At present, Vostok is also a receiving station for the Doppler-shift network—involving Byrd, Pole, and

McMurdo—for observing traveling ionospheric disturbances. These programs interrelate with the Soviet programs at Vostok.

The Soviets maintain an active meteorological program, occupying the work of four men in 1969. The ionospherist operates a standard ionosonde, generating records of very good quality by international standards. Vostok also has a three-component magnetometer system making absolute measurements (the U.S. program at Vostok observes only magnetic fluctuations). A neutron monitor is operated standardly in a cosmic-ray study. Even though the station is well inside the auroral belt, a full auroral program is in operation during the polar night, which runs from April 23 to August 18.

The medical research program at Vostok is extensive. During the 1969 winter, three doctors conducted studies of the physiological adaptation to isolation and climate. Data were obtained also for the sleep-study program of Dr. Jay Shurley, University of Oklahoma.

Glaciological samples were taken during the winter to supplement the work of the French glaciological team that was present at Vostok in the late austral summer. Dr. Manfred Schneider of East Germany conducted a research project of extremely fine accuracy concerned with earth tides.

The annual resupply tractor train from Mirnyy to Vostok—a distance of 1,410 km—arrived on February 23, 1969. With it was the French glaciological team, which was flown out again on the last aircraft on March 1, 1969, in order to meet *Ob'* for return to France. The tractor train left Vostok for Mirnyy on March 5, 1969, and its members had to winter over at Mirnyy since they arrived there long after the start of the austral winter and the departure of *Ob'*. This tractor train is the primary means of resupply for Vostok; in 1969 it was comprised of five large artillery wagons and sledges converted to antarctic use, and a large, self-propelled laboratory. Most personnel and a number of delicate supply items arrived by air from Mirnyy.

The daily routine at Vostok is generally similar to that at American stations. A seven-day work week begins at 8:00 A.M. with a hearty breakfast of porridge and cheese. Lunch at 1:00 P.M. is actually dinner and the largest meal of the day. Soup is always a major course, followed by a staple supply of meat and potatoes or rice. A stewed-fruit compote is served throughout the day in preference to melted-snow water. Supper at 8:00 P.M. is substantial. Following supper is a general conversation hour and then the nightly movie. Between 11 and 12 P.M. there is quite often a broadcast from Radio Moscow especially programmed for the antarctic expedition of the U.S.S.R. Occasionally, an individual Soviet antarctic station will be featured with special news from home including messages from loved ones. On festive occasions, such as birthdays or state holidays (Soviet and American), most of the station personnel would dress in suit and tie (and heavy antarctic boots) for a special dinner at 3:00 P.M. in place of the normal dinner and supper.

The work of the cook at Vostok should not be underestimated, if only for the fact that water boils at 86°C. instead of 100°C. Almost all preparations of food at Vostok involve boiling (the use of pressure cookers is not advocated). It takes 5–7 hours to cook beef, 3 hours to boil potatoes, and 10–14 hours to cook beans and peas. Foods sensitive to boiling-point changes, such as coffee and tea, do not retain their normal flavors.

Housekeeping chores, shared generally by all, include dishwashing and sweeping up after meals. This biweekly assignment is usually followed by a shower and personal laundering. Water is obtained by melting snow blocks, cut and stock-piled during the summer. Once a month, the entire station complement forms a human chain to replenish the supply maintained close to the snow melter.

During the winter, the game of dominoes generates a great deal of enthusiasm. It is basically a game of chance (or so it seems—the author placed dead last). Chess, billiards, ping-pong, and table hockey are played also.

Authority at the station is supremely vested in a leader who has absolute control in every situation and who has no other responsibilities. For the Soviets, this system has worked well.

The first plane was joyously welcomed to Vostok on December 20, 1969. An Il–14 from Mirnyy brought the leader of the 14th SAE, D. D. Maksutov, and fresh provisions as well as new equipment for the glaciological drilling project at Vostok. Two days later, an American C–130 brought supplies for the U.S. programs and picked up the preceding winter's records. A typical Vostok welcome was given to the visiting Americans. After $2\frac{1}{2}$ hours (while the aircraft engines idled the whole time), the plane was obliged to depart for McMurdo because of its range limitations, leaving the U.S. exchange scientist to organize the resupply and train the new Soviet operator, V. A. Ul'ev, who was not to arrive until the following week.

Departure from Vostok was on New Year's Day 1970. Flying in an Il–14, the route of the annual resupply tractor train, easily visible on the ground, was followed as a road to Mirnyy. Near the old site of Vostok–I (open from April 12 to November 30, 1957), supplies were dropped to the lonely men on the approaching tractor train below. The arrival at Mirnyy was fortuitous—just before a severe storm which might have prevented leaving on *Professor Vize* had not the flight preceded it. The ship was

MONTHLY TEMPERATURES AT VOSTOK IN 1969
(IN −°C.)

Month	Max.	Min.	Avg.
January	24.4	44.5	32.6
February	29.1	60.4	45.6
March	47.3	71.5	59.8
April	53.2	74.4	62.9
May	50.3	77.5	66.8
June	45.5	73.5	62.4
July	52.0	82.0	69.3
August	53.1	82.8	69.5
September	56.8	81.7	69.8
October	38.4	69.5	55.6
November	31.3	55.9	43.8
December	23.1	44.4	32.6

PRESSURE (MB) AND WIND (M/SEC.)
AT VOSTOK IN 1969

	Pressure			Wind	
	Avg.	Max.	Min.	Avg.	Max.
Jan.	638,7	653,4	629,1	5,6	13
Feb.	633,0	641,9	626,0	6,2	13
Mar.	622,6	639,9	612,8	7,4	18
Apr.	625,5	644,8	608,6	7,7	14
May	620,6	632,1	606,2	7,6	13
June	631,4	646,6	614,6	8,1	13
July	611,8	624,8	599,6	7,8	18
Aug.	613,8	628,4	602,0	6,8	12
Sept.	614,1	630,8	596,9	6,4	14
Oct.	623,6	638,1	606,6	6,9	16
Nov.	624,6	630,9	613,5	7,2	14
Dec.	632,3	638,6	624,1	6,8	14

docked at the edge of the annual sea ice, several kilometers from Mirnyy; the storm and accompanying whiteout delayed resupply efforts considerably, and she was unable to leave until January 8. The ship's northward course included stops at Cape Town in South Africa and Las Palmas in the Canary Islands.

The exchange-scientist program has been warmly received by the participating nations. The scientist-diplomats involved have furthered scientific exchange and harmony in Antarctica amongst the nations engaged. It seems clearly an axiom that man finds his warmest international relations in the coldest regions of the earth.

It is fortunate that the site of the earth's south geomagnetic pole can be shared and utilized by international scientific programs. The challenges are many, but the rewards are perhaps unequaled at any other place on the earth today.

REFERENCES

Nudel'man, A. V. 1965. *Soviet Antarctic Expeditions, 1961–1963.* Moscow, Academy of Sciences of the U.S.S.R. Translated for the National Science Foundation, 1968. 220 p.

Priestly, R. *et al.* 1964. *Antarctic Research.* London, Butterworths. 360 p.

Soviet Antarctic Expedition. Information Bulletin, Nos. 58 and 59, 1968.

Soviet Exchange Scientist at McMurdo

B. G. LOPATIN

Under the U.S.S.R.-U.S. Exchange Scientist Program I joined the U.S. Antarctic Research Program for more than a year in 1968–1969, spending about 4 months in field camps and 9 months at McMurdo Station, where I wintered over. My main objective was to carry out a geological reconnaissance of practically unexplored parts of West Antarctica: eastern Marie Byrd Land, Eights Coast, and Thurston Island. These areas, on the opposite side of the Continent from Soviet stations, are very important geologically because of their location relative to the Antarctic Platform [East Antarctic shield] and the Andean fold belt.

The facilities provided for geological investigations in both the Marie Byrd Land Survey and the Ellsworth Land Survey were excellent, especially the turbine helicopters. Motor toboggans were available, but the location of the field camps far from the exposed rocks to be studied curtailed their use. Unfortunately, the area's notoriously bad weather frustrated many of our plans; on the average, we had

8–9 days a month for field work. Nevertheless, we managed to collect very interesting data which, after laboratory analysis, should elucidate some problems of structure, age, and petrology of geological formations.

Along with the Americans, representatives of three other nations took part in the reconnaissance. The spirit of friendly cooperation in the survey group was very high. We discussed mutual problems, helped each other in collecting rock samples, and are now going to exchange scientific information.

My second objective was to carry out a detailed investigation of the basement complex of the Transantarctic Mountains in the "McMurdo Oasis" (Victoria Land). The dry valleys are outstanding objects for detailed petrology work because of their excellent exposure. The basement complex has not drawn as much attention hitherto as glaciology, the Beacon group, or Cenozoic history. Because of the season (February and September–October), I had to work independently in the dry valleys. I was provided with helicopter support from McMurdo and lived for several days in temporary camps at Lakes Vanda and Bonney. There, I was joined by voluntary assistants, who cooked and carried shoulder bags full of rock samples. I should like to mention their names: Lt. Elliott Freeman, USN, and Grahame Champress from New Zealand's Scott Base.

The work in the dry valleys was also successful: a stratigraphic section of the metamorphic rock was compiled, and the composition and structure of intrusions—mostly granitic—were studied. My third goal was to study volcanic rocks around McMurdo.

In the winter, I kept busy in the Earth Sciences and Biological Laboratories at McMurdo, using diamond saws, microscopes, and other equipment for preliminary examination of my rock specimens. For recreation, I thoroughly enjoyed the social get-togethers at McMurdo and Scott Base. Foremost among my impressions was a sense of continuous friendly attitude of all the foreign colleagues with whom I lived and worked. This greatly encouraged me during the long polar night. I believe that, besides advantages in scientific research, the exchange program in Antarctica is very important for establishing close personal contacts and better understanding among nations. We had a lot of fun playing chess, ping-pong, and other games, some of which are unknown in the U.S.S.R. I gave lessons in the Russian language, but my pupils found this language too difficult.

In conclusion, I should like to thank Philip Smith, Jerry Huffman, Richard Przywitowski, Kerby La-Prade, Alton Wade, and many others for friendly assistance in carrying out my scientific program. The first American I have ever met was Edward Goodale, who received me at the Christchurch International Airport; this agreeable veteran of antarctic exploration made a deep impression upon me.

With the Japanese Antarctic Research Expedition to Antarctica, 1969–1970

HERMAN R. FRIIS

Japanese interest in Antarctica began perhaps with the notable expedition of Lieutenant Nobu (Choku) Shirase in the auxiliary schooner *Kainan-maru* to the Bay of Whales in 1911–1912.[1] Several pioneering land reconnaissances and oceanographic surveys of the nearby Ross Sea were made. Since 1934, Japan has engaged extensively in whaling activities, particularly in the waters fringing East Antarctica.[2] These activities kept alive and encouraged Japanese interest in Antarctica until plans for the International Geophysical Year (1957–1958) spurred Japanese scientists to active participation in research.[3] These plans culminated in 1955 with the establishment of an Antarctic Committee in the Science Council of Japan and an Antarctic Program in the Ministry of Education.[4] The latter was responsible for preparing the plans and actively undertaking the first Japanese Antarctic Research Expedition

(J.A.R.E.).[5] The Japanese Maritime Safety Board provided the transportation—a reconstructed 4,200-ton ice-strengthened patrol ship named *Soya*.

J.A.R.E.–1 (1956–1958), under Dr. Takesi Nagata's leadership, sailed with 53 scientists and logistic support personnel, 240 tons of supplies, 18 Sakhalin sledge dogs, and a Cessna 180 light airplane.[6] Also aboard *Soya* when she left Japan on November 8, 1956, were two Bell 47–G helicopters, primarily for ice reconnaissance. The expedition carried out a reconnaissance of the Lützow-Holm Bay area of East Antarctica and erected Showa Station on the bare rock of the northeast portion of East Ongul Island at 69°00′22″S. 39°35′24″E. This site is 5 km west across the ice-covered Ongul Sound from the ice front of the continental plateau. The station was erected on schedule, and an 11 man group of scientists under Dr. Eizaburo Nishibori became the first wintering-over party. Strategically located as this site is for various operational and reconnaissance activities and local scientific research, it also has proven to be one of the most difficult to reach by ship because of the severe weather and ice conditions.

Japanese occupation of Showa ceased temporarily in February 1962 as J.A.R.E.–6 returned home aboard the *Soya* after sealing the station and storing its equipment.

While Showa Station was closed between 1962 and 1965, the Japanese antarctic program underwent significant changes, particularly with respect to logistics.[7] During this period, the Japanese Government built a modern icebreaker, *Fuji*, especially for the antarctic program. This icebreaker has a normal displacement of 7,760 tons, a draft of 8.3 m (27 ft), a length of 100 m (330 ft), and a beam of 22 m (73 ft). It is powered by diesel-electric engines delivering a maximum of 12,000 hp, has a cruising speed of about 15 knots, and a maximum speed of 17 knots. It can

break ice up to 6 m (19 ft) thick. While essentially a
logistic support vessel, *Fuji* has excellent facilities
for research. Also aboard are two long-range Sikorski helicopters, capable of carrying 26 passengers or
about 1,800 kg of cargo, and a Bell 47–G helicopter,
primarily for short-range reconnaissance.

Each year since 1965, the Japanese Government
has invited the United States Government to appoint
an Exchange Scientist to accompany the expedition.[9]
The author boarded the Japanese Maritime Self-
Defense Force icebreaker 5001 *Fuji* at Fremantle,
Australia, on December 14, 1969, and was greeted by
the Scientific Leader of J.A.R.E.–11, Dr. Tatsuro
Matsuda. Throughout the voyage and into Lützow-
Holm Bay, there were frequent conferences between
the scientists and technicians and logisticians about
the pending off-loading and construction operations
at Showa Station. The scientists, especially the biologists, made a variety of observations en route to
Showa, until the heavy pack ice restricted some of
them.

Adjoining the Captain's bridge on *Fuji* is a well-
equipped meteorological laboratory from where a
continuous program of observations was carried out
on weather, the state of the sea, and ice conditions.
From a station on the deck below the helicopter pad
aft, the biologists and oceanographers conducted
periodic surveys, including surface-water sampling
and routine chemical analysis of seawater, observations of zooplankton and phytoplankton, recording
of temperature and salinity at selected depths, measurements of currents, bathythermographic observations, and drag-net collection of marine organisms.

At 40°, 50°, and 60°S., the Australian Exchange
Scientist released 500 plastic plates bearing a request
that, if found, the plate should be sent to the Australian Oceanographic Laboratory in Adelaide. It is
hoped that enough plates will be returned to give

some indication of currents and drift. The U.S. Exchange Scientist made a photographic and descriptive study of the structure of the ice, especially the effect of plankton on its color and composition.

The first iceberg was sighted on December 23 at 59°12'S. 105°43'E. Then followed a rapid increase in the number of icebergs and a succession of fields of pack ice and a rapid drop in temperature to nearly 0°C. Near midnight on the 23rd, at 61°33'S. 105°34'E., the track of *Fuji* was directed to a nearly due west course through successive fields of berg-studded pack ice and open water. On Christmas Eve, the scientists and officers and crew gave a dinner party for the two exchange scientists, complete with gifts, decorated cakes, and Christmas decorations.

On December 26, a map of the area of East Antarctica between Queen Mary Coast and Queen Maud Land showing the state of the ice, the various leads, and the distribution of the pack ice was compiled from information received from a variety of sources, notably the ESSA satellite and Soviet flights over the area (Fig. 1). The map showed a long, narrow, open-water highway between the edge of the fast ice and the pack leading west almost to the entrance to Lützow-Holm Bay. In order to reach this open-water lead, *Fuji* first had to break through a wide area of pack ice and communities of icebergs. On December 28, the Bell and Sikorski helicopters carried out extensive flights of ice reconnaissance. On December 29, *Fuji* entered the heavy continuous pack ice. Early in the morning of December 30, the U.S. Exchange Scientist was invited by the Captain to accompany him on a two-hour-long Sikorski helicopter flight west to the wide entrance to Lützow-Holm Bay to reconnoiter the ice for the best approach into the Bay. The open-water highway, clearly shown on the ESSA map, was followed west.

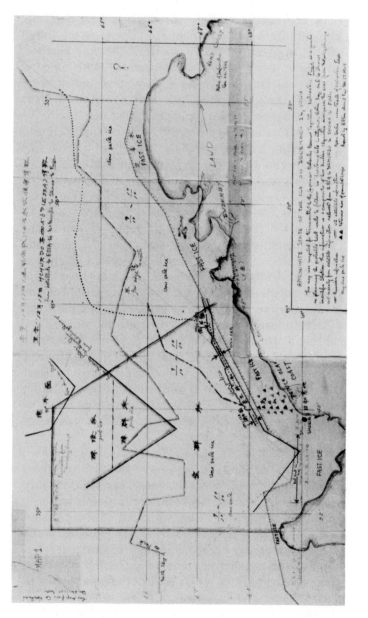

FIGURE 1. *Map based on ESSA Nimbus satellite photography showing the state of the ice on December 26, 1969.*

In the evening of the 31st, *Fuji* was carefully nudged into a narrow channel in the pack ice 150 m off the open-water highway. Here she was berthed, and New Year's Eve was celebrated with rousing festivities. On New Year's Day, ceremonies were held on the helicopter deck and promotions were given to certain officers and crew members.

Shortly after the return of the last Sikorski flight, *Fuji* began the final leg of her voyage to Showa. She proceeded southwest to a point almost directly north of Showa and then due south into and through the heavily berg-studded fast ice of Lützow-Holm Bay. With relative ease, she charged and cut a path through the fast ice to a small pond of open water in a small embayment in the west coast of Langhovde Hills. Here, on January 4, the Australian Exchange Scientist dropped and anchored an instrument capsule in about 100 fathoms of water to record for one month various data such as tides and temperatures. (Unfortunately, successive attempts to retrieve the capsule at the end of one month were unsuccessful.) *Fuji* then continued her track through the fast ice to a mooring in the ice about 150 m east of East Ongul Island and 1,250 m southeast of Showa Station (Fig. 2). The first major leg of the voyage had now been successfully completed on schedule (January 5).

Off-loading began almost immediately after *Fuji* was moored to the fast ice. One of the first activities was to transfer oil, by rubber hose, between the ship and the large new fuel-oil storage tank located on a hard-rock promontory about a third of the distance to Showa. The scientists, working in close harmony with the crew, were responsible for selecting, arranging, and supervising the removal of clearly identified items of cargo, from small boxes of canned goods to a large over-snow vehicle. Cargo, selectively off-loaded from *Fuji* onto the fast ice, was loaded onto sleds and pulled by snow cars to one of two staging

PHOTO BY YASUSADO OHTO

FIGURE 2. *Showa Station.*

areas on the fast ice—one about 600 m north of *Fuji* and the other about 60 m southwest of her. The latter included a large platform of heavy timber for landing and securing the Sikorski helicopters during the loading operations. The north staging area tended to be mostly for heavy items, such as drums of gasoline, oil, and the like, which were sling-lifted by helicopter for transport to Showa Station. The helicopter landed on the wooden platform to be loaded with a wide variety of relatively light items for delivery to Showa Station. Some of the heavy items, such as instruments, machinery, and rocket-related equipment were also transported by helicopter to the rocket-launching site. Between January 5 and 20, 1970, two Sikorski helicopters in 248 hops carried 573.3 tons of cargo from *Fuji* to Showa Station.

Occasional snowstorms and severe katabatic winds precluded work on several days. The changes from optimum sunny conditions to severe, treacherous, stormy conditions generally were rapid and posed problems for the helicopters and personnel in the open staging areas.

The last cargo to be off-loaded was the frozen food, of which there was considerable variety and supply. Except for these items, which were quickly flown to Showa and placed in frozen-food lockers, most of the cargo was placed at specified sites in an acre or so of undulating bare-rock surface to the north of the station proper (Fig. 3). Small Japanese trucks were used to move various smaller bits of cargo to assigned localities (Fig. 3). These trucks appeared to negotiate the rough terrain reasonably well, although they were badly shaken in the process.

Immediately following the completion of off-loading, all hands cooperated in a broad program of construction. Facilities at the end of J.A.R.E.–10 included 20 principal buildings. During the several weeks of summer work, all of the planned construc-

FIGURE 3. *Recently off-loaded cargo and various transport vehicles on a bare-rock site next to the main buildings of the station.*

tion was completed on schedule, including the telemetry, observation, launch, and accessory buildings and the table and platform for the launching of two rockets. In addition, two large prefabricated warehouses were built, a special nonmagnetic seismological station was installed (on a sand- and gravel-covered floor over a Precambrian gneiss base), and a concrete-making plant was completed in time to make the mix for the floors of the warehouses and the base for several of the structures at the launch site. A tall steel tower for micrometeorological measurements was built immediately east of the meteorological station. On it are four cup anemometers, two supersonic anemometers, and two air-temperature platinum thermometers. Construction of a permanent airfield, to be used especially by the Lockheed Cessna aerial-photography monoplane, was begun on the ice of the polar plateau about 20 km east of Showa Station. A mobile structure and a marked airfield were completed and successfully used by helicopters as well as the Cessna.

The wintering-over (February 1969–February 1970) group of 29 men was under the leadership of

Dr. Kou Kusunoki, Chief of the Department of Polar
Research and Information of the Polar Research
Center in Tokyo. During the period November 1969–
January 1970, an oversnow traverse was made to the
Queen Fabiola Mountains to study geology, geomor-
phology, glaciology, and meteorology.

Special research projects proposed by individual
scientists and academic and other professional institutions and approved by the Science Council of Japan
numbered 15. The overall program of the J.A.R.E.–11
wintering-over party is rather comprehensive and is
largely a continuation of the systematic studies of
preceding expeditions. The program includes observations of aurora and airglow, the ionosphere, VLF
emissions, geomagnetism, cosmic rays, meteorology,
infrasonic pressure waves, gravity, oceanography,
glaciology, seismology, cartography, geology, geography, biology, and medical research. During the first
weeks of February, there were several successful balloon flights to record cosmic rays. The 5,000-m^3 he-
lium balloons were scheduled to reach an altitude of
35 km.

In January, shortly after arrival, an over-ice traverse was made along the south coast of East to West
Ongul Island for the purpose of taking cores of the
ice and water nutrient samples below it. Numerous
samples for chlorophyll and phaeophytin were taken
in the ice and water of the ponds on East and West
Ongul Islands, Langhovde Glacier, and Byvågåsane
Peaks, and in the sea water circumjacent to northeast East Ongul Island. In several of these and other
areas, studies were made of mosses, lichens, benthos,
and phyto- and zooplankton.

An important mission of the summer program was
the continuation of a systematic aerial survey of
Lützow-Holm Bay, done from the Cessna aircraft
that was shipped to and returned from the Bay
aboard *Fuji*. In late January, Mr. Kozuo Matsuoka,

the pilot, flew the Cessna to the polar plateau near the Queen Fabiola Mountains to parachute spare parts to the returning traverse party which had a disabled vehicle. During one of his flights across Lützow-Holm Bay, Mr. Matsuoka discovered a small island surrounded by fast ice. On February 14, the U.S. Exchange Scientist accompanied Captain Isobe and a small group of scientists and technicians to the island for a brief survey of the lithology and moss cover.

Another successful scientific program during February was the placement of a glaciological field party at the western margin of Langhovde Glacier to establish a small base and place a line of markers on the ice to study the lateral and meridional movement of the glacier. Samples of snow and ice were obtained for studying crystallography and composition.

A most significant scientific accomplishment was the successful launch of two ionospheric rockets from the pad on the northwest corner of East Ongul Island (Fig. 4). Dr. Takeo Hirasawa, a geophysicist from the University of Tokyo, was largely responsible for the development of the instrumentation and the operation, as well as the analysis of the data. The two rockets (S160 JA1 and S160 JA2) achieved the projected altitude of 90 km. The first launch was on February 10 and the second on February 17 (Fig. 4). The total length of the rocket was 3,889 mm; its outer diameter, 160 mm; total weight, 113 kg; and payload, 5.4 kg.

On February 17, *Fuji* departed East Ongul Island for home by way of Bouvet Island. Early in the morning of February 20, she stopped her northward drive. The Captain and several personnel, including the U.S. exchange Scientist, flew by Sikorski to Showa Station for ceremonies officially transferring the leadership from Dr. Kou Kusunoki to Dr. Tatsuro Matsuda. Included in these memorable events was

PHOTO BY TAKAO HIRASAWA

FIGURE 4. *Launch of S160 JA2, the second of two rockets with instrument packages fired from the pad on the northwest corner of East Ongul Island, February 17, 1970.*

the gift to the U.S. Exchange Scientist of the now wind-tattered Stars and Stripes that had flown on the hilltop overlooking the station since his arrival on January 2.

Shortly after our return from Showa, *Fuji* got under way north across the transition between the fast ice and the pack ice. Then she entered a long, narrow lead toward the west which led into pack ice. The next day she encountered increasingly thick, hard ice, and by late afternoon forward progress was all but impossible. On February 22, a series of ice reconnaissances was carried out by helicopter. Several leads were found, but an extensive bank of enveloping fog obscured the northern portion of the pack ice. In the meantime, *Fuji* was maneuvered about in successive counterclockwise charges and then retraced her track to near the fast ice of Lützow-Holm Bay. This ended the planned possibility of scientists flying to Riiser-Larsen Peninsula and visiting Bouvet Island en route to Cape Town. On the 23rd, forward progress was resumed northeastward through the open-water lead and into the pack ice, which became increasingly heavier and more brittle. Relatively little progress was made. A prevailingly north and northeast strong wind, which had blown consistently for a number of days, was an ill omen because it is a prime element in compacting the pack as it presses it toward the continent. This became distressingly clear, and on the 24th, the total forward progress was measured in but a few meters.

Shortly after noon on February 25, *Fuji*, making very little forward progress (412 rams had advanced her but 720 m), was stopped dead in her track. All four blades of the starboard screw had been sheared to the hub by the ice. The ship was securely beset at 68°24′S. 38°51′E. in a vast sea of iceberg-strewn, heavily hummocked pack ice. The *Fuji* was about 75 km north of Showa Station, from which she had departed a week earlier.

The ice-strengthened Soviet cargo ship *Ob'*, near Mirnyy, was closest to *Fuji* and responded to the call for assistance, but she was unable to approach closer

than 28 km. Subsequently, USCGC *Edisto* departed
Wellington with a Japanese Maritime Self-Defense
Force liaison officer, and blankets, mattresses, food,
and special equipment, planning to make her way
east around Antarctica to a rendezvous with *Glacier*
at the edge of the pack ice in front of *Fuji* to attempt
a release of the ship. If that were not possible, the
scientists, technicians, and some crew members
were to be flown to the icebreakers for return home,
possibly by way of Cape Town. A skeleton staff was
to remain aboard to winter over.

The personnel aboard *Fuji* were placed on rations,
and plans were made to meet various kinds of emergencies, especially as they related to the conservation
of resources for a potential winter-over. Water and
heat were the first commodities to be rationed. Freshwater was obtained from blocks of ice chopped from
selected hummocks of pack ice adjacent to the ship
and hand-passed to reservoirs within the ship. A
"University of *Fuji*" was inaugurated to sponsor a
series of lectures on various scientific topics. Various
moral-boosting activities such as skits and commemo-
rations were instituted.

On March 17, an afternoon was given to a succession of humorous skits imploring the "God of the Big
Wind" to cause a south wind to blow the pack ice
away and free the ship. By coincidence, the pack ice
opened during that night, and the next morning the
Captain, by a succession of skillful maneuvers of the
ship and with the assistance of helicopters on ice reconnaissance, gradually inched the ship on its one
screw to a strategically developed lead that fortunately led to more open pack. *Glacier* and *Edisto*
were informed and returned to their assigned tasks.
During the 23 days of beset, *Fuji* had drifted 10 km
to the southwest into the entrance of Lützow-Holm
Bay.

During the day and night of the 19th, *Fuji* sailed through a succession of open-water leads, increasingly thinner pack ice, and communities of towering icebergs. Shortly after midnight, the ship was once again in ice-flecked open water. In this relatively calm water, *Fuji* stopped for several hours to batten down the hatches, clear the decks, and secure the cargo on the open decks for the rough seas expected ahead. All hands were notified that the destination was to be Cape Town, South Africa.

Late in the afternoon of March 20, at about 63°30'S., the last iceberg was sighted in a partial fog and increasingly heavy seas. During the evening, *Fuji* entered very heavy seas and at times gale-like conditions, which lasted for most of six days. Lists of 42° were recorded. Because of the heavy seas and delayed schedule, no oceanographic observations were made. *Fuji* docked at the main wharf in Cape Town on March 29, and the U.S. Exchange Scientist left the ship on the 31st.

REFERENCES

1. Hamre, I. 1933. The Japanese South Polar Expedition, 1911–1912. *Geographical Journal,* 82(5): 412–423.
   Shirase, Choku. 1912. The First Japanese Polar Expedition. *Independent,* October 3: 769–773.
   Kizaki, Koshiri. 1958. A note on the rocks of King Edward VII Land collected by the Japanese Antarctic Expedition, 1911–1912. *Antarctic Record,* 5: 57–73.
   Appendix to Nankyokuki, The reports of the Japanese Antarctic Expedition, 1910–1912. *Antarctic Record,* 1: 38–44; 2: 51–59; 3: 41–51; 4: 57–63; 5: 74–83.
2. Hanessian, John, Jr. 1963. Japan and the Antarctic. *American University Field Staff. Polar Area Series,* 3(1): 1–29.
3. *Ibid.,* p. 18–21.
4. *Ibid.*
5. Watanabe, Hyoriki. 1958. Report of the outline of the Japanese Antarctic Research Expedition I, 1956–1957. *Antarctic Record,* 5: 1–8.

Tatsumi, Tatsuo. 1958. Outline of [the] operation of the first wintering party, 1957–1958. *Antarctic Record*, 5: 9–17.

6. Japan Antarctic Society. 1958. *The Antarctic*. Tokyo, Bunkyo Tsushin Kyokai. 258 p.

Yoshikawa, Torao. 1963. Nihon no nankyoku kansoku, 1956–1962. (Activities of the Japanese Antarctic Research Expedition, 1956–1962). *Journal of Geography*, 73(1): 8–24.

7. Matsuda, Tatsuro. 1968. Report of the wintering party of the 7th Japanese Antarctic Research Expedition, in 1966–67. *Antarctic Record*, 32: 1–24.

8. Ono, Yoshihiko, *et al.* 1966. New antarctic observation ship 'Fuji.' *Nippon Kokan Technical Report-Overseas*, 35–64.

9. The U.S. Exchange Scientists with J.A.R.E. have been Henry S. Francis, Jr., National Science Foundation, 1965–1966 (see note 9); Wakefield Dort, Jr., University of Kansas, 1966–1967 (see *Antarctic Journal of the U.S.*, II(3): 78–80, 1967); Martin P. Sponholz, Environmental Science Services Administration, 1967–1968; Gerard A. Roach, University of Denver, 1968–1969; Herman R. Friis, The National Archives, 1969–1970.

Antarctic Research, a Prelude to Space Research

ERNST STUHLINGER

In the northern winter of 1966–1967, four members of the National Aeronautics and Space Administration had the good fortune of being invited by the National Science Foundation to spend a week of observing and learning on the Antarctic Continent. This voyage proved for each of us the most exciting, fascinating, and impressive trip we ever took. By far the deepest impression I received was from a hut built in 1911 by Captain Robert Falcon Scott on Ross Island in McMurdo Sound. This hut is still in excellent shape. On one of the walls there are a number of shelves filled with instruments for scientific research: glasses and bowls, scales, anemometers, thermometers, transits, even Bunsen burners with bottled gas. It is known that Scott carried and used research instruments on his ill-fated march to the Pole in 1911–1912, and that he recorded scientific observations up to the last days of his life.

Many of the early antarctic travelers, beginning with James Cook in 1772, combined the keen eye of the scientific observer with the adventurous spirit of the true explorer. However, the hardships of antarctic travel with its continuous struggle against a thoroughly hostile environment, together with the lack of suitable instruments for antarctic research, did not leave much room for early scientific observations.

The period of technological development of transportation and housing in Antarctica lasted from 1928 till about 1961, when the Antarctic Treaty among 12 member nations was ratified. With the Antarctic Treaty, the Continent developed into a research laboratory of the first order.

The development of Antarctica into a continent for science was a great and challenging experiment in itself. The basic problem was how to provide a group of scientists in a remote antarctic outpost with the necessary support which would permit them to live and to work under extremely hostile conditions. This problem, which is simple to formulate, but very difficult to solve, was encountered in a very similar form by those who were preparing the astronauts' flight to the moon, and later to the planets. The great similarity between the logistic support problems for the U.S. Antarctic Research Program and the forthcoming program of lunar exploration was indeed the reason why the four of us, Drs. Robert R. Gilruth and Maxime A. Faget, from the Manned Spacecraft Center in Houston, and Dr. Wernher von Braun and I, from the Marshall Center in Huntsville, spent a week with USARP in Antarctica in January 1967.

We wanted to learn how the Office of Antarctic Programs and the U.S. Navy have solved the many problems of maintaining productive research under environmental conditions which are certainly the most extreme and the most unforgiving to be found on Earth. Very simply, the four of us wanted to go to Antarctica because this was as close to lunar conditions as we could get here on Earth. Admittedly, there are some differences. There is an atmosphere in Antarctica, there is gravity six times that on the moon, and the nearest hospital, in New Zealand, is only 8 to 10 flight hours away, weather permitting. However, at a remote outpost in the mountains or on a glacier, where the few men of a scientific team may spend weeks or months in field studies, human life depends entirely on the technological reliabilities of a stove and of a radio transmitter. If both failed, death would be imminent unless safety measures had been carefully prepared.

SCIENTISTS
AND THE SUPPORT FORCE

When the four of us from NASA looked at the many fascinating activities through the eyes of space-project developers, we were greatly impressed by the large and complex machinery needed for logistic support of the U.S. Antarctic Research Program. During the austral summer about 200 scientists live in Antarctica; the logistic system employs about 2,000 uniformed men to support these scientists. Logistic support includes transportation of men and materials between the U.S.A. and Antarctica, and all across Antarctica; building and maintenance of permanent stations; supply of field stations; communications; mail; food and kitchen services; medical care; electrical power; heating; water supply; vehicle maintenance; clothing; shipment of scientific instruments and collected samples; and emergency evacuation. Scientists are responsible only for their own housekeeping, and, of course, for their scientific projects. At all the smaller field stations, however, scientists voluntarily and gladly help with such mundane chores as snow shoveling, snow melting, and station upkeep.

This very comfortable situation for the scientists

has evolved from practical field experience during the first years of continuous antarctic research. I am sure that many scientists in the U.S.A. envy their fortunate colleagues in Antarctica for this excellent support.

Each field station, as well as each permanent base, has a station scientific leader who is directly responsible to the Office of Antarctic Programs in Washington. Each station also has an officer-in-charge who, through channels, is the representative of the Commander, U.S. Naval Support Force, Antarctica. He is responsible for the safety and welfare of all persons at the station, and for the support of their activities. In case of an emergency, declared jointly by the station scientific leader and the officer-in-charge, the latter directs station activities. We felt that this system, which has proved highly satisfactory in Antarctica, may well set the prototype for the organization of future stations in Earth orbit and on the moon.

Easy movements and close-up observations familiar to antarctic explorers would not be possible on the moon, at least not during the first landings; however, the collection of rock samples, a very rewarding and fascinating activity for geologists in the ice-free parts of Antarctica, would of course be possible on the moon with simple tools.

Another severe limitation presently imposed upon lunar exploration is the lack of mobility. In Antarctica at the present time it is achieved most conveniently with helicopters and with a variety of surface vehicles, from the big Tucker Sno-Cat down to small motor-driven one-man vehicles, or even by a team of dogs. A lunar roving vehicle has been developed, although it does not yet fully reflect the lesson which antarctic explorers have been taught during many years of polar exploration: There should be a variety of vehicles available for different purposes. The largest should offer sufficient well-protected space within its cabin to permit travelers to live and work in comfort. The smallest vehicle should offer access to a driver in a heavy and clumsy suit; it should be so small and light that the driver can manually pull it out of a ditch; engine, tracks, and other components should be replaceable under field conditions. Of course, it is desirable that none of the various types of vehicles should ever have any malfunction or breakdown.

We were greatly interested in hearing about the safety measures in effect at the small field stations. Besides the plans for normal operations, complete plans and provisions for emergency situations must exist. In Antarctica one of the main dangers is that of fire. When the four of us visited Antarctica in January of 1967, we did not fully realize the magnitude of that danger also for the space program. Two weeks after our return, the very tragic accident at Cape Kennedy, in which three astronauts lost their lives, made it clear that fire is a most imminent danger for space explorers. All buildings in Antarctica, even temporary shelters, are amply equipped with fire-warning systems, fire extinguishers, and quick exits. All camps and stations have "fall-back" camps a few hundred meters away which are equipped to provide shelter, food, and communications. Should the main camp be damaged or destroyed by fire, the crew can survive in this emergency camp for days or even weeks until a rescue party arrives. It is obvious that a similar arrangement on the moon, and even in Earth orbit, will significantly increase the safety of the astronauts.

*

The exploration of space began with observations made from the surface of the Earth; balloon flights extended our observational capabilities, and high-altitude rockets added even more to this capability.

The advent of satellites meant a big leap forward for space research, as illustrated by the discovery of the Van Allen belts with the first Explorer satellites. Probes to the planets and flights to the moon have already resulted in a wealth of new knowledge about our neighbors in space. Very slowly, man is now taking his place in this program of space exploration, at first as a pilot, and gradually as an explorer and scientist.

Polar exploration evolved the other way. It began with human travel and discovery. The new territories were seen and recorded first by human eyes, and the storing, sorting, and analyzing of observational data were done by human minds long before, and even long after, such instruments as magnetic tape and the high-speed computer were developed.

Obviously, these two great exploration programs can mutually benefit from each other's methods. How little we would know about the polar regions of the Earth if we had only photographed them from high-flying airplanes, and if instrumented capsules, dropped by parachute, had provided the only data on surface features, rock formations, fossils, plants, and animals!

On the other hand, would it not be reasonable to leave to automated stations many of the routine observations in Antarctica of temperature, snowfall, weather, aurora, cosmic rays, ionospheric activity, whistler signals, micropulsations, and seismic waves? The space program has produced remarkable technological knowledge of, and practical experience with, automatic sensing and data-handling systems; why not use them now at remote places on the Earth's surface? Unmanned stations on the polar ice cap are far cheaper to establish and maintain than permanently manned stations. Manned stations and human sensors should be reserved for those research objectives that need the presence of a human mind to

Antarctic Landscape: A section of the Sentinel Range, Ellsworth Mountains.

be really successful, such as biological studies, fossil search, and a number of geological investigations.

Possibilities of automated stations for polar research have been studied repeatedly. Stanford University recently made a detailed and very interesting study concerning an automated data-taking and -transmitting station for environmental parameters. The cost to build an automatic station and maintain it on a year-round basis in Antarctica is about one-tenth of the cost of an equivalent manned station. Surprisingly, the most expensive single component of the station turns out to be the electrical power supply. Isotope-heated, thermoelectric supplies would appear very appropriate. Such power sources have been developed for space projects; the SNAP 27, for example, powers the ALSEP package of scientific instruments for lunar exploration. However, all space power sources are very expensive. As a consequence of the very high transportation cost to the moon or even into Earth orbit, all space instruments must be small, light, and reliable. In fact, a reliability factor of 99.9 percent is desirable for space instruments. This very high reliability requirement is the main reason for the high cost of space experiments. Ground-based automatic instruments are quite satisfactory with a reliability factor of about 95 percent. As an indication of the cost of attaining this degree of reliability, it would be cheaper in most cases to develop a new instrument of a 95 percent reliability than to improve the reliability of an instrument from 95 percent to 99.9 percent.

Another factor contributing to the high cost of space experiments is the need to minimize weight. Transportation to Antarctica is far cheaper than space transportation, and a few extra pounds on antarctic instruments would not hurt. In the specific case of an isotope-heated power source, an isotope with a shorter lifetime could be used for earthbound

*Lunar Landscape: Portion of the crater Copernicus, photo-
graphed by Lunar Orbiter II.*

power supplies. Semiannual replacement would be satisfactory for antarctic use as servicing visits could be made in October and in March. Another alleviating factor on the Earth's surface is the atmosphere, which helps by carrying the heat away from surfaces through convection and by providing an efficient heat transfer between adjacent metallic surfaces.

Research projects in Antarctica fall into two distinct categories according to their objectives: First, the survey-type measurements, such as recordings of cosmic rays, aurora, ionospheric activity, magnetic fields, winds, temperatures, glacier movements, whistler signals; and second, the exploration-type studies, which include geological observations, paleontological searches, and biological studies. Survey-type observations are generally carried out by young scientists who fabricated and tested their equipment at home in close cooperation with their senior colleagues. In Antarctica, their main objective is to operate the instruments, to record data, and to send the observational material home to their laboratories for analysis and evaluation. It is conceivable that this type of research work will be taken over more and more by automated stations in the future.

Exploration-type observations in Antarctica are carried out by experienced senior scientists, ably assisted by younger associates. Geologists, paleontologists, and biologists spend as much of their time as possible in the field in direct personal association with the objects of their research. The success of this work depends on the ability of the scientist to reach his area of interest, to look for the right objects, to recognize important specimens, facts, and relations, to draw conclusions while exploring, and continuously to adjust, modify, and develop his research program as his exploration proceeds and his knowledge increases. The biologists among these explorative scientists may maintain a small laboratory at the McMurdo Station to supplement and expand their research activities. It should be quite obvious that this exploration-type research cannot be automated; it definitely needs the live scientist as the most important factor in the project.

This fact was driven home to us NASA visitors very vividly when we visited the dry-valley area together with Dr. Roy E. Cameron, from the Jet Propulsion Laboratory, and Dr. Russell W. Strandtmann, from Texas Technological College, in January of 1967. As we walked over the ice-free terrain of Marble Point, Dr. Strandtmann pointed out to us the various forms of algae and arthropods that live in that region, and he described their ingenious ways of adaptation to this unusual environment. Each rock sample which he selected with the trained eyes of the research biologist contained on its protected underside some specimens of algae, mites, or small insects; the samples which we untrained space engineers picked up did not show any traces of life. "No wonder," said Dr. Strandtmann. "This is the difference between a live, alert, intelligent, highly trained and motivated scientist, and a lifeless robot.

The most significant contributions that antarctic research will make to our basic scientific knowledge in the next several years will very likely concern the genesis of the Earth and the evolution and adaptation of life. The Antarctic Continent has probably gone through more drastic changes than the rest of the Earth; furthermore, some of the evidences of early stages of development, both geological and biological, may be better preserved and less contaminated in Antarctica than at other places on our globe. The recent find of a jawbone of an ancient amphibian, a Labyrinthodont, which also lived in Africa and India, appears to give powerful support to the hypothesis of the old Gondwanaland and the subsequent drift of its fragments to the places where we find Asia, Africa, Australia, and Antarctica today.

The division of antarctic research into survey-type and exploration-type activities has a very interesting parallel in space research. Numerous survey-type observations of the Earth, the sun, other celestial bodies, and the space between will certainly be made on a continuing basis from Earth-orbiting satellites. These observations will not require the continuous presence of man in orbit. However, there are other observations of an exploratory type which simply should not be left to the operation of a programmed machine, as pictures obtained from the recent Lunar Orbiter project prove. These pictures show many unexpected features, such as lava flow channels, outcrops of deep layers of materials, strong color differences, and other peculiarities which geologists feel must be seen *in situ* by a scientist who could mentally record, sort, analyze, and integrate thousands of visual pictures from a millimeter to a kilometer in scale within minutes and arrive at a satisfactory understanding of a geological situation unobtainable from TV pictures alone.

The need for the presence of a scientist who can interact immediately with his subject of research is even more obvious when we think of the search for life on the planet Mars. How complex would an instrument have to be in order to substitute for a human mind trained in experimental biology and highly motivated to detect any possible indications of living organisms? I believe that it would be hopeless to try to make such a substitution.

We found the scientists in Antarctica invariably in high spirits, filled with strong motivations for their work. They greatly appreciate the opportunity of doing research in Antarctica. They read much (scientific books, travel, fiction), listen to music, and tend to their scientific activities.

Support personnel, lacking the strong personal motivation of the scientists, also display a pleasant spirit, but they often find life somewhat boring under antarctic conditions, and they look forward to their trip home.

A few simple rules on how to avoid psychological problems arising from the unusual circumstances of antarctic life have resulted from the long experience gained in Antarctica. A single small room for each man is far preferable to larger rooms with multiple occupancy. Privacy of a few hours per day appears to be of great importance. A man should know beforehand that the next few hours will belong to him alone and that nobody else will sit at his table, whistling the "Bridge on the River Kwai," or inhaling vigorously through his nose every 15 seconds, or oscillating his leg toward the table. I feel that the lessons learned in Antarctica should be, and will be, heeded in the planning and designing of the quarters for astronauts on prolonged journeys through space. Antarctica has the lowest population density of all continents; only outer space has a lower density. However, it is easier to escape the omnipresence of people in New York than in Antarctica, or in outer space. A man who is "allergic" to close contact with others simply should not be picked for either isolated assignment.

Experience dictates that living quarters in isolation should be as comfortable, and as much like home, as possible. At the long-wire station near Byrd, for example, we met a few young chaps who had their snow-covered quarters beautifully equipped with walnut paneling, easy chairs, sofa, coffee corner, house bar, and an excellent hi-fi set with a large collection of classical records.

It may be interesting to note in this context that there is a strong tendency among space planners at the present time to provide simulated gravity for astronauts on prolonged space flights by rotating the spacecraft. Medical or biological effects would probably not demand this, but the "gravitational" force, even if it amounted to only a fraction of one g, would contribute toward a homelike environment.

After we had lived for a week among the antarctic researchers and their support personnel, we had developed the greatest admiration for the remarkably effective cooperation between the support organization, which is a part of the U.S. Navy, and the scientific projects, which are coordinated by the National Science Foundation. The great flexibility, the immediate response to the need of scientific teams, the absolute minimum of red tape in Antarctica and in the New Zealand staging area, and the high degree of motivation for accomplishment often appeared to us like a dream come true. It is realized that this excellent cooperation and high degree of efficiency certainly did not come into existence by themselves; they are the result of a very determined and sincere effort by both parties, and the fact that this effort has led to such a remarkable success reflects greatest credit upon both the U.S. Naval Support Force, Antarctica, and the Office of Antarctic Programs.

We were equally impressed by the high degree of cost-effectiveness of the antarctic program. A large number of parties, some of them wintering at one of the permanent stations, are doing research work in about 15 major fields of scientific endeavor, among them geology, aeronomy, physics, biology, medicine, glaciology, oceanography, astronomy, geophysics, paleontology, and psychology. For all of them, Antarctica represents an open frontier with vast opportunities to acquire new scientific knowledge. Perhaps even more important, it offers the opportunity to create new scientists trained in scientific research work under unusual circumstances. The steady growth of scientific capabilities is certainly one of the most important objectives a nation can have. When compared to the rich scientific harvest which USARP has yielded in the past and promises to yield in the future, the yearly expenditures of $8 million for scientific projects and $20 million for logistic support certainly are modest and exceedingly well spent.

There are, very obviously, a number of significant differences between antarctic exploration and space exploration. The two programs differ in their subjects, their histories, their environments, their total costs. But, there are also many similarities between the two programs, and there is in particular one feature in which the two programs are painfully similar: They both have to fight hard to obtain the funding necessary for their continuation. Their prime product is scientific knowledge, something not easily measured in dollars-and-cents benefits that accrue to each taxpayer every year. Scientific knowledge frequently can be valued in hard money, or as improved living, or for contributions to health, but this process takes a time which often is longer than the memory of the average citizen. In view of this fact, our argument for the continuation of strong research programs in Antarctica as well as in outer space should be based very simply and directly on the assertion that the acquisition of scientific knowledge is one of the very basic fibers in the makeup of a healthy, strong, and progressive society. It ranks on an equal status with such other basic fibers as a modern technology, a high living standard, advanced medical capabilities, an efficient governmental system, and a satisfactory national defense system. Even during times of rising living costs and dwindling resources, a nation which wishes to maintain prominence among other nations cannot afford to let its support of science shrink. A recent public opinion poll to assess the respect in which the various professions are held by the citizens revealed that physicians and scientists together ranked highest. This show of public esteem and confidence is quite reassuring; however, it also imposes an obligation, not only on the scientists, but on those charged with providing the support needed in order to retain the high level of accomplishment characteristic of scientific work in our country.

The two programs, antarctic exploration and space exploration, are so similar in many respects that the same arguments hold for both of them. In both, the scientific efforts can succeed only when adequately supported by a complex and costly line of logistics. In both, the potential value of the research is very high, but cannot be counted in dollars and cents at the end of each fiscal year. Also in both, the profits will not be limited to scientific knowledge, but will extend far into the areas of technology, organization, program planning, and management. And finally a most valuable product in both cases will be a group of men motivated by the spirit of exploration and experienced in the handling of large and complex projects involving science, industry, and government.

The Role of
Icebreakers
in the Antarctic

EDWIN A. MacDONALD

The United States first employed icebreakers in the Antarctic in 1946, in connection with *Operation Highjump*. The prominence of these ships in the antarctic scene is demonstrated in the table which shows that at least three and usually four of them have been assigned to each of the 14 *Deep Freeze* seasons to date. Only two other nations send icebreakers into the region: Argentina first dispatched ARA *General San Martín* there in 1954, and Japan introduced *Fuji* in 1965.

In the Antarctic, the main duty of our icebreakers is to break the ice defenses surrounding the Continent so that supplies can be delivered to ports of entry, which for the United States program are McMurdo Station on Ross Island and Palmer Station on Anvers Island. The vital importance of icebreakers can be summed up in one sentence: Over 95 percent of the matériel used by the U.S. program is delivered to Antarctica by ships. Without icebreakers, there is no assurance that the cargo ships and tankers can get

385

through to their destinations, especially in the Ross Sea sector.

The annual ice in McMurdo Sound almost never breaks up before late January, even under the most favorable conditions. Sometimes, no annual breakup occurs at all, as was the case during Scott's first (1902–1904) expedition, when his ship *Discovery* was forced to remain a second year for lack of such help from nature.

Perhaps ships could reach McMurdo without ice-breaker assistance after a natural breakup occurs, but the operating period would be short indeed and somewhat hazardous due to the onset of stormy weather in March. In contrast, the breaking of a ship channel into McMurdo Sound enables ship transport to begin in late December or early January at the latest. (In 1964 and 1967, the channel was pushed through to Winter Quarters Bay on the unusually early date of December 5.) One must also remember that the mooring site at Hut Point has usually been readied by icebreakers, and that the carving of the ship channel in the early part of the season has certainly aided, if not precipitated, the annual Ross Sea ice breakup.

Sea ice is never a solid, homogeneous mass, except in sheltered sounds and bays. Rather, it is constantly being broken into floes as variations in temperature, wind, and current create cracks and channels. Those same forces propel the sections or pieces of ice apart and together in an accordion-like manner that alternately increases and decreases pressure in the pack.

The term "icebreaking" is actually a misleading description of how a passage is opened through sea ice; the mechanics of the process are better described as "ice displacement." Ice forward of the icebreaker is shoved aside to accommodate the underwater portion of the vessel. Where the ice coverage is too solid

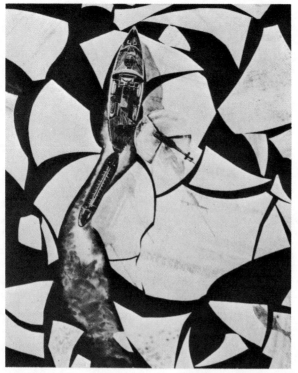

Water color by Comdr. Standish Backus, Jr., USNR, depicting USCGC Eastwind *towing a gasoline barge during Deep Freeze I.*

to permit lateral displacement, it is necessary to shove the ice over or under adjacent layers.

Only those pieces of ice too large to be readily shoved aside are broken. Breakage is accomplished either by the shock of impact or by cleaving action, in which the bow rises up (Fig. 1) and cuts through because of weight and the leverage applied at the bow section by the buoyancy of the depressed stern. The broken pieces must still be forced into nearby ice-free areas or the icebreaker will be impeded in its progress. Occasionally, ice is forced under the hull, to

FIGURE 1. *USCGC* Glacier *carving a channel in the ice pack.*

be caught in the propeller stream and driven astern. Under such circumstances, a piece of ice may become entangled with a propeller, sometimes resulting in a broken blade or shaft or in tripping a shaft off the line. The friction of the ice may also bring the ice-breaker to a halt.

The cushioning effect of snow can prevent the upraised bow from returning to the water. As a countermeasure, liquid ballast can be transferred laterally between healing tanks to impart a rolling motion to the icebreaker, breaking the snow's sticky grip. Sometimes, however, even this method, combined with the sudden application of full-astern power, is of little use.

In McMurdo Sound, where 5- to 7-foot-thick bay or fast ice ordinarily exists most of the year, two or three icebreakers usually start in late November or early December to carve a channel that will accommodate the thin-skinned supply ships scheduled to come later. This 25- to 40-mile-long channel is cut in the shape of a huge V with the open end to the north and its center axis aligned as much as possible in the direction of the prevailing southerly winds to facilitate

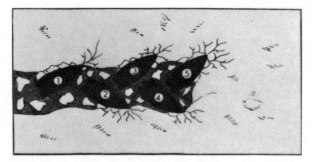

FIGURE 2. *The basic herringbone pattern involves charging alternately to port and starboard.*

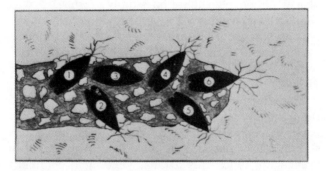

FIGURE 3. *In the modified herringbone pattern, each pair of angled cuts is followed by a head-on charge.*

the escape of the broken ice, or brash. In spite of these precautions, clogging of the channel by ice rubble sometimes reaches serious proportions. The icebreakers themselves may have difficulty negotiating the ice conglomerate that accumulates when northerly winds blow or when there are extended periods of calm. At such times, the situation can be improved only by a slow process of attrition wherein the icebreakers work up and down the channel, breaking large ice chunks into smaller ones and stirring the icy debris with screw currents to promote melting.

To cut a channel through an extensive area of fast

ice, as in McMurdo Sound, either of two basic methods may be used. If only one icebreaker is available
to lengthen the channel—perhaps because its partner
is occupied in reworking the undispersed ice rubble
—it will alternately charge the ice at a small angle to
port of the basic course, and then to starboard, re-
peating the process over and over in a herringbone
pattern (Fig. 2). (A channel cut by making repeated
straight-ahead charges would not give the icebreaker
any maneuvering room and might cause it to become
wedged at the head of the narrow cut; such a channel
also would be inadequate for supply vessels.) A wider
channel can be achieved by first making two blows to
port and starboard at greater angles than in the basic
herringbone method, and following each pair of these
with a third blow in the direction of the basic course
(Fig. 3).

The other basic method, sometimes called the rail-
road-track technique, requires two icebreakers. They
make two straightforward, parallel cuts, about three
ship-widths apart (Fig. 4). The intervening ice
breaks up under this attack, yielding a channel of
greater width than does the modified herringbone
pattern. This method has the added advantage of
being at least three times as fast as the single-ship
approach.

Having cut a channel to McMurdo, the icebreakers
do not desert the approaching supply vessels. Even if
favorable winds have cleared the channel of broken
ice, there is the drifting pack to the north of the
channel to cope with, except perhaps during January
and February, when ships sailing the route from
New Zealand to McMurdo usually require escort
south of 67°S. During severe ice years, escort has
been necessary throughout the austral summer.

The escorting icebreaker, with the aid of its helicopters searching ahead, attempts to locate the easi-
est paths through the jigsaw-puzzle pattern of ice

FIGURE 4. *USCGCs* Southwind *and* Westwind *employing the railroad track technique to cut a channel during Deep Freeze 68.*

floes. Ease of transit, however, is not the only criterion. Compromises must be made in order that the course taken is straight enough for the supply ships to negotiate and so that the general heading never strays further than 45° from the direct one to the destination.

The character and pattern of the ice floes and the fact that the icebreaker, due to its relatively short length (Fig. 5), tends to follow the path of least resistance, make the channel behind the icebreaker a meandering one that is often quite difficult for the supply ships to follow. Another difficulty is that the

FIGURE 5. *USCGC* Glacier *breaking out the Norwegian sealer* Polarhav *in Deep Freeze 60.*

ice-free path cleared by the wide beam of the ice-breaker, while at first adequate, tends to close rather quickly, making it necessary for the following ship (or ships in column) to keep closed-up tightly behind the icebreaker. In thick pack—or even in a channel previously cut through fast ice but still clogged with brash—it may be necessary to take a cargo ship or tanker in tow. Likewise, if a supply ship becomes severely damaged or has an engine casualty, the ice-breaker has the added task of towing the cripple to a safe place, an operation which involves placing the vessel's bow in the icebreaker's stern towing notch, or towing at a short scope of hawser, so that the ship will receive maximum protection from the ice.

Other complications can arise during escort. Should a particularly heavy section of ice be encountered, the icebreaker may have to range ahead in order to cut through a thick ice bridge. It may even be expedient to make the escorted ship wait while the icebreaker attempts charging and backing tactics, as in fast ice. It is possible, too, that a supply vessel may become stuck in the ice. In the corrective maneuver, the icebreaker clears the ice from the lee-ward side of the beset ship so that it will have its stern free to take a proper course.

With its barrel-like hull and no keels, an icebreaker rolls hideously in rough seas. Every one of them boasts of a record roll at one time in the 60°-range. But in the ice, where the vertical movement of the seas is dampened, an icebreaker ride is an entirely different affair. While in light to moderate ice, there is an almost imperceptible rising and lowering of the bow as the vessel rides up to break the larger floes.

If charging and backing tactics must be employed, however, the effect is something like riding a freight car over a railless track. When in solid, homogeneous ice, or pack of eight oktas concentration, where these tactics are employed, the bridge controllers are advanced to full ahead. The diesel engines respond with a roar, the ship charges ahead, and momentum builds up. Bow metal grinds into hard ice, and the ship slows. The bow rises sharply as the icebreaker comes to a complete stop after an advance of about one length. The propellers are then reversed and the ship backs off for another charge. It is a slow operation that is extremely hard on men and machinery.

On quite a few occasions, U.S. icebreakers have gone to the assistance of other nations' vessels operating in antarctic waters. In 1959, for example, a plea for help was received from the Belgian expedition, when the Norwegian sealer *Polarhav* was its resupply vessel. *Polarhav*, loaded heavily with the relief party, dogs, supplies, and equipment, became beset in heavy pressure ice some 200 miles from the Belgian station. The situation had appeared so hopeless to those aboard *Polarhav* that they had elected a "town council" to govern themselves during the long months ahead.

When *Glacier* finally broke through to circle the entrapped ship, men cheered lustily from the rigging

of *Polarhav,* her whistle tooting merrily, and her flag
dipping in the traditional salute of a merchant vessel
to a warship on the high seas. (The last action was
so unexpected under the circumstances that it took
a long time to get a seaman aft on *Glacier* to return
the honor.) After a struggle with the ice, *Glacier*
finally managed to escort the tiny *Polarhav* out to
the fringes of the pack. Then, having taken the dogs,
relief party and cargo aboard, *Glacier* went on to relieve Roi Baudouin Station.

During that same operating season, the British
were having problems supplying and relieving their
bases in the Antarctic Peninsula area. *Northwind*
and *Edisto* helped RRS *John Biscoe* overcome these
difficulties.

Typically, the vessels requesting such aid are small
and of dual capability, combining moderate icebreaking ability with cargo-carrying capacity. The situations, always urgent in character, have been caused
by unusually severe ice conditions: either the vessel
was beset and could not extricate itself, or it needed
help in carrying supplies and personnel to one or
more stations. Countries which have requested such
assistance in the past are Argentina, Australia, Belgium, Great Britain, Japan, New Zealand, and South
Africa.

Icebreakers have many supplementary uses in the
Antarctic, some scientific and some logistic. For one
thing, they are the only surface vessels rugged and
powerful enough to conduct oceanographic operations within the ice pack. The oceanographic and
marine data collected from icebreakers have added
appreciably to our knowledge of the Antarctic, and
of the Arctic as well. Especially notable instances in
which icebreakers have been employed in scientific
endeavors are the *Glacier-Burton Island* and *Glacier-
Staten Island* penetrations into the Bellingshausen

Sea during the early months of 1960 and 1961, respectively, and the *Glacier-General San Martín* oceanographic operations in the Weddell Sea during 1968 and 1969.

Icebreakers can be a valuable supplement to photographic aircraft in charting and exploring the coastline of Antarctica and off-lying islands. Using the combined mobility of the icebreaker and its helicopters, survey personnel can be put ashore at almost any location around the periphery of the Antarctic Continent. An outstanding example was the 1947–1948 venture of *Burton Island* and *Edisto* that determined the geographic coordinates of prominent terrain features along the antarctic coast. Known unofficially as "Operation Windmill," that effort was undertaken to make the numerous aerial photographs taken the season before during *Operation Highjump*, usable for mapping by establishing control points at recognizable features.

The configuration of our present icebreakers evolved from the experience of nearly a century of icebreaking, during which shipbuilders made many design improvements. That is not to say, however, that further improvement is impossible. Shipbuilding technology has advanced tremendously since our icebreakers were laid down, and our antarctic operations have more than doubled our icebreaking experience in the past 20 years. Yet as of 1971 the U.S.A. had not launched a new icebreaker since 1954.

Many suggestions can be made for the design of better icebreakers. Conventional propulsion machinery certainly can be improved; better propeller designs seem possible: using three propeller shafts—a feature of some Soviet and Canadian icebreakers— rather than two may have considerable merit. Perhaps propellers, which are very susceptible to ice damage that is reparable only in dry dock, should be eliminated in favor of hydrojet propulsion. Nuclear power appears to offer an answer to the cruising-range limitations now imposed by fuel capacity.

Hull design can also be improved. A Massachusetts Institute of Technology study indicates that a different bow profile would be more effective for ramming. It also suggests several means (including the use of a coating such as Teflon) for reducing the frictional force to be overcome in the backing phase of the ramming maneuver.

An interior improvement that would be welcomed by both the ship's operators and her embarked scientists would be larger, better-equipped research laboratories. This need will become greater if nuclear propulsion is adopted, permitting year-long cruises in the ice fields.

Action to construct new icebreakers may have to be taken soon. Icebreaking produces metal fatigue and engine wear of unusual severity, and all of the *Wind*-class icebreakers have more than 20 years of arduous service. In fact, their age exceeds the prescribed life of other, comparable naval vessels. *Glacier,* while launched in 1954 with some advanced features, is essentially an enlarged version of the basic *Wind*-class design.

There seems to be no question that more modern icebreakers could do a more efficient job for us, but the tasks our present ships accomplish are still considerable. They ensure that the cargo ships and tankers get through with vital supplies; they permit oceanographic research over a wider area; and they perform a combination of services that cannot be matched by other types of vessels.

Without our icebreakers, we—and perhaps several other nations—could not plan antarctic research programs with such assurance of success as we now do. Certainly, the icebreakers must be given their share of credit for what has been accomplished thus far in the Antarctic.

REFERENCES

MacDonald, E. A. "Our Icebreakers are not Good Enough," *United States Naval Institute Proceedings*, vol. 92, no. 2, February 1966.

Preserving the Environment in Antarctica

KURT G. SANDVED

It used to be that only two things were considered inevitable—death and taxes. Recently we have come to recognize two more as apparently equally unavoidable—inflation and pollution. Contrary to death and taxes, there is no benefit in the latter two. The price tag, in goods and social comfort, to eliminate them is enormous. Both of them are of concern to the U.S. antarctic program. On the following pages we look briefly at one of them—pollution.

It used to be also that the polar regions, and especially Antarctica, were looked upon as the last remaining clean and unspoiled areas of earth. In comparison with the rest of the world they still are, but local and the so-called worldwide pollutants have long since reached even Antarctica.

Slowly but surely, DDT and other chlorinated hydrocarbons have advanced to the antarctic shores and even to the polar plateau; radioactive fallout from atmospheric tests has left its message in the snow; and some of the less desirable trademarks of modern man are becoming visible—the garbage dump, the smog, the abandoned equipment, the noise.

Although perhaps it had to be expected, it was nevertheless sobering to learn in 1965 that DDT had been found in antarctic animals. Since then, a number of papers have been published on research leading to the identification of pesticides in various animate and inanimate samples, first in the Ross Island area, then in the South Orkney Islands. The seemingly irrepressible expansion of the limit of contaminated territory eventually reached Plateau Station where, at 3,600 m above sea level and thousands of miles from any populated area, DDT was found in melted snow samples. The U.S. Antarctic Research Program presently includes a study of chlorinated hydrocarbons and polychlorinated biphenyls (found in many plastics) in West Antarctica to determine the extent of contamination and the fallout patterns.

Observations of radioactive fallout from nuclear explosions have been made at many antarctic stations and from ships at sea, often with the primary or secondary objective of identifying snow layers or studying atmospheric-stratospheric circulation. The rate of fallout from bomb tests has been relatively low in both the atmosphere and the oceans of the Southern Hemisphere.

Other types of fallout that have been studied in the antarctic snow include silver and iodine, from the large-scale cloud-seeding operations that began in the early 1950s, and lead, injected into the atmosphere by industries in the Northern Hemisphere. The gradual increase in carbon dioxide and other chemical constituents of the air has also been measured.

The extent of local pollution has not been well documented, partly because it has not been considered of very great importance by national expeditions and partly because members of expeditions have been reluctant to criticize their own pollution. Also, it is well known that many nations, including the U.S.A., have invested much effort in developing efficient waste disposal systems and methods for the polar regions. These systems, developed principally for use in the Arctic, are treated only ephemerally in this brief survey.

Concern for local pollution at U.S. antarctic stations has been present for years, and on the following pages are described some of the precautions that have been and will be taken to minimize it. Of concern are garbage disposal methods, audio and electrical noise, vehicular traffic, human activities, and spillage of fission products. To the traditional expeditionary polluters has been added a source with a somewhat unpredictable future—the tourists.

On a continent the size of Antarctica it may seem unnecessary to worry about pollution by a few individuals. In the icy wastes of the interior, where everything is eventually mercifully buried in the snow, it may be just that. At the larger stations along the coast, in the precious dry valleys, and near rookeries, however, pollution is a very real threat to animals, area pristinity, and scientific studies.

The close cooperation of the U.S.A. and New Zealand around McMurdo Sound and at Hallett Station is reflected in the following articles. Beyond that, the coverage is limited, except in the bibliography, to the situation in the U.S. antarctic program.

THE CASE FOR
CONSERVATION
IN ANTARCTICA

BRUCE C. PARKER

Antarctica and its circumpolar waters may soon face an irreversible pollution crisis. Efforts to keep this last outpost of our global environment in its pristine state must be prodigious to offset the harmful effects of increases in scientific exploitation, tourism, and perturbations caused by pollution problems elsewhere in the world. While these efforts to preserve and use wisely the resources of Antarctica may seem ludicrous to some in the light of pollution crises closer to home, the gains from the undertaking will be not only aesthetic and scientific but also of economic and social relevance.

One finds a growing awareness of antarctic pollution problems and conservation needs that stretch beyond the local disturbances of wildlife populations. By 1970, Rudolph recognized that a number of disturbances (foreign microorganisms, insects, toxic substances, etc.) had reached antarctic and subantarctic regions from outside those territories without having been introduced deliberately. His observation affords proof for the well-known ecological concept that the biosphere—the part of the world wherein life occurs—is a discrete unit that cannot be divided entirely and successfully into two or more parts. Thus, the antarctic continental land mass cannot be separated from its atmosphere or its circumpolar waters. Furthermore, misuse of antarctic resources will

401

have relevance to resources and human beings elsewhere in our world. This concept is further elucidated by several pollution trends recognizable in Antarctica.

A prime example of the inseverable connection between Antarctica and the rest of the world is the occurrence there of synthetic organochlorine pesticides, even though there is no record of their previous use in that region. Sladen *et al.* (1966) found traces of DDT in the fatty tissues of six Adélie penguins and one crabeater seal collected at Cape Crozier on Ross Island. George and Frear (1966) confirmed the presence of DDT in Adélie penguins and also found it in several Weddell seals, numerous skuas, and one fish. The skuas also had DDE, a toxic metabolite of DDT. However, water, snow, an emperor penguin, and a variety of marine invertebrates also collected in the McMurdo and Ross Island area lacked detectable pesticides. Tatton and Ruzicka (1967) identified DDT and a number of other organochlorine pesticides in penguins, penguin eggs, skuas, blue-eyed shag, one fish, krill (*Euphausia*) from penguin stomachs, and sheathbills, all collected near Signy Island. The skuas possessed the exceptionally high concentrations of 26 parts per million of DDE and 2.5 ppm of DDT in their fat.

A number of possibilities have been proposed to explain the movement of these persistent pesticides through the biosphere and their accumulation in animal fatty tissues. Among the more plausible routes, they could be trapped in airborne dust, which can travel great distances in the winds and then fall or be carried to earth in rain or snow. Risebrough *et al.* (1968a) have demonstrated such transatlantic movements of pesticides in the northeast trades. Another mechanism of long-distance movement might be the oceans. Wurster (1968) has found DDT in oceanic phytoplankton, and Tatton and Ruzicka (1967) have observed that there are lower concentrations of several pesticides in krill than in Adélie penguins and that there are traces of several compounds in subantarctic waters. These findings suggest that migration of marine organisms or passive transport in currents, in addition to airborne transport, may carry these pesticides to Antarctica. Finally, the poor solubility of many of these substances in water suggests that they may concentrate in surface slicks on the ocean, where they may spread rapidly over great distances (Parker and Barsom, 1970). Such a mechanism of transport would increase in efficiency in the presence of oil slicks, which have been increasing steadily worldwide since the advent of tankers.

The pesticide picture is by no means complete. Soon other related toxins like the polychlorinated biphenyls (Risebrough *et al.*, 1968b) may be detected or may reach antarctic ecosystems from elsewhere in our biosphere. Studies are under way to assess the current concentrations of lead and vanadium in airborne dust and to measure their precipitation over Antarctica. These and other toxic metals already may have had an initial impact on the antarctic biota. Because silver iodide may be used increasingly in cloud seeding to induce rain in arid parts of the world, in future years we may be concerned with atmospheric ionic silver, an exceptionally potent biocide.

Radioactive substances as pollutants in Antarctica resemble the pesticides and heavy metals in that they can be borne in air, water, soil, and biota. However, prior global awareness of the lethal effects of excess radioactivity has tended to minimize indiscriminate use of nuclear explosives and careless disposal of radioactive waste material. Nevertheless, as nuclear power increases in the world, the hazards from accidental release of radioactivity into the biosphere will increase also. As with pesticides, the problem of radioactivity is global, and Antarctica cannot remain immune.

Because of the slow metabolic rates of antarctic cold-blooded animals, plants, and microorganisms, the accumulation of radioactivity in them may be orders of magnitude greater than in organisms of warmer climates. Indeed, the situation could be worse were it not for the Antarctic Treaty, which prohibits use of nuclear explosives and disposal of radioactive waste material in the Treaty area. So far, great care has been taken to achieve these goals, as exemplified in the meticulous studies that preceded and have followed installation of the nuclear power plant at McMurdo Station (D'Emidio, 1962; Brewer, 1963).

Of course, not all antarctic pollution originates from areas outside the continent and its circumpolar waters. Solid and chemical pollution near the bases themselves poses local problems in conservation that are vital to the conservation of the entire region and deserve immediate attention. Stations at the ocean's edge, such as McMurdo, Hallett, and Palmer, frequently use the ocean as their chief disposal system for solid, chemical, and domestic waste. Some of these activities will disturb—indeed already have disturbed—local ecosystems.

At Palmer Station on Anvers Island during the austral summer of 1969–1970, we noted frequent oil slicks in Arthur Harbor. On several occasions, Adélie penguins on nearby Humble Island emerged from the water with noticeable oil slicks on their bodies. Neither the fate of the birds nor the exact source of the slicks was ascertained, but the potential hazard posed by this slick to local marine and terrestrial wildlife was obvious. Because of the slow rates of microbial decomposition and chemical recycling at polar temperatures, the absolute dependence of terrestrial life upon the marine ecosystem, and the simplicity of antarctic ecosystems, seemingly small pollution problems of this type often may shift the natural balance locally. The length of time for recovery of such a disturbed ecosystem in Antarctica has never been determined, but from experience with more complex, more stable ecosystems in the Arctic, some have estimated the recovery time to be more than a century.

Solid waste and domestic waste disposal pose additional problems (Fair, 1963; Drobny, 1965; Sassani, 1966). Temporary solutions, such as the flushing chemical toilet (Nehlsen and Halton, 1964) and the incinerator latrine (Smith, 1963) have been suggested for small camps, but they do not seem practical for large stations, especially in light of the predicted increase in tourism. An enclosed sewage treatment system heated by the surplus thermal energy from a nuclear reactor might be economically feasible. Once in operation such a plant could produce surplus methane and other combustible gases that could be burned as a secondary energy source. Chlorination would no doubt be necessary since sewage bacteria are known to survive in sea water at $0°C$. (U.S. Naval Civil Engineering Laboratory, 1963).

Another of the more local problems is that of the destruction of terrestrial vegetation. Numerous case histories substantiate the steady retreat of these slow-growing lichens, mosses, liverworts, algae, and, on the Peninsula, two angiosperms. At McMurdo Station, lichens once occurred within a short walk of the base, but no longer (G. A. Llano, personal communication). The depletion of vegetation along with appearance of solid waste (paper cups, beer cans) was even apparent on Humble Island, 3 km from the several-year-old Palmer Station. There, a noticeable change had occurred between 1970 and 1971 (G. L. Samsel, personal communication). Numerous cases of declines in populations of marine and terrestrial wildlife have been reported (Carrick, 1960, 1963; Murphy, 1962, 1967; Dasmann, 1968; Rudolph, 1970).

The need for pollution abatement and the conservation of Antarctica with its circumpolar waters is obviously greater now than it was 7 years ago, when outside and local stresses upon this environment were less. The need for preserving the simple terrestrial ecosystems of interesting vegetation and wildlife remains important aesthetically and scientifically. Even small antarctic lakes and melt pools are vital as undisturbed sites for scientific study. This is borne out by the discovery that chemical eutrophication, a man-induced pollution problem found throughout the inhabited world, occurs naturally in antarctic lakes entirely free of human influence (Samsel and Parker, in press). Such scientific discoveries on remote antarctic ecosystems can thus lend new insights and new approaches to pollution prevention and control outside the antarctic region.

Most of us were at first surprised to learn that chemical pollutants such as pesticides could travel through the biosphere and reach remote areas of Antarctica. Since the interactions in the biosphere are multidirectional, and since we have discovered just a few ways that pollution in the rest of the world can affect Antarctica, one should ask, "How might pollution and exploitation of Antarctica affect the rest of the world?" This question implies many others, such as: What might overexploitation of krill do to antarctic marine ecosystems, and how might this affect migratory fishes, whales, and birds? In short, I believe that a major disturbance of the ecosystem in Antarctica could have an economic impact on other parts of the world; such feedback mechanisms are well recognized in nonpolar regions.

A satisfactory solution to the global pollution problem obviously is beyond the capability of any conservation program in Antarctica. Similarly, little can be done in Antarctica to prevent pesticides, toxic metals, and other biosphere-wide pollutants from entering antarctic ecosystems. However, scientific investigation to detect new pollutants and changes in their concentrations, to identify their pathways of transport, and to understand their ecological and physiological effects in antarctic ecosystems can bring about more serious global concern and may lead to discovery of remedial measures.

At the stations, a more vigorous research effort to find new techniques for minimizing pollution will be necessary before additional persons (tourists, scientists, and support personnel) visit antarctic bases. Techniques must be developed to preserve freshwater ecosystems, to improve sanitation and sewage disposal, and to minimize marine slicks, underwater deposition of refuse, terrestrial solid wastes, distribution of water-borne, airborne, and soil-borne pathogens, local atmospheric pollution and fallout, and radioactive and thermal release. Some of these new techniques may prove applicable to nonpolar pollution problems as well.

The Antarctic Treaty nations must continue to evaluate and develop their conservation programs. Additional "specially protected areas" must be established with their restrictions on plant collecting and animal killing. The Treaty countries should seek further to improve the regulation of conservation in antarctic circumpolar waters and pack ice zones, as these areas have been proved an integral part of food chains that support life on the continent and ice shelves now covered by the Treaty.

The United States has a large and complex program in Antarctica and consequently runs the risk of being a major polluter. It therefore seems only proper that the U.S. should have a comprehensive, effective conservation program. As shown in other articles below, a start has been made. One way to continue in this direction might be to have a conservation officer (a scientist) at each base with the necessary knowledge and authority and with the responsibility for educating personnel, establishing local conservation procedures, and seeing to it that the procedures are implemented.

REFERENCES

Anderson, D. 1968. The conservation of wildlife under the Antarctic Treaty. *Polar Record,* 14: 25–32.

Brewer, P. W. 1963. Nuclear power in the antarctic environment. *American Society of Civil Engineers. Proceedings,* 89(SA 4): 45–56.

Budker, P. 1966. Les grands cétacés menacés de disparition totale. *Science Progres Nature,* 3369: 11–13.

Carrick, R. 1960. Conservation of nature in the Antarctic. *Polar Record,* 10: 299–306.

Carrick, R. 1963. Problems of conservation in and around the southern ocean. *Polar Record,* 11: 506.

Cockrill, W. R. 1965–1966. Deep sea whaling—an industry in decline? *Ciba Journal.* 36: 52–57.

Dasmann, R. F. 1968. Conservation in the Antarctic. *Antarctic Journal of the U.S.,* III: 1–6.

D'Emidio, J. A. 1962. Radioactive waste disposal in the Arctic and Antarctic. *Navy Civil Engineer,* 31: 36–38.

Drobny, Neil L. 1965. Survey of antarctic water supply and waste disposal facilities, practices, and problems. *U.S. Naval Civil Engineering Laboratory. Technical Note N–708, Type C,* 24 p.

Fair, G. M. 1963. Sanitary engineering in polar regions. *World Health Organization. Public Health Papers,* 18: 116–137.

George, J. L., and D. E. H. Frear. 1966. Pesticides in the Antarctic. *Journal of Applied Ecology,* 3 (Supplement): 155–157.

Murphy, R. C. 1962. Antarctic conservation. *Science,* 135: 194–197.

Murphy, R. C. 1963. Conservation of the antarctic fauna. *Polar Record,* 11: 505–506.

Murphy, R. C. 1967. The urgency of protecting life on and around the great southerly continent. *Natural History,* 76: 18–31.

Nehlsen, W. R., and J. E. Halton. 1964. Flushing chemical toilet for temporary polar camps. *U.S. Naval Civil Engineering Laboratory. Technical Note N–666, Type C*, 13 p.

Panzarini, R. N. 1962a. Wild life. *UNESCO Courier,* 15: 36–40.

Panzarini, R. N. 1962b. La protección de la naturaleza en el Antártico. *Instituto Antártico Argentino. Contribución,* no. 66. 23 p.

Parker, B. C., and G. Barsom. 1970. Biological and chemical significance of surface microlayers in aquatic ecosystems. *BioScience,* 20(2): 87–93.

Risebrough, R. W., *et al.* 1968a. Pesticides: transatlantic movements in the northeast trades. *Science,* 159: 1233–1236.

Risebrough, R. W., *et al.* 1968b. Polychlorinated biphenyls in the global ecosystem. *Nature,* 220: 1098–1102.

Roberts, B. 1966. Wildlife conservation in the Antarctic. *Oryx,* 8: 237–243.

Rudolph, E. D. 1970. Conserving the antarctic terrestrial ecosystem. *Biological Conservation,* 3: 52–54.

Samsel, G. L., and B. C. Parker. In press. Comparison of two antarctic lakes with different trophic states. *Virginia Journal of Science.*

Sassani, M. J. 1966. Sanitary and hydraulic engineering in the Antarctic. In: *International Conference on Permafrost, Lafayette, Indiana, 1963. Proceedings,* p. 442–447. National Academy of Sciences.

Sladen, W. J. L., C. M. Menzie, and W. L. Reichel. 1966. DDT residues in Adélie penguins and a crabeater seal from Antarctica. *Nature,* 210: 670–673.

Smith, G. D. P. 1963. An incinerator latrine. In: *Symposium on Antarctic Logistics (1962),* p. 202–205. National Academy of Sciences.

Stonehouse, B. 1965. Animal conservation in Antarctica. *New Zealand Science Review,* 23: 3–7.

Tatton, J. O'G., and J. H. A. Ruzicka. 1967. Organochlorine pesticides in Antarctica. *Nature,* 215: 346–348.

U.S. Naval Civil Engineering Laboratory. 1963. Survival of sewage bacteria in zero-Centigrade sea water. Its *Technical Report, R–256,* 6 p.

Wace, N. M. 1966. Last of the virgin islands. *Discovery,* 27: 36–42.

Winterbottom, J. M. 1963. The antarctic fauna. *South African Journal of Science,* 59: 559–560.

Wurster, C. F., Jr. 1968. DDT reduces photosynthesis by marine phytoplankton. *Science,* 159: 1474–1475.

McMURDO SOUND

PAUL K. DAYTON
and
GORDON A. ROBILLIARD

There are three possible sources of marine pollution in McMurdo Sound near McMurdo Station: heated sea water released from the nuclear-powered distilling plant, inorganic trash dumped on sea ice, and organic food wastes and sewage dumped on sea ice that is eventually broken *in situ* by icebreakers.

Although the hot water outlet of the distilling plant technically is a source of thermal pollution, the authors have made a number of dives near the outlet and are convinced that, at the current level of discharge, there are no noticeable ecological consequences whatever. The sea water temperature within 0.5 m of the elevated outlet is at the ambient (−1.8°C) temperature. Nevertheless, in a small area (25–35 sq m) in the vicinity of the outlet, the invertebrates have been killed, possibly as a result of flushing the distilling system. Should the plant ever be drastically enlarged, the effects of thermal pollution ought to be considered.

Inorganic litter on the bottom at McMurdo is dramatic: fuel lines, barrels, honey buckets, rope, clothing, tractors, pieces of airplanes, thousands of beer cans, and many other types of trash are everywhere. On many of our transects, the beer cans outnumber some of the sponge species. The density of litter decreases as one moves away from the station, but litter is commonly seen as far as 6 km to the north. Although this litter is an eyesore, it probably has not seriously damaged the benthic biota. The most detrimental effect of this inorganic litter is simply in its covering of the bottom. The sponges are particularly sensitive to being covered, and even beneath such seemingly insignificant materials as cardboard and clothing all the sponges are dead. Probably because of the cold, bacterial decomposition in the Sound is slow: even paper, old clothing, and waterlogged wood last for many years. We are especially concerned about the recent introduction of plastic litter, not readily broken down by microbial activity even in warm water. At McMurdo, the plastic will last practically forever and will kill all organisms beneath it. Considering the amount of this litter that has accumulated in the past 10 years and unless some other method of disposal is found, it is reasonable to predict that, in place of the fascinating community there now, eventually the bottom at McMurdo will be covered by a veritable rug of litter.

Another form of inorganic pollution, apparent only in the vicinity of the hot water outlet and at Hut Point, is siltation. In both those places landfill has introduced some siltation, but in neither does it appear to have affected the benthic community significantly. If extensive construction is ever planned for Cape Armitage or Hut Point, siltation should be considered, because it could smother the sponges.

The introduction of pesticides and such inorganic chemicals as lead, mercury, sulfur, and cadmium into the sea is fraught with long range implications. However, we have no evidence that these materials are being released from local sources around McMurdo, and there is no obvious indication that they have begun to affect the benthic community there.

While the effects of this inorganic pollution are immediate and apparent, the effects of organic pollution are more subtle. But, potentially, the most devastating form of pollution to the benthic community is the large amounts of nutrients introduced in the form of food wastes and accumulated sewage.

The destructive effects of organic enrichment to recipient ecosystems in lakes has been well documented both experimentally (Nelson and Edmondson, 1955) and as a result of pollution studies (Whipple, 1918; Edmondson, 1968; California Water Quality Control Board, 1967). Major disturbances in marine communities resulting from organic enrichment have been documented also (North, 1964). The recent history of southern California kelp suggests that a shift in the ecological balance has resulted from organic pollution. A major die-off of kelp beds, coincident with unusually warm sea water temperatures and the increased release of sewage effluents in some areas, occurred in the late 1950s and in 1960 (North, 1964, 1965). Heavy exploitation of the declining kelp beds by the major grazers, the sea urchins *Strongylocentrotus purpuratus* and *S. franciscanus,* apparently hastened the disappearance of the kelp beds and prevented their recovery. It is hypothesized that enrichment of coastal water by sewage effluent increases recruitment of the urchins and helps maintain their high populations after they have consumed all the species of macroalgae in the community (North, 1965, 1969; North and Pearse, 1970).

A potentially similar situation may be found at McMurdo, as there are detritus-feeding urchins and starfish whose populations would respond relatively quickly to an increase in organic detritus. The result of such population increases is predictable with some confidence. The larger population would consume the detritus much more efficiently and thus would probably reduce the larval recruitment of many species. Since the same starfish species also eats sponges, it would eventually eliminate most of the benthic community at McMurdo by overexploiting a food source that would be unable to recover.

P. K. DAYTON

A paint bucket at the bottom of McMurdo Sound

Preliminary observation of the currents in the vicinity of McMurdo shows that organic pollution introduced in front of McMurdo Station would be spread over the bottom from Cape Armitage past Hut Point to Arrival Heights. The distribution of litter we have observed supports this finding. This organic enrichment resulting from sewage and local sinking of garbage is probably spread over the bottom community in the McMurdo area and could very likely result in a shift of the ecological balance. The accompanying consequences would be disastrous.

It is true that the level of pollution at McMurdo is much lower than that in southern California, but there are two critical differences between those two ecological systems. First, the small area near Cape Armitage may be the only experimentally accessible part of a community that exists only below the Ross Ice Shelf and in very deep water elsewhere off the continental shelf (Bullivant and Dearborn, 1967). Thus, instead of a whole seacoast and continental shelf as in southern California, a relatively small area is jeopardized at McMurdo. Second—and most important—the southern California kelp, with the reduction of the urchin population, can recover completely in 1 to 3 years (North, 1964), but the turnover rate at McMurdo must be considered in terms of hundreds, perhaps thousands, of years. The natural productivity in McMurdo Sound is so low that slight changes in productivity effected by organic enrichment may have profound effects on the populations of the detritus-feeding animals. Once there is a differential increase in their populations, these animals will not immediately starve if the organic enrichment is reduced, but they will begin to eat the extremely slow-growing sponges, which form the foundation of the community. Therefore, any changes wrought by pollution of McMurdo Sound would be permanent in effect.

Unlike many situations where there seem to be no realistic solutions to pollution problems, the situation at McMurdo does have acceptable alternatives. A planned sewage disposal plant will remove most or all of the polluting material before the effluent is pumped into the sea. If the outlet for any remaining material extends into deep water well beyond Hut Point, the dilution will probably be sufficient to prevent the type of disturbance to the benthic community discussed above. In addition to the sewage treatment plant, an incinerator is planned that will burn the combustible trash. The remaining trash and slag from the incinerator should be hauled out onto the ice far beyond the channel to be cut by the icebreakers. Then, when the ice does break up, this material will be carried out to sea where it presumably will sink in different, distant areas and will not affect the restricted benthic community in the McMurdo area. If these improvements come in time, a community very much worth preserving will probably survive.

REFERENCES

Bullivant, J. S., and J. H. Dearborn. 1967. The fauna of the Ross Sea, part 5: Ecology of the Ross Sea benthos. *New Zealand Department of Scientific and Industrial Research. Bulletin,* 176: 49–75.

California Water Quality Control Board. 1967. Eutrophication—a review. Its *Publication,* 34: 1–188.

Dayton, P. K., G. A. Robilliard, and R. T. Paine. 1970. Benthic faunal zonation as a result of anchor ice at McMurdo Sound, Antarctica. In: *Antarctic Ecology,* vol. 1, 244–258.

Edmondson, W. T. 1968. Water-quality management and lake eutrophication: the Lake Washington case. In: *Water Resources Management and Public Policy,* University of Washington Press, 139–178.

Nelson, P. R., and W. T. Edmondson. 1955. Limnological effects of fertilizing Bare Lake, Alaska. *U.S. Fish and Wildlife Service. Fishing Bulletin,* 56(102): 413–436.

North, W. J. 1964. On investigation of the effects of discharged wastes on kelp. *California Water Quality Control Board. Publication,* 26: 1–124.

North, W. J. 1965. *Annual Report 1964–1965, Kelp Habitat Improvement Project.* California Institute of Technology, Pasadena.

North, W. J. 1969. *Annual Report 1968–1969, Kelp Habitat Improvement Project.* California Institute of Technology, Pasadena.

North, W. J., and J. S. Pearse. 1970. Sea urchin population explosion in southern California coastal waters. *Science,* 167: 209.

Pearse, J. S. 1969. Antarctic Seastar. *Australian Natural History,* 16: 234–238.

Whipple, G. C. 1918. Technical and sanitary problems. In: *Freshwater Biology,* First edition. John Wiley and Sons, New York.

HALLETT STATION

LEIGH H. FREDRICKSON

Conservationists have become increasingly concerned about the effects of trash disposal and station activities on the beauty, fauna, and flora of Cape Hallett (72°19′S. 170°13′E.). Skuas and Adélie penguins provide unique opportunities for biological studies within walking distance of Hallett Station. Populations of insects and mites associated with the rich growth of lichens and mosses in a nearby specially protected area offer other research opportunities.

The facility was opened as a year-round station in 1957. Rough terrain required use of the flat rookery area on Seabee Hook as the only suitable site for the station. Encroachment on the fauna of the area began immediately when 7,850 penguins were fenced from their breeding areas (Eklund, 1959) and the station was constructed on their former nesting sites. After several years the tradition for these nesting sites was broken. As the station developed, more buildings were constructed and additional antennas were established within the rookery. The debris from construction, empty oil drums, and discarded and broken equipment were transported to dumps or left where they fell. Debris from dumps on sea ice located near the beach was washed ashore. Human wastes and kitchen garbage added to the waste disposal problem. Roads were constructed to dumps and to a glacier that provided fresh water.

The accumulation of trash covered some penguin nesting sites. Snow that accumulates around station

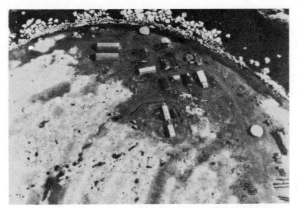

Hallett Station and adjacent Adelie penguin rookery. Penguins (seen as black dots on snow-covered areas) once occupied the entire area.

buildings during the winter was pushed into piles that encroach on some colonies. Melt water from this snow flooded nests in depressions. Certain scientific activities proved detrimental to the success of breeding penguins (Reid, 1964).

Nesting pairs of penguins and skuas have declined during the last 10 years at Cape Hallett (Reid, 1964; Tenaza, 1971). Skuas have suffered a high mortality as the result of direct killing by unknowing persons. The lack of nesting penguins in areas of intense activity suggests the inability of the species to tolerate continuous disturbance. Counts of both species in 1970 verified their further decline (Jeremy J. Hatch, personal communication, and author).

Several steps have been taken to improve the situation at Hallett. Disturbance to penguins and skuas has been reduced by discontinuing the use of the glacier as a source of fresh water and by restricting dumping to a small area near the station. This should result in return of penguins to nest sites near roads and dumps that now lack nesting birds. The dump on the sea ice was located a mile from the station in 1971. The removal of oil drums from the rookery and their deposition at sea has reduced the problem of drifting snow and melt water. Plans are being made for a systematic cleanup of all trash within the rookery and beaches. Nonfunctional radio antennas will be removed.

CLEANING UP
U.S. STATIONS

PHILIP L. HALL

Antarctica is a vast area with a sparse population —about 500 in winter and not 10 times that figure in summer. Thus, the threat to the ecology by locally produced pollution is probably limited to the immediate vicinity of the stations. Even so, active steps are being taken at U.S. installations to dispose of local pollutants and to counter their effects. At McMurdo Station, an incinerator and a sewage treatment plant have been delivered. The sewage treatment plant will eliminate the dumping of raw sewage into McMurdo Sound. The incinerator will handle almost all the waste material that now goes to the unsightly McMurdo trash dump. If available, commercial equipment will be installed to convert nonburnable trash and the ash residue of the incinerator into landfill material.

At the new Pole Station, diesel generator exhaust systems will be equipped with catalytic afterburners that will remove over 90 percent of the pollutants.

This 1967 photo shows some of the litter that once was scattered about Palmer Station.

In the past, snow that was melted to provide the water supply was contaminated by diesel exhaust.

Palmer Station was once a prime example of land pollution in the Antarctic. Construction crews and station operating and scientific personnel had strewn the entire area with construction materials, station supplies, scientific supplies, packing materials, tin cans, bottles, and other refuse. Much of the problem was caused by a lack of storage space. During *Deep Freeze 70* a combined warehouse, garage, and storage building, which added a considerable amount of inside storage space to the station, was completed. This additional space, coupled with a sincere desire to clean up the entire station area, led to an extensive and highly successful cleanup campaign in March 1970 by the construction forces, station personnel, and personnel from the Coast Guard icebreaker *Glacier*. A similar campaign had been conducted at the old Palmer Station site during *Deep Freeze 69*.

The most recent cleanup took place at Hallett Station. Cooperation between USARP personnel and the

Naval Support Force, Antarctica, led to a cleanup this past season, and further cleaning of the rookery is planned for next season.

Two originally unrelated events have given impetus to pollution abatement in the Antarctic and are expected to provide much of the needed technology and equipment. One is the awakening of the American people and the United States Government to the pollution crisis in the United States. The other is the Alaskan oil strike, which has focused technology on small, isolated bases that operate in a hostile environment. Rapid advancements are being made in the development of sewage treatment equipment for small applications. One such unit recently tested in Alaska is contained in an air-transportable van; its effluent reportedly is so clean that it has passed Alaska's standard for drinking water.

UNITED STATES
AND NEW ZEALAND
COOPERATION

ROBERT B. THOMSON

After the First Antarctic Treaty Consultative Meeting, held at Canberra in July 1961, representatives recommended to their governments that "they recognize the urgent need for measures to conserve the living resources of the Treaty area and to protect them from uncontrolled destruction by man." At the third consultative meeting, at Brussels in June 1964,

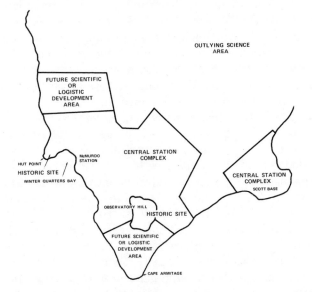

Boundaries on Hut Point Peninsula set by New Zealand's Department of Scientific and Industrial Research and the U.S. National Science Foundation.

the representatives agreed on special conservation measures that have since been implemented by all nations working in Antarctica. These measures are known as the Agreed Measures for the Conservation of Antarctic Fauna and Flora, or simply the Agreed Measures.

The position of New Zealand and the United States is unique: the two countries are close neighbors in Antarctica, they successfully operate joint stations, they pool their logistic resources, they cooperate fully in their scientific projects, and they operate for the most part from one country—New Zealand—where there is much public interest in Antarctica. The two countries aim at achieving a high degree of coordination in implementing the Agreed Measures.

Informal discussion in 1965 between New Zealand's Department of Scientific and Industrial Research (DSIR) and the U.S. National Science Foundation (NSF) led to the drawing up of a map of Ross Island's Hut Point Peninsula that set aside science reserves, logistic work areas, central station complexes, historic sites, and future logistics and scientific development areas (see fig.).

It was easy to produce the map, but there was still the problem of marking the boundaries and enforcing the new regulations. Further, a means was needed for interested parties to get together quickly should there be a specific requirement that would impinge on the boundaries. To fulfill these important functions of coordination and control, the McMurdo Land Management and Conservation Board, consisting of representatives of DSIR, NSF, and the U.S. Navy, was formed in 1967. Its first work was to arrange for tidying up and generally improving Hut Point Peninsula and for establishing underwater study areas. Since 1968 the Board has increased its responsibilities by arranging for cleanup and control in the ice-free valleys and at Capes Royds, Evans, and Hallett.

For 13 seasons, field parties from many countries, but mainly the United States and New Zealand, have carried out research in the ice-free Taylor and Wright Valleys. In the early days, helicopter support was minimal, and there were no semipermanent bases or huts for storage or shelter. Researchers had to take along enough food and equipment for a stay of months. Many cached their supplies at numerous points. When their projects were over, the researchers often did not retrieve these supplies; they were content with the thought that the caches would come in handy for some future expedition. Often, this was not to be the case. Sand blown by the wind hid unflagged, unmapped caches, and the wind itself, tear-

PHOTOS: R. B. THOMSON

The joint New Zealand-United States controlled visitor site at Cape Royds includes Shackleton's historic hut and a penguin rookery. Sign requests visitors to keep 10 ft. from nests.

ing at weakly anchored caches, littered the valley floors with supplies.

In January 1969, the McMurdo Land Management and Conservation Board took action. Supported by U.S. Navy helicopters, parties formed from NSF, DSIR, and U.S. Navy personnel cleaned up the worst of the litter, thus halting pollution of this unique, otherwise uncontaminated area. Now, field parties in the ice-free valleys are generally more closely supported, thus reducing the amount of supplies they need to carry. They are also instructed to cache at specific locations only, and even these caches must be retrieved before the close of the season.

Another development stemming from the close relationship of the United States and New Zealand was the decision in early 1969 to set aside an area of Cape Royds as a controlled visitor site. Everyone going to Antarctica wants to see and photograph penguins, and many also wish to visit an historic hut. As both can be done at Cape Royds, we developed this area as a small zoo-museum and thus considerably reduced the number of people disturbing other sites. Two caretakers provided by the New Zealand Antarctic Society took up residence at Cape Royds during the peak activity period of the 1969–1970 summer. The caretakers marked out a track that would allow visitors to see and photograph penguins without the usual need for getting in amongst them, and they guided visitors through Shackleton's hut. During nonvisitor periods the caretakers attended to hut maintenance, area tidiness, penguin counts, and meteorological observations. This scheme proved so successful that it was repeated during November 1970 and is likely to be continued indefinitely.

Preserving the Environment:
A Selected Bibliography

WORLDWIDE CHEMICAL POLLUTANTS

Brewerton, H. V. 1969. DDT in fats of antarctic animals. *New Zealand Journal of Science*, 12(2): 194–199.

Brown, Craig W., *and* Charles D. Keeling. 1965. The concentration of atmospheric carbon dioxide in Antarctica. *Journal of Geophysical Research*, 70(24): 6077–6085.

George, J. L., *and* D. E. H. Frear. 1966. Pesticides in the Antarctic. *Journal of Applied Ecology*, 3 (Supplement): 155–167.

Murozumi, M., T. J. Chow, *and* C. Patterson. 1969. Chemical concentrations of pollutant lead aerosols, terrestrial dusts and sea salts in Greenland and antarctic snow strata. *Geochimica et Cosmochimica Acta*, 33(10): 1247–1294.

National Science Foundation. 1965. DDT traces found in Antarctica; other pesticides absent. *NSF News Release 65–138*.

Peterle, Tony J. 1969. DDT in antarctic snow. *Nature*, 224(5219): 620.

Risebrough, Robert W. 1970. The Antarctic as a study area for problems in marine pollution. *Antarctic Journal of the U.S.*, V(4): 124.

Sladen, William J. L., C. M. Menzie, *and* W. L. Reichel. 1966. DDT residues in Adélie penguins and a crabeater seal from Antarctica. *Nature*, 210(5037): 670–673.

Tatton, J. O'G., *and* J. H. A. Ruzicka. 1967. Organochlorine pesticides in Antarctica. *Nature*, 215(5099): 346–348.

Warburton, J. A., *and* L. G. Young. 1970. Determination of silver and iodine in antarctic precipitation. *Antarctic Journal of the U.S.*, V(4): 115.

RADIOACTIVE FALLOUT

Ardouin, B., *et al.* 1961. Measurement of radioactivity of artificial origin in the Southern Hemisphere. *Bist*, 56: 12 p.

Begemann, F., *and* W. F. Libby. 1957. Continental water balance, ground water inventory and storage times, surface ocean mixing rates and worldwide circulation patterns from cosmic-ray and bomb tritium. *Geochimica et Cosmochimica Acta,* 12: 277–296.

Botter, R., C. Lorius, *and* G. Nief. 1960. The deuterium concentration of precipitation in Victoria Land. *Académie des Sciences. Comptes-Rendues,* 251: 573–575.

Crozaz, G. 1969. Fission products in antarctic snow, an additional reference level in January 1965. *Earth and Planetary Science Letters,* 6 (1) : 6–8.

Fairhall, A. W., *et al.* 1969. Radiocarbon from nuclear testing and air-sea exchange of CO_2. *Antarctic Journal of the U.S.,* IV (5) : 184–185.

Labeyrie, Jacques, *and* Gérard Lambert. 1963. On the existence of a diffusion barrier between the Northern and Southern Hemisphere tropospheres. *Académie des Sciences. Comptes-Rendues,* 256 (12) : 2664–2667.

Lockhart, L. B., Jr. 1960. Atmospheric radioactivity in South America and Antarctica. *Journal of Geophysical Research,* 65 (12) : 3999–4005.

Picciotto, E., *and* S. Wilgain. 1963. Fission products in antarctic snow, a reference level for measuring accumulation. *Journal of Geophysical Research,* 68: 5965–5972.

Popov, N. I. 1966. Concentration of nuclear-test long-lived fission products on the surface of the world ocean during the 1959–1961 moratorium. *Akademiia Nauk SSSR. Institut Okeanologii. Trudy,* 82: 35–41.

Popov, N. I., *and* S. A. Patin. 1966. Main features of the global distribution of strontium-90 on the surface of the world ocean. *Akademiia Nauk SSSR. Institut Okeanologii. Trudy,* 82: 42–55.

Rafter, T. A. 1965. Carbon-14 variations in nature: Part 2—increase in C^{14} activity in the atmosphere of the Southern Hemisphere from the testing of nuclear weapons. *New Zealand Journal of Science,* 8 (4) : 472–493.

Shen, S. P., S. A. Korff, *and* H. A. C. Neuberg. 1963. Tritium content of antarctic snow. *Nature,* 199 (4888) : 60–61.

Taylor, C. B. 1966. Tritium in Southern Hemisphere precipitation 1953–1964. *Tellus,* 18 (1) : 105–131.

Wilgain, S., E. Picciotto, *and* W. de Breuck. 1965. Strontium-90 fallout in Antarctica. *Journal of Geophysical Research,* 70 (24) : 6023–6032.

Woodward, R. N. 1964. Sr^{90} and Cs^{137} in antarctic snows. *Nature*, 204: 1291.

LOCAL POLLUTION

Buchinger, Maria. 1964. Undisturbed conditions for research. In: *U.S. Department of the Interior. National Park Service. World Confedernce on National Parks, 1st, Seattle, Washington, June 30–July 7, 1962*, p. 69–76.

Carrick, Robert. 1964. Conservation in the Antarctic, In: *U.S. Department of the Interior. National Park Service. World Conference on National Parks, 1st, Seattle, Washington, June 30–July 7, 1962*, p. 281–286.

Chichvarin, V. A., *and* V. I. Ptitsyn. 1966. The conservation of the natural resources of the Antarctic—an international problem. In: *Antarktika. Doklady Kommissii*, 1965, p. 95–102.

Dasmann, Raymond F. 1968. Conservation in the Antarctic. *Antarctic Journal of the U.S.*, III(1): 1–6.

Drobny, Neil L. 1965. Survey of antarctic water supply and waste disposal facilities, practices, and problems. *U.S., Naval Civil Engineering Laboratory. Technical Note N–708*. 24 p.

Holdgate, M. W. 1970. Conservation in the Antarctic. *Antarctic Ecology*, vol. 2, p. 924–945.

Llano, G. A. 1967. Terrestrial life of Antarctica. Introduction. *Antarctic Map Folio Series*, 5: 1–2.

Murphy, Robert Cushman. 1962. Antarctic conservation. *Science*, 135(3499): 194–197.

Murphy, Robert Cushman. 1967. The urgency of protecting life on and around the great southerly continent. *Natural History*, 76(6): 18–31.

Panzarini, Rodolfo N. 1962. The protection of nature in the Antarctic. *Instituto Antártico Argentino. Contribución No. 66*. 23 p.

Reinhold, Robert. 1967. City life and city problems come to the Antarctic. *New York Times*, December 22.

Roberts, Brian. 1966. Wildlife conservation in the Antarctic. *Oryx*, 8(4): 237–243.

Rudolph, E. D. 1970. Conserving the antarctic terrestrial ecosystem. *Biological Conservation*, 3: 52–54.

Shimoizumi, J. 1970. Conservation around Showa Base. *Antarctic Ecology*, vol. 2, p. 946–948.

Stonehouse, Bernard. 1956. Animal conservation in Antarctica. *New Zealand Science Review*, 23(1): 3–7.

Antarctic Engineering

PHILIP M. SMITH

Dean Chauncey Starr of the Engineering College, University of California, Los Angeles, said recently that he thought the engineer was today's true social revolutionary. Whereas in the past, social change may have been a function primarily of political, philosophical, or humanitarian thought, Dean Starr believes that it is created today primarily by the engineer. In some cases, technology has outstripped man's ability to adjust to change; it is here that the social role of the engineer is most exposed.

The role of the engineer as an agent in social change is nowhere better demonstrated than in Antarctica. Our past progress, our present social relationships, and our future prospects in Antarctica are functions of technology. That this is true is illustrated by considering that man's day-to-day experience in Antarctica extends back only to the winter of 1898, when *Belgica* was entrapped in the Bellingshausen Sea. Her crew became the first men to cope with the severe climate of the south polar winter. They had no radios, no electric power for either science or amenities, and no hope of rescue by any means other than their own. Today, by contrast, men live in comfort year around at the coldest place on Earth.

In 1928, about 30 years after *Belgica*'s entrapment, the engineer's revolutionary role in Antarctica had become clearly apparent with the operational use of aircraft, tracked vehicles, and far-reaching communications on the first Byrd expedition. In other areas —management and financing—change had not yet become apparent. The Byrd expedition still depended on the solicitation of much private support, in contrast to the government support now in effect. In 1928 and 1932, one took what one could get and was grateful for it. One oldtimer told me that the donated supply of a breakfast cereal was so abundant that the dog kennels were floored with it.

In the 40 years since the first Byrd expedition, the antarctic engineering revolution intensified, changing the whole pattern of activity on the Continent. Now, we successfully work throughout the winter in comparative comfort in the interior of the Continent, although we have sometimes come close to disaster and hardship when our equipment or its maintenance has failed. In the austral summer, we place parties all over the Continent virtually at will.

This revolution has also brought changes which are not beneficial. Wastes are visible at many antarctic stations. At McMurdo, for example, smog became a problem a few years ago. On some occasions, smoke from burning trash has reduced visibility on the Williams Field runway. Life style on the expedition has also been affected by specialization and by growth. Tragically, many individuals at McMurdo have become alienated from the program's objectives. Many sailors and officers involved in the support of the operation are so far from the "front-line" that they have no identification whatsoever with the scientists in the laboratories and aviators and scientists in the field.

*

Our experience in Antarctica will not seem unusual if we compare it with events that have taken place on other continents. Through such an examination, we can learn to plan new engineering for the future. In the history of American cities, one finds certain parallels between the development of McMurdo Station and the growth of cities such as Pittsburgh, Pennsylvania, and Louisville, Kentucky. In the period between 1780 and 1820, these frontier cities served as staging areas for man's further travel into the North American interior. In a brief 40-year period, frontier trading gave way to well-organized business and the phenomenon of suburban development. The records of the cities reveal problems of waste disposal, street construction and lighting, and fire protection. In this same period, construction along the river fronts proceeded with no thought for scenic protection; other patterns of land use, which are apparent today when one visits Pittsburgh or Louisville, emerged in this early period.

The struggle in this period of frontier urbanization is paralleled in developments at McMurdo Station in the 13-year period of our tenure. We also have struggled, sometimes vainly, in our effort to improve community services and utilities, often under restrictions created by our earlier construction decisions and outmoded planning principles. We have been somewhat unappreciative of our "million-dollar view" of the Royal Society Range, having obscured it with a maze of telephone poles and wires which offends the eye of the most insensitive person. The history of Pittsburgh and Louisville shows that a continuing planning effort should have been adopted at

PHOTOS BY W. R. CURTSINGER, USN

the outset. The future could not then be predicted, much as we could not in 1955 predict the future of McMurdo Station. But we are not now in the position of the early town fathers in Pittsburgh, for we have some notion of our future in Antarctica. Indeed, we have opportunities today that the planners in North America would find a source of envy.

We did not believe at the time of the IGY that we would be in Antarctica for more than three or four years. Little America V and the central core of present-day McMurdo were designed as "gold rush" towns. When the new Byrd Station was built in 1961, we knew that the antarctic program would continue for some time, but the decision to extend the program had been so recent that a really effective analysis of our requirements at that station was not possible. Today, Byrd Station provides visible evidence of the evolving program management. Palmer Station is the first station which truly bears the imprint of our new opportunities in planning.

Planning can be done more easily for Antarctica than for most other areas of the world. Dr. A. P. Crary, who until recently was Chief Scientist of the Office of Antarctic Programs, has pointed out that there are no pressing demands of private interests to contend with in the Antarctic. There is no need for crash programs, although some programs seem to take on that appearance at the last minute. Furthermore, there is a store of planning information available. Perhaps most important, there are relatively precise figures available for the cost of the various support services. When a new scientific program is contemplated, the logistic costs can be considered. Our plans are updated annually, giving planners the opportunity to regroup when they fail.

There are also some difficulties in planning for Antarctica. Some problems relate specifically to the mission of the National Science Foundation (NSF), which is responsible for the coordination and funding of the scientific activity. NSF is a nonoperational agency supporting basic research; while our plans may call for certain projects, we cannot hire scientists to carry them out. Instead, we must hope that our plans will be a true reflection of academic and governmental scientific interests. Otherwise, we must hope that some persuasion may bring the opportunities to the attention of qualified workers. Another feature of our planning is that both the Office of Antarctic Programs and the U.S. Naval Support Force, Antarctica operate on level budgets. In planning, a level budget is painful, for it means that any innovation necessitates the curtailment of funds for a project already in progress. Budgetary restrictions can also be advantageous, however, for they provide an opportunity to weed out the moribund. Coordination of our two budgets is particularly important. It would be unwise, for example, for NSF to curtail programs which were at the same time receiving re-newed logistic emphasis by the Navy.

Our five-year plan for the period 1968–1972 is now in effect. What does it mean from the standpoint of engineering? First, it is clear that by the mid-1970s, we will operate only three permanent year-round sta-tions—Palmer, Pole, and McMurdo. By then, Byrd Station will be 12 to 14 years old; its maintenance costs will have increased greatly, probably to the point where the station no longer will be economically useful in its present large size. Portable, temporary stations like Plateau may be in continued use, but will have short occupation at any one location. New instrumentation such as the radio ice-thickness sounder will lead to extended use of remote-sensing aircraft. Submersibles and other vehicles will have been introduced. Automatic stations are certain to be in operation by virtue of the perfection of isotopic power supplies, communications through synchron-ous satellites, and other spinoffs of the space age.

Exciting new investigations that heretofore have been technically impossible to conduct will become feasible. One of the most important of these—sam-pling by remote techniques beneath the Ross Ice Shelf, which is the size of France—has long fasci-nated workers in several fields. Biologists want to know if life exists there. Oceanographers believe that the bottom water of the world ocean may originate beneath the shelves. Glaciologists have long debated whether the underside is melting or freezing. Conse-quently, there is a desire to drill a hole, perhaps 4 ft. in diameter, through the floating shelf and lower automatic, remote-sensing equipment into the water beneath. These new and heady projects demonstrate the revolutionary role of the engineer, for none of them would be possible without him.

How do we proceed in the years ahead to exploit

our planning opportunities? We should think carefully about and adopt the systems-analysis approach, now widely used in government for planning, programming, and budgeting. It has a few shortcomings. One of them is that we generally relate it to the inanimate. Actually, our "system" in Antarctica is a human one to a very real extent. If one of us fails in the accomplishment of his responsibility, the whole system breaks down. In thinking of a systems approach to antarctic engineering, I urge that attention be given to the human elements—the interaction of personnel from the design phase on through to the operation and maintenance of a station. A systems-analysis approach does not relieve the individual of responsibility; instead, it strengthens the individual's performance.

The implications of a projected activity become known through the analysis of all elements of the problem, including, in our instance, such diverse factors as transportation schedules, procurement, and ongoing operational expenses. It is quite possible, I believe, to define our needs for a systems examination, since we have better projections of our overall objectives than most planners have. And, we have one major advantage in our use of the systems approach: we can obtain very good feedback. In many engineering activities, such a user feedback is quite difficult to obtain. We know right away from our users—especially the wintering personnel—whether they are happy with our engineering.

As we think of a systems approach to our engineering, we can consider the following factors, all of which are important elements of a systems analysis along with specific objectives about the project itself.

Our stations are physically isolated, much in the manner of ships at sea. The ebb and flow of trade, supply, and resupply can be precisely measured. Our construction and maintenance is actually more like the construction and operation of a ship—a total environmental system—than a shore facility in the sense that the term is used in regard to naval installations in the United States. It might have been well to include the Naval Ships System Command, which knows the problems of isolation, in the development of a station such as Plateau.

We must use our knowledge of antarctic environmental differences. When the preparations were being made for the first winter support flight to Antarctica, antarctic environmental differences were summarized in messages from the ice. At McMurdo, the terminal of the fly-in, the temperatures were in the neighborhood of $-30°C$. At Palmer, temperatures were above freezing and there was a drizzle. Meanwhile, at Plateau, it was down to nearly $-75°C$. The fact that Antarctica is a large continent with many different environments escapes some engineers.

Standardization rather than diversification is possible. We are less dependent on the artificially stimulated demands of society than are most engineering activities. The most modern and the best-looking do not have to be obtained for Antarctica because they are so advertised or even because they are the least costly.

Consolidation of utility systems is possible. All utilities can be maintained by a single operating organization. We do not have separate electric, power, and fuel companies. Consider, for example, the desirability of placing the power lines alongside the water distribution system. This would eliminate the overhead wires and their hazardous maintenance during winter storms. It would permit simultaneous physical inspection by utility men of the water, waste, and power-distribution systems.

Further in our systems analysis, we have the opportunity to consider the efficiency which comes through manpower reduction, not its increase. We have no need for full employment in Antarctica and do not have to make work.

Pressure for the continuation of a bad antarctic plan is small. There are relatively few political and economic implications in our work. Our investment is our own, not the investment of corporate stockholders. It should be noted that we are responsible to the U.S. taxpayer—the real stockholder of our enterprise. Few taxpayers willingly promote increased costs, especially those arising from a planning failure.

In our work, there is the opportunity to utilize new developments from the Arctic. There are cities, such as Inuvik near the mouth of the Mackenzie River, which are a little further along the line from frontier village to city. Our planning should take into account the rapid northward push into Canada and Alaska and the way that the engineering requirements are met.

There is one element of antarctic systems planning on which I would like to dissent from the generally held opinion. Among working engineers in the Antarctic, one hears a good deal about the "simplicity principle," the rationale for which is that complex devices will fail more quickly in Antarctica. In some earlier, expeditionary phases of the antarctic program such a principle may have been applicable. Today, however, we are too committed to the engineering revolution to retain or achieve simplicity. But the main reason that I object to the simplicity principle is that it insults man's capability! Man seeks challenge in the unknown and in technological development. The leveling process of simplicity also levels man.

We have a requirement for a new South Pole Station by the early 1970s. There are new scientific projects—some of which I have mentioned and some which I have not—all requiring new technology. Systems analysis can be employed in all of these undertakings.

In Antarctica, we have three great advantages which elude most planners. I have talked at some length about the planning cycle. Secondly, there is the umbrella provided to the program by the Antarctic Treaty: we operate in a favorable national and international climate as a result of the 12-nation agreement of 1961. A third important factor is that, to a large degree, we are in control of our destiny. Our activities in Antarctica are more nearly similar to the emerging development of the North American Continent 100 years ago than they are to the adventures of man in space. We have a handful of engineers at work on our projects, while there are thousands involved in NASA programs. That we have control of our destiny should stimulate desire for excellence on the part of all, and should develop a sense of collective responsibility for our projects.

How Antarctica fits into the distant future cannot be forecast, but it is certain that it will. It is less than a century since the *Belgica* expedition in 1898. What we are building at McMurdo today will surely be useful for 20 or 30 years—till the end of this century —in Antarctica. We must constantly think of our broader responsibility for the Antarctic Continent and our collective involvement in planning as we carry out our individual tasks in construction and engineering. At some future point, we will be judged, for the wisdom of our decisions will be evaluated just as we now look back on an earlier phase of antarctic activity and on man's use of North America.

Appendix I

Antarctic Treaty

The Governments of Argentina, Australia, Belgium, Chile, the French Republic, Japan, New Zealand, Norway, the Union of South Africa, the Union of Soviet Socialist Republics, the United Kingdom of Great Britain and Northern Ireland, and the United States of America.

Recognizing that it is in the interest of all mankind that Antarctica shall continue forever to be used exclusively for peaceful purposes and shall not become the scene or object of international discord;

Acknowledging the substantial contributions to scientific knowledge resulting from international cooperation in scientific investigation in Antarctica;

Convinced that the establishment of a firm foundation for the continuation and development of such cooperation on the basis of freedom of scientific investigation in Antarctica as applied during the International Geophysical Year accords with the interests of science and the progress of all mankind;

Convinced also that a treaty ensuring the use of Antarctica for peaceful purposes only and the continuance of international harmony in Antarctica will further the purposes and principles embodied in the Charter of the United Nations;

Have agreed as follows:

ARTICLE I

1. Antarctica shall be used for peaceful purposes only. There shall be prohibited, *inter alia,* any measures of a military nature, such as the establishment of military bases and fortifications, the carrying out of military maneuvers, as well as the testing of any type of weapons.

2. The present Treaty shall not prevent the use of military personnel or equipment for scientific research or for any other peaceful purpose.

ARTICLE II

Freedom of scientific investigation in Antarctica and cooperation toward that end, as applied during the International Geophysical Year, shall continue, subject to the provisions of the present Treaty.

ARTICLE III

1. In order to promote international cooperation in scientific investigation in Antarctica, as provided for in Article II of the present Treaty, the Contracting Parties agree that, to the greatest extent feasible and practicable:

(a) information regarding plans for scientific programs in Antarctica shall be exchanged to permit maximum economy and efficiency of operations;

(b) scientific personnel shall be exchanged in Antarctica between expeditions and stations;

(c) scientific observations and results from Antarctica shall be exchanged and made freely available.

2. In implementing this Article, every encourage-

ment shall be given to the establishment of cooperative working relations with those Specialized Agencies of the United Nations and other international
organizations having a scientific or technical interest in Antarctica.

ARTICLE IV

1. Nothing contained in the present Treaty shall
be interpreted as:

(a) a renunciation by any Contracting Party of
previously asserted rights of or claims to territorial
sovereignty in Antarctica;

(b) a renunciation or diminution by any Contracting Party of any basis of claim to territorial
sovereignty in Antarctica which it may have
whether as a result of its activities or those of its
nationals in Antarctica, or otherwise;

(c) prejudicing the position of any Contracting
Party as regards its recognition or non-recognition
of any other State's right of or claim or basis of
claim to territorial sovereignty in Antarctica.

2. No acts or activities taking place while the
present Treaty is in force shall constitute a basis for
asserting, supporting or denying a claim to territorial sovereignty in Antarctica or create any rights
of sovereignty in Antarctica. No new claim, or en-
largement of an existing claim, to territorial sovereignty in Antarctica shall be asserted while the
present Treaty is in force.

ARTICLE V

1. Any nuclear explosions in Antarctica and the
disposal there of radioactive waste material shall be
prohibited.

2. In the event of the conclusion of international
agreements concerning the use of nuclear energy,
including nuclear explosions and the disposal of

radioactive waste material, to which all of the Contracting Parties whose representatives are entitled to participate in the meetings provided for under Article IX are parties, the rules established under such agreements shall apply in Antarctica.

ARTICLE VI

The provisions of the present Treaty shall apply to the area south of 60° South Latitude, including all ice shelves, but nothing in the present Treaty shall prejudice or in any way affect the rights, or the exercise of the rights, of any State under international law with regard to the high seas within that area.

ARTICLE VII

1. In order to promote the objectives and ensure the observance of the provisions of the present Treaty, each Contracting Party whose representatives are entitled to participate in the meetings referred to in Article IX of the Treaty shall have the right to designate observers to carry out any inspection provided for by the present Article. Observers shall be nationals of the Contracting Parties which designate them. The names of observers shall be communicated to every other Contracting Party having the right to designate observers, and like notice shall be given of the termination of their appointment.

2. Each observer designated in accordance with the provisions of paragraph 1 of this Article shall have complete freedom of access at any time to any or all areas of Antarctica.

3. All areas of Antarctica, including all stations, installations and equipment within those areas, and all ships and aircraft at points of discharging or embarking cargoes or personnel in Antarctica, shall

be open at all times to inspection by any observers designated in accordance with paragraph 1 of this Article.

4. Aerial observation may be carried out at any time over any or all areas of Antarctica by any of the Contracting Parties having the right to designate observers.

5. Each Contracting Party shall, at the time when the present Treaty enters into force for it, inform the other Contracting Parties, and thereafter shall give them notice in advance, of

(a) all expeditions to and within Antarctica, on the part of its ships or nationals, and all expeditions to Antarctica organized in or proceeding from its territory;

(b) all stations in Antarctica occupied by its nationals; and

(c) any military personnel or equipment intended to be introduced by it into Antarctica subject to the conditions prescribed in paragraph 2 of Article I of the present Treaty.

ARTICLE VIII

1. In order to facilitate the exercise of their functions under the present Treaty, and without prejudice to the respective positions of the Contracting Parties relating to jurisdiction over all other persons in Antarctica, observers designated under paragraph 1 of Article VII and scientific personnel exchanged under subparagraph 1(b) of Article III of the Treaty, and members of the staffs accompanying any such persons, shall be subject only to the jurisdiction of the Contracting Party of which they are nationals in respect of all acts or omissions occurring while they are in Antarctica for the purpose of exercising their functions.

2. Without prejudice to the provisions of paragraph 1 of this Article, and pending the adoption of measures in pursuance of subparagraph 1(c) of Article IX, the Contracting Parties concerned in any case of dispute with regard to the exercise of jurisdiction in Antarctica shall immediately consult together with a view to reaching a mutually acceptable solution.

ARTICLE IX

1. Representatives of the Contracting Parties named in the preamble to the present Treaty shall meet at the City of Canberra within two months after the date of entry into force of the Treaty, and thereafter at suitable intervals and places, for the purpose of exchanging information, consulting together on matters of common interest pertaining to Antarctica, and formulating and considering, and recommending to their Governments, measures in furtherance of the principles and objectives of the Treaty, including measures regarding:

(a) use of Antarctica for peaceful purposes only;
(b) facilitation of scientific research in Antarctica;
(c) facilitation of international scientific cooperation in Antarctica;
(d) facilitation of the exercise of the rights of inspection provided for in Article VII of the Treaty;
(e) questions relating to the exercise of jurisdiction in Antarctica;
(f) preservation and conservation of living resources in Antarctica.

2. Each Contracting Party which has become a party to the present Treaty by accession under Article III shall be entitled to appoint representatives to participate in the meetings referred to in para-

graph 1 of the present Article, during such time as that Contracting Party demonstrates its interest in Antarctica by conducting substantial scientific research activity there, such as the establishment of a scientific station or the despatch of a scientific expedition.

3. Reports from the observers referred to in Article VII of the present Treaty shall be transmitted to the representatives of the Contracting Parties participating in the meetings referred to in paragraph 1 of the present Article.

4. The measures referred to in paragraph 1 of this Article shall become effective when approved by all the Contracting Parties whose representatives were entitled to participate in the meetings held to consider those measures.

5. Any or all of the rights established in the present Treaty may be exercised as from the date of entry into force of the Treaty whether or not any measures facilitating the exercise of such rights have been proposed, considered or approved as provided in this Article.

ARTICLE X

Each of the Contracting Parties undertakes to exert appropriate efforts, consistent with the Charter of the United Nations, to the end that no one engages in any activity in Antarctica contrary to the principles or purposes of the present Treaty.

ARTICLE XI

1. If any dispute arises between two or more of the Contracting Parties concerning the interpretation or application of the present Treaty, those Contracting Parties shall consult among themselves with a view to having the dispute resolved by negotiation, inquiry, mediation, conciliation, arbitration,

judicial settlement or other peaceful means of their own choice.

2. Any dispute of this character not so resolved shall, with the consent, in each case, of all parties to the dispute, be referred to the International Court of Justice for settlement; but failure to reach agreement on reference to the International Court shall not absolve parties to the dispute from the responsibility of continuing to seek to resolve it by any of the various peaceful means referred to in paragraph 1 of this Article.

ARTICLE XII

1. (a) The present Treaty may be modified or amended at any time by unanimous agreement of the Contracting Parties whose representatives are entitled to participate in the meetings provided for under Article IX. Any such modification or amendment shall enter into force when the depositary Government has received notice from all such Contracting Parties that they have ratified it.

(b) Such modification or amendment shall thereafter enter into force as to any other Contracting Party when notice of ratification by it has been received by the depositary Government. Any such Contracting Party from which no notice of ratification is received within a period of two years from the date of entry into force of the modification or amendment in accordance with the provisions of subparagraph 1(a) of this Article shall be deemed to have withdrawn from the present Treaty on the date of the expiration of such period.

2. (a) If after the expiration of thirty years from the date of entry into force of the present Treaty, any of the Contracting Parties whose representatives are entitled to participate in the meetings pro-

vided for under Article IX so requests by a communication addressed to the depositary Government, a Conference of all the Contracting Parties shall be held as soon as practicable to review the operation of the Treaty.

(b) Any modification or amendment to the present Treaty which is approved at such a Conference by a majority of the Contracting Parties there represented, including a majority of those whose representatives for under Article IX, shall be communicated by the depositary Government to all the Contracting Parties immediately after the termination of the Conference and shall enter into force in accordance with the provisions of paragraph 1 of the present Article.

(c) If any such modification or amendment has not entered into force in accordance with the provisions of subparagraph 1(a) of this Article within a period of two years after the date of its communication to all the Contracting Parties, any Contracting Party may at any time after the expiration of that period give notice to the depositary Government of its withdrawal from the present Treaty; and such withdrawal shall take effect two years after the receipt of the notice by the depositary Government.

ARTICLE XIII

1. The present Treaty shall be subject to ratification by the signatory States. It shall be open for accession by any State which is a Member of the United Nations, or by any other State which may be invited to accede to the Treaty with the consent of all the Contracting Parties whose representatives are entitled to participate in the meetings provided for under Article IX of the Treaty.

2. Ratification of or accession to the present

Treaty shall be effected by each State in accordance with its constitutional processes.

3. Instruments of ratification and instruments of accession shall be deposited with the Government of the United States of America, hereby designated as the depositary Government.

4. The depositary Government shall inform all signatory and acceding States of the date of each deposit of an instrument of ratification or accession, and the date of entry into force of the Treaty and of any modification or amendment thereto.

5. Upon the deposit of instruments of ratification by all the signatory States, the present Treaty shall enter into force for those States and for States which have deposited instruments of accession. Thereafter the Treaty shall enter into force for any acceding State upon the deposit of its instrument of accession.

6. The present Treaty shall be registered by the depositary Government pursuant to Article 102 of the Charter of the United Nations.

ARTICLE XIV

The present Treaty, done in the English, French, Russian, and Spanish languages, each version being equally authentic, shall be deposited in the archives of the Government of the United States of America, which shall transmit duly certified copies thereof to the Governments of the signatory and acceding States.

IN WITNESS WHEREOF, the undersigned Plenipotentiaries, duly authorized, have signed the present Treaty.

DONE at Washington this first day of December, one thousand nine hundred and fifty-nine.

Appendix II

Statement by
The White House

The President announced today that he had completed a review of United States policy for Antarctica, reaffirming a continuing U.S. interest in Antarctica and in the scientific work which is undertaken on that continent in cooperation with the other eleven nations signatory to the Antarctic Treaty.

In conducting his review of United States policy for Antarctica, the President has directed changes in the funding and program management of U.S. activities to bring about a more effective administration. In the past, the funding for the U.S. program in Antarctica has been divided among the National Science Foundation, which has funded and managed the scientific programs, and the Departments of Defense and Transportation, which have provided logistic support to these programs.

Because the U.S. effort in Antarctica is primarily scientific in nature, and in order to achieve maximum effectiveness in developing a national program, the President has decided to consolidate funding and program management responsibilities for all U.S. activities in Antarctica within the National Science Foundation.

The increase in the National Science Foundation budget for Antarctic activities will not cause a net increase in the total Federal budget, as the Foundation will be assuming budget items for logistic support currently provided by the Department of Defense and the Department of Transportation. The President directed the agencies to commence now the orderly transfer of administration and budgetary responsibilities.

The President noted that the United States policy in Antarctica includes several objectives:

To maintain the Antarctic Treaty and ensure that this continent will continue to be used only for peaceful purposes and shall not become an area or object of international discord.

To foster cooperative scientific research for the solution of worldwide and regional problems, including environmental monitoring and prediction and assessment of resources.

To protect the antarctic environment and develop appropriate measures to ensure the equitable and wise use of living and non-living resources.

United States interests in Antarctica extend back 150 years. It was then that Nathaniel Palmer of Stonington, Connecticut, made the first known sighting of Antarctica. The national exploration by Charles Wilkes in 1840 charted 1500 miles of the Antarctic coasts. In this century, the well-known exploits of Rear Admiral Richard E. Byrd, Dr. Laurence M. Gould and other explorers and scientists have constantly attested to the U.S. interest in Antarctica.

In 1958, President Eisenhower extended invitations to the Governments of the eleven nations which had conducted scientific research programs in Antarctica during the International Geophysical Year (1958) to participate in a conference with a view to writing a treaty "dedicated to the principle that the vast uninhabited wastes of Antarctica shall be used only for peaceful purposes". The Treaty was signed by the United States and the eleven other nations (Argentina, Australia, Belgium, Chile, France, Japan, New Zealand, Norway, the Union of South Africa, the Union of Soviet Socialist Republics, and the United Kingdom) on December 1, 1959, and entered into force on June 23, 1961.

President Eisenhower noted that the "Antarctic Treaty and the guarantee it embodies constitute a significant advance toward the goal of a peaceful world with justice". Of the guarantees in the Treaty, any signatory country may satisfy itself that the pledge is being observed by inspecting any station or expedition anywhere and at any time.

The Treaty has provided an effective framework for the continued peaceful use of the area by the twelve nations conducting research and working together on the icy continent, an area as large as the United States and Europe, where national differences are no barrier to practical and mutually beneficial cooperation. Each year the United States welcome foreign scientists to its stations and sends American scientists to do work at stations of other countries. Annually the U.S.S.R. and the U.S. make bilateral exchanges of scientists to winter at a station of the other country. Science has provided a successful basis for international accord, and the Antarctic is the only continent where science serves as the principal expression of national policy and interest.

OCTOBER 13, 1970

The Authors

J. CAMPBELL CRADDOCK — Professor of Geology at the University of Wisconsin, former geologist for Shell Oil Company; served with Minnesota Geological Survey and New Zealand Geological Survey; has specialized in Antarctic geology.

ALBERT P. CRARY — Director of the Division of Environmental Sciences in the National Science Foundation. Was chief scientist of the United States Antarctic research program during the International Geophysical Year of 1957–58 (IGY). Led a number of traverses across the Antarctic sheet.

PAUL C. DANIELS — Nursed the Antarctic Treaty of 1959 through many months of delicate negotiation; was one of the State Department's leading specialists in Latin American affairs, having for a time headed the department's division concerned with the American states. Now retired.

PAUL K. DAYTON AND GORDON A. ROBILLIARD — With, respectively, the Scripps Institution of Oceanography at the University of California in La Jolla and the Department of Zoology at the University of Washington.

451

GEORGE H. DENTON, RICHARD L. ARMSTRONG,
AND MINZE STUIVER — Geologists with the University of Maine, Yale University, and the University
of Washington, respectively.

YEVGENY K. FEDEROV — Played a key role in the
I.G.Y. as chairman of the Soviet Working Group on
Rockets and Satellites. He later became vice president
of the Committee on Space Research (COSPAR) of the
International Council of Scientific Unions. He now
heads the Hydrometeorological Service of the U.S.S.R.
— the Soviet Weather Bureau.

JOSEPH O. FLETCHER — Heads the Office of Polar
Programs in the National Science Foundation. In 1952
established a scientific station on a drifting ice island
in the Arctic Ocean with Albert P. Crary as his geophysicist. The island has circled the ocean and served
repeatedly as a research station. It is known as Fletcher's Ice Island or T-3. Fletcher has become an authority on the effects of polar ice on climate.

LEIGH H. FREDERICKSON — With the Gaylord Memorial Laboratory of the University of Missouri.

HERMAN R. FRIIS — With the Center for Polar Archives of the National Archives, Washington, D.C. Was
Exchange Scientist with the Japanese Antarctic Research Expedition, 1969–1970.

SIR VIVIAN FUCHS — Led the British Commonwealth
Trans-Antarctic Expedition that made the first land
crossing of Antarctica during the I.G.Y., travelling
from the Weddell Sea, on the Atlantic side, via the
South Pole, to the Ross Sea on the Pacific side. He was
formerly in charge of British exploration in the area of
the Antarctic Peninsula.

LAURENCE M. GOULD — Professor of Geology at the
University of Arizona, was second in command of Admiral Byrd's first expedition to Antarctica in 1928, was
president of Carleton College in Minnesota for a number of years, and was chairman of the committee responsible for American polar research during the I.G.Y.

PHILIP L. HALL — Is a Captain in the U.S. Army who
served with the U.S. Naval Support Force, Antarctica.

ROBERT A. HELLIWELL — Professor of Electrical Engineering at the Stanford Electronics Laboratory, he is a pioneer investigator of "whistlers" and other forms of radio-wave propagation along the high-arching lines of the earth's magnetic field. In the years immediately following the I.G.Y. he has sponsored research involving simultaneous observations at "conjugate points"—the opposite ends of such high-arching lines in Antarctica and comparable latitudes in the North.

THOMAS O. JONES — Deputy Assistant Director for National and International Programs in the National Science Foundation. Long headed the Antarctic program within N.S.F.

C. C. LANGWAY, JR. & B. LYLE HANSEN — Both are associated with the U.S. Army's Cold Regions Research and Engineering Laboratory in Hanover, N.H. Landway heads its Snow and Ice Branch. Hansen is chief of its Technical Service Division and is a veteran Antarctic driller.

RICHARD S. LEWIS — Managing Editor of the *Bulletin of the Atomic Scientists,* former Science Editor of the *Chicago Sun-Times,* he is a science writer who has reported on Antarctic research at first hand. His book, *A Continent for Science* (1965), describes recent activities in that region.

GEORGE A. LLANO — Program Manager for Biological Sciences in the Office of Polar Programs at the National Science Foundation. His specialty is lichens, but he is also an authority on shark behavior and diverse other subjects. His concern with Antarctic biology is of long standing.

B. G. LOPATIN — With the Institute of Arctic Geological Research in the U.S.S.R. Was Exchange Scientist with the United States Expedition.

EDWIN A. MACDONALD — Captain, USN (Ret.), is director of ship and polar operations for Lindblad Travel, Inc. For four years was Deputy Commander, U.S. Naval Support Force, Antarctica. Formerly an icebreaker captain, he spent 15 years in polar ship operations.

F. MICHAEL MAISH — With the Environmental Research Laboratories of the National Oceanic and Atmospheric Administration. Was Exchange Scientist with the 14th Soviet Antarctic Expedition.

WILLIAM D. McELROY — Director of the National Science Foundation. A specialist in firefly luminescence, bacterial mutations, mold metabolism and other biochemical processes. Formerly chairman of the biology department at Johns Hopkins University.

BRUCE C. PARKER — Is with the Department of Biology, Virginia Polytechnic Institute and State University.

NEAL POTTER — Research associate with Resources for the Future, Inc. in Washington, D.C. Author of *Natural Resource Potentials of the Antarctic.*

GORDON de Q. ROBIN — Director of the Scott Polar Research Institute at Cambridge University in England. Took part in the ice-sounding trail expedition into Queen Maud Land in 1949–52.

MORTON J. RUBIN — Chief of the Office of Special Studies in the National Oceanic and Atmospheric Administration. As a meteorologist with the U.S. Weather Bureau he served as an Exchange Scientist at Mirnyy, the Soviet Antarctic base.

KURT G. SANDVED — Is editor of the *Antarctic Journal of the United States* and Director, Polar Information Service, Office of Polar Programs, National Science Foundation.

PHILIP M. SMITH — Deputy head of the Office of Polar programs in the National Science Foundation. Helped lay the original tractor trail from Little America to Byrd Station in Antarctica. As a speleologist, or cave explorer, he descended into crevasses to map a safe route.

FINN SOLLIE — Director of the Fridtjof Nansen Foundation at Polhogda, Norway, and a specialist in international law.

ERNST STUHLINGER — Director of the Space Sciences Laboratory at the George C. Marshall Space Flight

Center of the National Aeronautics and Space Administration in Huntsville, Ala. Took his doctorate in physics at the University of Tübingen and played a leading role as physicist with the V-2 missile development project. He then came to the United States and participated in early development of missiles in this country.

WALTER SULLIVAN — Science Editor of the *New York Times*, has accompanied four expeditions to Antarctica. Is author of *Quest for a Continent* (1957), an account of Antarctic exploration.

ROBERT B. THOMSON — Is with the New Zealand Department of Scientific and Industrial Research.